CHEMICAL DETECTION OF GASEOUS POLLUTANTS

An Annotated Bibliography
EDITED AND REVISED BY WALTER E. RUCH
School of Public Health, University of Michigan, Ann Arbor, Michigan

PREFACE

Originally published by the Office of Technical Services, U. S. Department of Commerce, in two volumes. These U. S. Government publications have been out of print for some time, were, in fact, all snapped up by the nation's scientists almost as soon as their availability was known.

The high regard in which this Bibliography is held prompted the decision to edit and revise. We believe it to be invaluable for use by industrial hygienists and safety engineers and to workers in the fields of education and chemical research. The bibliography should prove useful also to those working on the development of new detectors.

Credit for the original work is due the Los Alamos Scientific Laboratory, Los Alamos, New Mexico.

Published by Ann Arbor Science Publishers, Inc., 6400 Jackson Road, Post Office Box 1425, Ann Arbor, Michigan 48106.

Library of Congress Catalog Card No. 66-29577.

Printed in the United States of America
1st printing 1966
2nd printing 1967
3rd printing 1968
4th printing 1970

ABBREVIATIONS USED IN THIS WORK

AA — Analytical Abstracts

APCA — Air Pollution Control Association Abstracts.
Air Pollution Control Association (in cooperation with U. S. Public Health Service and the Library of Congress.) 4400 Fifth Avenue, Pittsburgh, Pa. 15213.

BOT — Bibliography of Ozone Technology. Vol. I, Analytical Procedures and Patent Index. Clark E. Thorp. Armour Research Foundation of the Illinois Institute of Technology, Technology Center, Chicago, Illinois 60616 (1954).

CA — Chemical Abstracts. American Chemical Society.

H — Organic Chlorine Compounds. Ernest Hamlin Huntress. John Wiley and Sons, Inc., New York, New York (1948).

IHD — Industrial Hygiene Digest.
Industrial Hygiene Foundation,
Mellon Institute, 4400 Fifth Avenue,
Pittsburgh, Pa. 15213.

U.S. A.E.C., OTX.
NSA — Nuclear Science Abstracts.

Add. Ref. — Additional Reference

TABLE OF CONTENTS

INTRODUCTION

The industrial hygienist has always based his recommendations for environmental health control measures on the analysis of air for airborne contaminants. Because many industrial hygiene organizations cannot, for economic reasons, have enough trained chemists to do the many and varied analyses necessary for all situations, the industrial hygienist must seek simple, reliable indicators for routine control measurement of air samples. The two extremes of attitude toward industrial hygiene analytical chemistry are those of the "purist" and the "practical." Without disrespect to either, there must be a common ground, which may well be the "standard" methods of industrial hygiene. Even these methods require elaborate laboratory equipment and, often, the industrial hygienist waits days for a result. The "practical" industrial hygienist wants some system which will give him a quick answer within limits established by the process or operation under investigation. The present day philosophy on air analysis is that there are three ranges of interest regarding contaminated air: the concentration of contaminant in the air is unsafe, safe, or absent. Each of these levels of contamination must be interpreted by the industrial hygienist for the given situation and for the analytical technique used to determine the level. If an analytical procedure shows no contaminant, then the interpretation must be that the level is below the sensitivity of the procedure; the sensitivity in turn must be well below that concentration which, if present, would be considered safe. Methods which are not specific may be adequate in atmospheres which contain only one of the substances for which the method is designed. It is difficult to define the concentration of a contaminant which is "safe." What level of contaminant in air is "unsafe" is left, in most cases, to the interpretation of the industrial hygienist, even though there are guides for his use. Because the industrial hygienist wants to know immediately whether the air contamination level is within "safe" limits, many industrial hygiene organizations use "field detectors." The designers of field detectors and field detector kits are rapidly eliminating many of the errors of the past and are making it possible to estimate the concentration of a contaminant with remarkable accuracy.

The Bureau of Standards, the U. S. Bureau of Mines, and other government agencies have contributed to this development because they recognize the need for rapid and continuous detection of air-borne contamination. The demand is so great for detection devices that many of the foreign and domestic health and safety equipment manufacturers maintain research programs, which provide new or improved detectors and field kits for industrial hygiene work. Most of the detectors listed in the bibliography section are from independent laboratories and public health laboratories. The British were the first to use the detector system routinely on a standardized basis.

Chemical detectors for the detection and estimation of air-borne contaminants are invaluable to the military services as well as to the industrial hygienist. Although chemical detectors are used chiefly for gases and vapors, they also may be applied to mists and fumes. Determinations of particulate matter generally are limited to the darkening of a white surface or to some other reflective measurement.

Most detectors are only semi-quantitative. Their accuracy depends largely on their preparation and on the care with which the given type of instrument is standardized. Because all detector procedures depend on personal observations by the operator, human error influences the final result. For example, the quantity of an unknown substance may be determined visually by comparing the stain made by it with a stain of equal intensity and hue made by a known amount of the substance. Other factors which influence the sensitivity and accuracy of a detector will be discussed in detail below.

There are essentially two types of detectors: liquid and solid.

1. LIQUID DETECTORS

In these, the solution is carried into the field with the sampling unit. For this rather inconvenient, but very sensitive, procedure often referred to as "air titration" or "air colorimetry," the reagent in the bubblers or impingers must trap, dissolve, and react with the contaminant either to form a color or to bleach a preformed color, and it must have constant efficiency over the range of the standards. If the product of the reaction is stable, it may be returned in some cases to the laboratory for a more precise analysis. Field use of solutions is more prevalent than the literature indicates because a number of laboratories have taken routine procedures and made reference solutions for direct comparison. Examples of these are the Saltzman method for oxides of nitrogen, the Goldman method for TNT, and the gold reaction for bromides; these can be applied to field analysis by comparing the final color with that of a series of synthetic colors. Air titration, such as the absorption of alkali in sulfuric acid containing an indicator, is used when the volume of air and the amount of alkali required to neutralize the acid in the sampling container are known (a constant end-point is difficult to maintain). Although these methods are not preferred by the analytical chemist (purist), they may, under proper control, be satisfactory for routine use.

Another liquid-using field method is the field laboratory. Its procedures are cumbersome and many errors may be introduced. The industrial hygiene chemist can recognize the limitations of the field unit and evaluate the interferences, contaminants, and other influencing factors.

2. SOLID DETECTORS

Solid detectors, though generally less accurate than liquid reagents, are much more easily handled. Three types of solid detectors used in industrial hygiene and chemical warfare are: a) impregnated paper, cloth, or other filtering media; b) impregnated granules such as silica gel diatomaceous earth, alumina, and titanium dioxide; and c) chalks or crayons which change when scratched on a surface, if contaminants either are on the surface, or in the air in contact with the surface, or if they enter the atmosphere at some future time.

a) *Impregnated papers,* which are easily prepared, are used widely, especially for the detection of toxic gases and vapors. The paper usually referred to is a high grade of washed filter paper. Cloth and filter mats of various materials also have been reported. One way to handle the filter papers is to hang them in the suspected atmosphere; the time required for a color to develop will be a function of the concentration of the contaminant in the air. This is a qualitative test, indicating the presence or absence of the contaminant. Some of these papers are prepared and used dry, while others are treated with a solution just before use and employed wet. Although to the experienced operator the detector papers thus used will indicate degree, the many factors which influence results obtained with the "free-hanging" filter suggest its omission from routine use. A second way to use the filter paper is to allow a given volume of air to pass over or impinge on the surface of the paper in a given length of time. This technique has been satisfactorily applied to hydrofluoric acid by a commercial manufacturer, and has been used for the detection of mercury with a pump to force the air over the sensitive paper. A third and more desirable method of handling a filter paper, which permits more control of the various factors that affect the sensitivity and quantitative color development, is to place the paper in a suitable holder and aspirate air through the filter at a definite rate and constant volume. The agents which influence the result of such an operation are discussed below in detail.

b) *Solid absorbents* impregnated with reagents are in popular demand because they can be stored for some time and they allow more accurate control of many factors. Units with this type of detector are available commercially. The detectors consist of suitably sized particles of silica gel, aluminum oxide, titanium oxide, pumice, etc. in a glass tube for simple reading. A definite volume of air is drawn through the tube at a controlled rate. This type of instrument is preferred to others because it meets most of the requirements of a good detector, is quantitative over a selected range of concentration, simple to use, and easy to prepare. The commercial units are expensive initially but give good reproducibility in the range covered by the particular instrument.

c) *Chalks and crayons,* some of which are available commercially, have the same disadvantage as the "free-hanging" papers, namely, lack of control over the many factors influencing the result obtained with them. The use

of these chalks, therefore, is to be questioned for routine industrial hygiene evaluations.

Difficulties similar to those of the chalk and "free-hanging" filter methods also affect the ampoule method for the detection of gases. Even though the solution in the ampoule is evenly distributed, there is no certainty that the reaction at a given concentration always will be quantitative, because the procedure invoves breaking the glass ampoule so that the solution wets the cotton or gauze surrounding the ampoule. Such tests are useful to indicate immediately that an environment definitely is not suitable for human life, but conversely they give no assurance that the environment is completely safe if the test is negative.

FACTORS INFLUENCING THE VALIDITY OF A DETECTOR

The following factors are significant to the industrial health and safety officer who uses detectors to measure quantitatively the environmental concentration of toxic substances. The factors become less important if a detector is used solely for qualitative work at high concentrations.

1. Air Volume

The total volume of contaminated air passing through the detector affects the final result because the color change to be expected is a function of the concentration per unit volume. Neither chalks, "free-hanging" filters, nor ampoules meet this requirement. Mounted filter papers, granules, and solutions can be calibrated for a given air volume.

2. Rate of Air Flow

The rate at which air passes through the detector affects the time the contaminant is in contact with the reagents, and this is a controlling factor in the over-all accuracy and reproducibility of the test. Whether by mechanical or hand pump, the air must flow through the detector at a rate consistent with the calibration of the original reference standards. When stain length is the measure of concentration, the rate of air flow must be controlled precisely and must be linear over all the surfaces of the impregnated material.

3. Humidity

Although humidity usually cannot be controlled in the environment being tested, it may be controlled in the detector. Some reactions need water for greater rapidity or for completion; then a humectant, such as glycerine or a glycol, is added to the detector to help retain the water necessary for the reaction. When water must be excluded from the reaction a dehydrating agent, on a separate paper or on granules, precedes the test material. Silica gel is satisfactory for drying only if the contaminant is not absorbed by the silica gel.

4. Time

Since the length of time a detector is exposed to the contaminated air influences the final result, this element also must be controlled. Regulating the total amount of air is as important as fixing the rate at which the air is drawn through a detector. In some detectors the air itself plays a significant role and causes bleaching or deterioration of the reagents.

5. Area

The size of the surface which the detector exposes to the contaminated air definitely influences the accuracy of the result. The paper detector's sensitivity is based on an air flow rate per unit area so that at the same velocity, and with uniform sampling time and contaminant concentration, different areas produce the same color or density change. When color change only of impregnated granules is to be read the area size is less consequential, but it is extremely important when stain length is to be measured. In the stain length procedure, the reaction between the contaminant and the reagent is rapid and is a function of the flow rate, total volume, and amount of reagent exposed to the contaminated air; while with impregnated granules, in which the reaction is usually incomplete, the color change is slow and becomes a function of the flow rate and the total volume of contaminated air. In both cases, the particle size of the granules (surface area) is controlled for reproducibility.

6. Reagents

The reactant must be chosen to be as specific as possible; it must combine stability with sensitivity sufficient to detect the suspected substance in the necessary volume of the contaminated air in the concentration range desired. All of the reagents should be pure and each batch preparation should be standardized for reproducibility.

PREPARATION OF SOLID (DRY) DETECTORS

The preparation of various dry detectors—paper, silica gel or other granules—is essentially the same. After reagents are made and materials for impregnation readied, the final colorimetric process will be affected by several factors:

1. Immersion Time

Immerse each batch of material treated for the same length of time, because some supporting materials act as ion exchange beds and absorb the reagent to the point of saturation. This may be desirable in some instances.

2. Removal of Excess Reagent Solution

Always remove the solution the same way. Decant the liquid from granules, allow them to drain for a fixed period, and dry them each time under the same conditions of desiccation, temperature, and final storage. Drain, blot, and dry filter papers so as to retain the same amount of reagent on the paper of each batch.

3. Storage

Store papers, as well as silica gel and other granules, so as to prevent contamination, and protect them from light and extreme temperatures. In some detectors several reagent granules are mixed thoroughly before use to form almost a solid solution. The age or shelf life for each system must be known. Migration of reagents in two or three component systems has been noted in the literature.

4. Interferences

Interfering compounds are reduced in number or eliminated primarily by selection of specific reactants. Water already has been mentioned; particulate matter not desired on a white paper may be removed first on an untreated paper. Elimination of hydrogen sulfide with lead acetate before testing for arsine with silver or mercury compounds is an example of the chemical removal of an interfering compound. Silica gel removes organic vapors before a test for carbon monoxide in the typical carbon monoxide analyzer. Some authors use bubblers in which reagents to remove interfering compounds precede paper and silica gel detector systems. A thorough knowledge of the detector's sensitivity prevents misinterpretation of the final results. Detectors that react to a broad spectrum of compounds—for example, those sensitive to reducing or oxidizing compounds, acids and/or bases—should be used only with a complete understanding of the composition of the air being tested.

5. Handling

The detectors must be handled so as to avoid contaminating the surface of the materials. Oils from the hand can coat the particles or the paper surfaces and prevent an even distribution of the color or stain.

6. Measurement

After the sample has been taken, the color must be compared or the stain length measured for a quantitative result. Few reactions are so specific that different colors are produced with different concentrations of a contaminant, although one is reported for a "free-hanging" filter paper. Sometimes the first color change is the end-point and the time is a function of the concentration. In most papers and granules the color changes and deepens as the concentration increases. The intensity of these colors then is compared with color charts for concentration estimation. Paper detectors often are referred to a single color. Air is drawn through the detector until this color is matched, then time, volume, and number of strokes on the hand or other pump become a function of the concentration. Tubes with granules are compared in the same way. With stain length, the function usually is logarithmic and suitable graphs can be prepared. Some commercial kits have a rotating tube on the barrel of the unit, which is labeled for the length of stain produced from a given number of aspirations of air. Charts accompany other test kits and include temperature, humidity, column height, and volume corrections.

Colored glass reels, synthetic solutions, and color charts are used with liquid detectors. This type of comparison has been developed to a great extent by the sanitary industry, and the units commercially available have been modified for routine work in industrial health.

7. Special Paper

Although many filter papers and filters are described in the literature, a particular one is worth mentioning here. The Yagoda confined spot filters help to control many of the variables. A known volume of a reagent solution or solutions can be added to the paper without fear of dispersion throughout the paper. The area is consistent from one paper to the next, and the paper may be cut to fit any holder up to 1½ inches, with the concentration of reagents per square centimeter remaining the same. In some cases, standards are easily prepared by adding liquid solutions of the contaminant.

8. Holders

There are as many holder designs as there are laboratories doing this type of analytical work; a description of any one holder is unnecesary. However, any filter holder must have:

a) An opening in front equal to the area of the spot or area of the paper to be exposed to the air stream.

b) A suitable back-up that will give a flat surface without contaminating the filter; this may be another filter which is untreated, such as a glass fiber filter.

c) An easily removable cover to prevent exposure of the paper before sampling the contaminated atmosphere.

Holders for granules are glass tubes with glass wool or cotton plugs in both ends. Some granules have been rubbed into the surface of filter papers; however, most authors do not recommend this treatment. The granules must be packed so that they are evenly and consistently distributed. Commercial units are designed to take into account most of the above mentioned factors.

STANDARDIZATION AND EVALUATION

Several industrial hygiene and public health laboratories in the United States have established for their own use an evaluation method for detectors and field kits, and are beginning to publish their findings to date. The methods of evaluating are essentially the same, that is, known concentrations of the contaminant are established in either a dynamic or a static system and the results of the detector analyses are compared with standard laboratory analytical procedures. Factors such as sensitivity, reproducibility, etc. are determined. Recent publications contain complete mathematical treatments of the physical properties of detectors. The most important single factor in the use of a detector regardless of its form is an understanding of the detector's limitations.

Recently the army chemical research and development laboratories have developed detector systems based on biochemical-enzymic reactions. These detectors are extremely sensitive and can detect even the most toxic agents in parts per billion with accuracies comparable to classical chemical methods. These studies introduce a new field of detector investigation.

SUMMARY

The olfactory senses are not reliable enough to detect air-borne contaminants. A properly used chemical detector can give sufficient information so that qualified persons can appraise intelligently the degree of hazard involved. A chemical detector should be used primarily for rapid estimations; it should not replace classical analytical techniques in the field of industrial health and safety. Standardization and familiarization are the most important elements in determining the validity of any quantitative result interpreted from a detector or from a field analysis.

SECTION 1
Reviews and General Bibliography

1—SIMPLE METHODS FOR THE DETERMINATION OF GASEOUS IMPURITIES IN THE AIR OF FACTORIES

Hahn, Martin. Gesundh. Ing. **31,** 693-697 (1910); CA **4,** 1074 (1910).

Colorimetric methods for the determination of ammonia, carbon dioxide, chlorine and sulfur dioxide are described. Ammonia is determined by nesslerization while the method for carbon dioxide is a modification of the well-known Lunge-Zeckendorf method. The analysis for sulfur dioxide is accomplished by determining the amount of air required to bleach the color of a 0.25000 N solution of iodine treated with starch. A similar method is satisfactory for chlorine.

2—TITLE NOT GIVEN

Arndt, Max. Ger. (Pat. No.) 216, 468, Feb. 17, 1907; CA **4,** 694 (1910).

An apparatus for making qualitative determinations of certain contaminant gases in the atmosphere is described. The presence of a certain gas is determined by utilizing a colored ribbon saturated with a liquid reagent appropriate for the gas being determined. The apparatus consists of a container for the reagent and ribbon and a spreading device for the liquid.

3—DETECTING POISONOUS GASES IN AIR

Lamb, A. B. and C. R. Hoover. U. S. (Pat. No.) 1, 321, 061, Nov. 4, 1920; CA **14,** 163 (1920).

This invention serves to provide a method which is useful in determining small amounts of oxidizable gases in the atmosphere. Among these gases are carbon monoxide, arsine, phosphine, ammonia or the sewer gases. Two methods are given for preparing the material, which is named "hoolamite." The material produced is a white solid and the analysis is carried out by drying the test air and then contacting the dried air with the reagent. In the presence of oxidizable gases the reagent turns green to brown in color.

4—DETECTING POISONOUS GASES IN AIR

Lamb, A. B. and C. R. Hoover. U. S. (Pat. No.) 1, 321, 062, Nov. 4, 1920.

20-40 mesh pumice is treated with varying ratios of fuming sulfuric acid, sulfur trioxide, iodic anhydride, and iodine to form a color with oxidizable gases. Carbon monoxide is discussed as an example (q.v.). Depending on the pre-absorber used (charcoal, etc.), the detection tubes and aspirator bulbs will serve for other substances. The base and reagents, termed "hoolamite," are described in U. S. (Pat. No.) 1, 321, 061 by the same authors and dated the same (see above). Add. Ref.: CA **14, 163** (1920).

5—QUALITATIVE ANALYSIS OF THE ELEMENTS OF THE FIRST TO THIRD GROUPS WHEN PRESENT TOGETHER, WITH SPECIAL REGARD TO SPOT TESTS

Tananaev, N. A. Z. anorg. allgem. Chem. **140,** 320-334 (1924); CA **19,** 1108 (1925).

Test papers are described for the detection of silver, mercury, lead, bismuth, copper, aluminum, iron, nickel, cobalt, manganese, chromium, zinc, and cadmium.

6—MACRO-MICRO REACTIONS

van Eck, P. N. Pharm. Weekblad **62,** 365-376 (1925); CA **19,** 1828 (1925).

The authors describe 51 test paper reactions for the following substances: ozone, water, hydrogen peroxide, nitric acid, ammonia, hydrogen cyanide, benzidine, chlorine, hydrochloric acid, bromine, iodine, carbon monoxide, sulfur dioxide, hydrogen sulfide, phosphorus, arsenic, copper, mercury, iron, magnesium, potassium, glycerol, . . . furfural. Add. Refs.: BOT 226, p. 93; Welcher, Frank J. "Organic Analytical Reagents," Vols. I, II, III, IV (Van Nostrand, New York, N. Y., 1948).

7—MACRO-MICRO METHODS

van Eck, P. N. Pharm. Weekblad **63,** 913-917 (1926); CA **20,** 3143 (1926).

The author describes test paper reactions for hydrogen chloride and hydrogen sulfide.

8—CHEMICAL DETECTION OF RESPIRATORY POISONS

Smolczyk, E. and H. Cobler. Gasmaske **2,** 27-33 (1930); Wasser u. Abwasser **28,** 95 (1930); CA **26,** 1214 (1932).

The description of an apparatus, which indicates the composition and concentration of gases, is given. Paper strips which have been sensitized are used and the reactions involved as well as their sensitivity to hydrogen chloride, sulfur dioxide, ammonia, hydrogen sulfide, hydrogen cyanide and nitric oxide are given.

9—DETECTION OF GASEOUS IMPURITIES OF AIR AND TECHNICAL GASES

Nicolas, E. A. J. H. Chem. Weekblad **27,** 103-104 (1930); CA **24,** 3195 (1930).

Silica gel granules moistened with the appropriate reagent are used instead of filter paper for the qualitative determination of gases.

10—ANALYSIS OF ETHYLENE FOR ANESTHETIC USE

Busi, M. and C. Collina. Atti soc. ital. progresso sci. **19,** 195-199 (1931); CA **26,** 1707 (1932).

A description of methods of detection of carbon dioxide, sulfur dioxide, acetylene, formaldehyde, phosphine, arsine, and hydrogen sulfide in ethylene is given.

11—DETECTION OF POISONOUS GASES

Smolczyk, Ed. Gasmaske **5**, 36-39 (1933); CA **27**, 2397 (1933).

Methods of detection of industrial poisonous gases and chemical war gases are discussed. The sense of smell is often the simplest and safest method for the detection of toxic gases even though simple chemical methods can be devised for these gases.

12—DRAEGER-SCHROETER GAS-DETECTION EQUIPMENT AND ITS USE IN GAS ATTACKS

Stampe, G. and G. A. Schroeter. Gas -schutz u. Luftschutz **4**, 16-18 (1934); CA **28**, 2222 (1934).

A small testing set is described. The method involves concentration of the gas by drawing a known volume of the contaminated atmosphere through silica gel by means of a small hand pump. Identification of the adsorbed gas is accomplished by means of a permanganate solution. A sensitivity of about 0.015 mg/l is attained and a single test requires less than three minutes.

13—DETECTING GASES AND VAPORS IN AIR

Draeger, Otto H. Fr. (Pat. No.) 774, 680, Dec. 11, 1934; CA **29**, 2260 (1934).

A mineral oxidizing-reducing agent, such as potassium permanganate, is used.

14—DETECTING GASES

Draeger, Otto H. Fr. (Pat. No.) 773, 964, Nov. 28, 1934; CA **29**, 2116 (1935).

The detection of small quantities of gases in air is accomplished by passing the contaminated air through silica gel which has been or can be impregnated with appropriate reagents that are colored by the gas to be detected.

15—THE MICRO-DETECTION OF GASES AND VAPORS

Blank, Eugene W. J. Chem. Education 11, 523-525 (1934).

The author has devised an apparatus with which very small quantities of gases can be detected. These laboratory methods are included here because of the unique way in which the detector systems are handled. Included are methods for carbon dioxide, hydrogen cyanide, fluorine, ammonia, hydrogen sulfide, sulfur dioxide, chlorine, and bromine. He refers to P. N. van Eck (Pharm. Weekblad **62**, 365 (1925), who describes fifty-one test paper reactions including tests for the gases ozone, ammonia, hydrogen cyanide, chlorine, hydrogen chloride, bromine, iodine, carbon monoxide, sulfur dioxide, and hydrogen sulfide. Add. Ref.: CA **28**, 6392 (1934).

16—THE DETECTION OF TOXIC GASES AND VAPORS

Leroux, Lucien. Rev. hyg. et med. prevent. **57**, 81-112 (1935).

Methods and techniques are given for the detection and determination of a large number of gases and vapors, together with their toxicity and the need for the various procedures. The following are tabulated: ethylene oxide, acetylene, ammonia, carbon monoxide, sulfur dioxide, chlorine, bromine, hydrogen sulfide, ozone, oxides of nitrogen, oxygen deficiency, hydrogen cyanide, silicon tetrafluoride, hydrogen fluoride, formaldehyde, phosgene, mercury, lewisite, adamsite, chloropicrin, benzyl bromide, arsine, carbon dioxide, phosphine, and mustard gas. Add. Ref.: CA **29**, 3627 (1935).

17—PROBLEMS OF PASSIVE DEFENSE AGAINST THE DANGER OF CHEMICAL GAS ATTACKS

Harsovescu, C. Antigaz (Bucharest) **9**, No. 9/10, 22-34 (1935); Chem. Zentr. **1936**, I, 4240; CA **31**, 7141 (1937).

The author presents a review of the properties and qualitative analyses for hydrogen cyanide, cyanogen chloride, carbon monoxide and chloroacetophenone. Methods for preventing contact of foods and drink with war gases are also discussed.

18—POSSIBILITIES OF DETECTION OF CHEMICALS USED IN WARFARE

Hoeriger, Max. Protar **1**, 197-201 (1935); Chem. Zentr. **1936**, I, 3952; CA **31**, 7141 (1937).

The detection of chemicals used in warfare is difficult because they are often present in minute quantities and also because other contaminating materials are also usually present. Filter papers which have been impregnated with dyes soluble in the material to be detected along with the Draeger-Schroeter apparatus (cf. CA **28**, 2222 (1934) are applicable to the field determination of war gases. Bleaching powder, which reacts with mustard gas with the formation of visible suffocating fumes, also can be used advantageously. For testing the air the portable pressure injector of Koelliker (cf. CA **27**, 4500 (1933), which can be utilized for the detection of low concentration of war gases, is recommended by the author. Particulate matter, e.g., dephenylchloroarsine can be captured on cotton, wool or similar filters.

19—SIMPLE METHODS FOR THE DETECTION AND DETERMINATION OF POISONOUS GASES, VAPORS, SMOKES AND DUSTS IN FACTORY AIR

Weber, Hans H. Zentr. Gewerbehyg. Unfallverhuet. **23**, 177-180 (1936).

The following compounds are discussed: hydrogen cyanide, arsine, phosphine, aniline, chlorine, nitric oxide, sulfur dioxide, hydrogen sulfide, carbon monoxide, halogenated hydrocarbons (halide lamp), smokes, mercury, and dusts of lead, copper, bismuth, tin, aluminum, and zinc by laboratory methods. Add. Ref.: CA **32**, 1609 (1938).

20—THE USE OF INDICATORS FOR THE DETECTION OF POISONOUS GASES AND VAPORS

Heering, D. Gasmaske **8**, 88-89 (1936).

Ammonia, aniline, stibine, arsine, ethylene oxide, bromine, chlorine, chloropicrin, hydrogen cyanide, carbon monoxide, oxides of nitrogen, phosgene, phosphine, mercury, sulfur dioxide, and hydrogen sulfide detection papers are tabulated, together with their sensitivities and reactions. The odor and toxicity of the compounds are given also. Add. Ref. CA **30**, 7059 (1936).

21—SOME METHODS FOR THE DETECTION AND ESTIMATION OF POISONOUS GASES AND VAPORS IN THE AIR (A Practical Manual for the Industrial Hygienist)

Zhithova, A. S., translated by J. B. Ficklen. (Service to Industry, Box 133, West Hartford, Conn., 1936).

The manual includes a large number of detection procedures. However, only five of them are applicable to this discussion. Most of the detector techniques presented are those which apply to air sample solutions, but the paper impregnation method is given for ammonia, chlorine, carbon monoxide, oxides of nitrogen, and hydrogen sulfide. Add. Refs.: CA **31**, 632 (1937); J. Ind. Hyg. Toxicol. 18, 681 (1936).

22—REAGENTS FOR TESTING GASES

Draeger, Bernhard and Otto H. Draeger. Brit. (Pat. No.) 448, 847, June 11, 1936 (addn. to Brit. (Pat. No.) 431, 809, cf. CA **30**, 6, 1936); CA **30**, 7500 (1936).

Potassium permanganate, or other colored oxidizing agent which can be absorbed in a colorless gel such as silica gel, is used. The addition of a buffer solution will maintain the required acidity.

23—MODERN METHODS OF DETECTION AND DETERMINATION OF INDUSTRIAL GASES IN THE ATMOSPHERE

Leclerc, E. and R. Haux. Rev. universelle mines **12**, 293-298 (1936).

Detection and instrumental techniques are given for hydrogen sulfide, hydrogen chloride, hydrogen fluoride, sulfuric acid, sulfur dioxide, nitrogen oxide, chlorine, bromine, carbon dioxide, ammonia, arsine, phosphine, carbon monoxide, combustible gases, turpentine, benzene and benzine. Add. Ref.: CA **30**, 6672 (1936).

24—APPARATUS FOR ESTIMATING POISONOUS GASES IN AIR BY ABSORPTION IN LIQUID REAGENTS

Budan, Gerhard. Fr. (Pat. No.) 822, 042, Dec. 18, 1937; CA **32**, 3212 (1938).

25—ROLE OF THE CHEMIST IN THE PASSIVE DEFENSE AGAINST WAR POISONS

Demanet, Leon. Ing. chim. **21**, 133-140 (1937); CA **31**, 8744 (1937).

The author describes briefly the detection and rapid analysis of the following poison gases and general toxic agents: hydrogen cyanide, cyanogen bromide, cyanogen chloride, carbon monoxide; the suffocating gases: chlorine, phosgene, chloracetyl chloride, trichloroacetyl chloride, chloropicrin (trichloronitromethane); the vesicants: lewisite, adamsite; the labyrinthine poison alpha-alpha'-dichloromethyl ether; the lachrymatory gases; omega-bromotoluene, alpha-bromodimethyl ether, alpha-chlorodimethyl ether, alpha-bromophenylacetonitrile, phenacyl chloride; the sternutatory: diphenylchloroarsine, diphenylcyanoarsine, etc.

26—OBJECTIVE METHOD FOR THE IDENTIFICATION OF WAR CHEMICALS

Webster, D. H. Pharm. Weekblad **74**, 742-759 (1937); CA **31**, 7557 (1937).

The classification of poisonous gases by their physiological effects and their chemical composition is given. Methods for the chemical determination of each class are briefly discussed.

27—DETECTION OF WAR GASES

Dijkstra, D. W. Chem. Weekblad **34**, 351-355 (1937); CA **31**, 7557 (1937).

The author describes simple methods to detect and identify several poison gases. These include chloropicrin, phosgene, diphosgene, mustard gas, hydrogen cyanide, and chloroacetophenone. The contaminant is first concentrated by adsorption on activated carbon. Hoogeveen's article (q.v.) is based on this work.

28—NEW DATA ON THE TOXICOLOGICAL ANALYSIS OF AIR

Kohn-Abrest, E. Rev. chim. ind. (Paris) **46**, 2-14, 40-45, 66-70 (1937).

The author discusses laboratory techniques for the detection and determination of carbon dioxide, carbon monoxide, phosphine, arsine, hydrogen cyanide, oxides of nitrogen, alkyl halogens, solids, and carbonaceous gases. Add. Ref.: CA **31**, 4619 (1937).

29—PROTECTION AGAINST GAS ATTACKS FROM THE AIR. III.

Thomann, J. Schweiz. Apoth.-Ztg. **75**, 37-45 (1937); CA **31**, 8744 (1937).

The author describes group detection methods for chlorine, phosgene, hydrogen chloride, nitrous gases, etc. using test papers. These materials do well as individual detection methods for carbon monoxide, hydrogen cyanide, and carbon dioxide.

30—IBID. VI. 297-300 (1937).

A new official tabulation of chemical warfare substances and their detection in the field is announced and discussed.

31—PORTABLE DEVICE FOR DETECTING THE PRESENCE OF FOREIGN GASES OR SUSPENSIONS IN AIR AND OTHER GASES

Hollman, Franz (to Otto H. Draeger). U. S. (Pat. No.) 2, 069, 035, Jan. 26, 1937; CA **31**, 1664 (1937).

The author presents details of an apparatus with a pump which forces the test gas through a detecting material in a steady stream.

32—GAS DETECTOR

S. van der Windt & Cie. Fr. (Pat. No.) 817, 955, Sept. 15, 1937; CA **32**, 1984 (1938).

Centrifugal force is used to spread out the liquid reagent into a thin layer. The reagent used is then contacted by the air stream to be tested.

33—SHORT SCHEME OF ANALYSIS FOR THE DETECTION OF POISON GASES

Studinger, J. (With Notes On Their Odour And Irritant Action by R. Mueller). Chem. and Ind. (London) **15**, 225-231 (1937). Translated by F. G. Crosse from the original article in Mitteilungen aus dem Gebiete der Lebensmitteluntersuchung und Hygiene **27**, 8-23 (1936) (see CA **31**, 6367 (1937).

Tests given in outline form for arsines, chlorine, chloropicrin, hydrocyanic acid, mono- and tri- chloroacetophenone, mustard gas, nitrogen oxide, phosgene, xylylene bromide, and most other known war gases. Add. Ref.: CA **31**, 3588 (1937).

34—DETECTING FOREIGN SUBSTANCES IN THE ATMOSPHERE

Etablissements Luchaire. Fr. (Pat. No.) 816, 128, July 30, 1937; CA **32**, 1984 (1938).

An apparatus for indicating poisonous gases is described. The gas is bubbled through the reagents. The presence of mercury vapor, gasoline vapor, fire damp, etc., is indicated.

35—WAR GASES AND THE PLANT WORLD

Grogg, Otto. Protar **4**, 144-150, 164-170, 184-192 (1938); CA **33**, 263 (1939).

The author describes test paper detection methods applicable to work with plants for bromine, chlorine, phosgene, diphosgene, chloropicrin, hydrogen cyanide, carbon monoxide, and hydrogen sulfide.

36—DETECTION METHODS OF WAR MATERIALS PROPOSED IN LITERATURE

Dultz, George. Wien. Pharm. Wochschr. **72**, 548-552 (1939); CA **34**, 542 (1940).

A review dealing with the following substances: B, B'-di-

chloroethyl sulfide, war chemicals containing arsenic (aliphatic and aromatic), phosgene, Perstoff, and chloropicrin. 20 references.

37—CHEMICAL DETECTORS FOR POISON GASES

Noriega del Aguila, M. Prim. congr. peruano quim. (Actas y trab.) 1938, 1001-1005; Chim. & ind. (Paris) **43**, 470 (1940); CA **34**, 4179 (1940).

Poison gases can be classified into different groups according to whether they contain chlorine, chlorine and sulfur, chlorine and nitrogen, chlorine and arsenic or a metal by utilizing tests for the halogens, nitrogen, sulfur and Pringsheim's test. Fluorescein formation is the technique used for the identification of Xylyl bromide. The detection of phosgene as diphenylurea, or by paper impregnated with a mixture of benzaldehyde, dimethylamine, and diphenylamine or by means of nitrosodimethylaminophenol is discussed. Several methods for the detection of yperite are given. These methods are: 1) chloride of lime, 2) sodium iodoplatinate paper, 3) the gold chloride or selenium oxide test, 4) Grignard's reagent, 5) the sodium sulfide or platinized asbestos test. Chloropicrin is identified by the Labat test, by reduction to nitrous acid or by the formation of potassium nitrite. Hydrochloric acid is used to decompose trichloroacetaldoxime to hydrogen cyanide, which is then identified.

38—THE SAMPLING AND DETECTION OF WAR GASES

Wlostowska, W. Przeglad Obrony Przeciwlotniczej i Przeciwgazowej Biul. Gaz. **9**, 14-19, 44-49 (1938); Chem. Zentr. **1938**, II, 3194; CA **34**, 5959 (1940).

Methods and equipment for collecting gas samples are described and characteristic reactions for the detection of the known war gases given. The gas-testing apparatus of Draeger-Schroeter is described.

39—DETECTING SMALL QUANTITIES OF ADSORBABLE GAS OR VAPOR IN AIR OR OTHER GASES

Schroeter, August G.-A. (to Otto H. Draeger). U. S. (Pat. No.) 2, 103, 187, Dec. 21, 1938; CA **32**, 1214 (1938).

The contaminated gas stream to be tested is passed through an adsorbing medium such as silica or titanium gel. The gel is treated with a substance which will react with the adsorbed gases to produce a change in the appearance of the adsorbing medium. The method can be used to test for the presence of ammonia or phosgene etc. in air.

40—DETECTING ABSORBABLE OXIDIZABLE GASES OR VAPORS IN AIR OR OTHER NEUTRAL GASES

Bangert, Friedrich K. G. (to Otto H. Draeger). U. S. (Pat. No.) 2, 103, 136, Dec. 21, 1938; CA **32**, 1214 (1938).

The contaminated air is drawn through silica gel where the contaminant is adsorbed and concentrated. The gel is then impregnated with a solution of an inorganic oxidizing agent such as potassium permanganate. The oxidizing agent changes color upon reduction by the contaminating gas.

41—NEW METHODS OF DETECTING WAR GASES

Kimpflin, Georges. La Nature No. **3021**, 174-175 (1938); CA **32**, 5529 (1938).

The preparation of a special reagent for the detection of war gases is described. 100 mg of bromophenol are triturated with 3 cc of 0.05 N sodium hydroxide, water is added to make a total volume of 250 cc. One cc of reagent plus 9 cc of ethyl alcohol along with 2 drops of 0.01 N sulfuric acid must produce a blue-violet color. Acids in contact with the reagent will shift the pH to 4 and produce a yellow color. Air samples suspected of containing these gases are led over heated platinum at the rate of 5000 cc per minute and the resulting materials bubbled through the reagent. It has been determined that at this aspiration rate 2 to 3½ minutes was adequate for the detection of 5 mg/cu.m. of surpalite, yperite, or chloropicrin; 4 minutes for the detection of 10 cu.m. of benzyl bromide. Seven μg of chlorine can be detected with 2 cc of reagent. Two cc of reagent will also detect 9.8 μg of phosgene, and 11 μg of chloropicrin.

42—A GENERAL AND RATIONAL METHOD OF DETECTING WAR GAS

Kling, Andre. Bull. acad. med. **119**, 75-82 (1938); CA **32**, 8034 (1938).

Gases which are hydrolyzed and absorbed in water cause a shift of pH in the solution. The pH change is detectable by adding bromophenol blue. Increased sensitivity of this reaction can be obtained by utilization of dilute ethyl alcohol as the solvent instead of water by by heating the gas stream in a platinum tube before its absorption. The method has been tested on surpalite, yperite, benzyl bromide, and chloropicrin.

43—DETECTING GASES OR MATERIALS SUSPENDED IN AIR

Degea A.-G. (Auergesellschaft). Fr. (Pat. No.) 832, 656, Sept. 30, 1938; CA **33**, 2440 (1939).

This method involves the use of an active gel applied to glass, quartz, a ceramic material, gypsum or some other similar material.

44—GAS DETECTOR

Bell Telephone Manufacturing Company. Belg. (Pat. No.) 435, 247, July 4, 1939; CA **36**, 3405 (1942).

The indicating papers stored hermetically sealed to keep them from air and light. When the bottom is pressed a cover opens and the indicator paper is pushed out by a spring. Belg. (Pat. No.) 437, 315, Dec. 9, 1939. Addn. to Belg. (Pat. No.) 435, 247 (above). The detector consists of two compartments, one contains the gas-indicating substance ready for use, the other contains additional indicator.

45—DETECTION OF GASES USED IN WARFARE

Gigon, A. and M. Noverraz. Schweiz. med. Wochschr. **69**, 859-860 (1939); CA **34**, 1589 (1940).

The air to be tested is bubbled through a tube containing 2 cc of an alcohol-water solution to which bromophenol blue has been added. The indicator changes color due to the acid action of the war gas. This method is a modification of Kling's technique. (cf. CA **32**, 8034 (1938).

46—TUBE FOR THE DETECTION OF POISONOUS SUBSTANCES

Chema, Ltd. and Jan Sigmund. Brit. (Pat. No.) 519, 957, April 10, 1940; CA **36**, 589 (1942).

The author describes a detector tube for the detection of war gases. The detector tube consists of a small tube in which one or more detecting layers are arranged. Examples of detection materials for use in the tube are: 1) wool impregnated with dimethylaminobenzaldehyde which reacts with phosgene; 2) silica gel impregnated with the catalyst copper sulfate (into which is dropped a benzodiacetate solution) which reacts with hydrogen sulfide, 3) and silica gel impregnated with palladium chloride which reacts with carbon monoxide.

47—DETECTOR FOR TOXIC WAR PRODUCTS

Chema Akciova Spolecnost. Fr. (Pat. No.) 850, 815, Dec. 27, 1939; CA **36**, 1870 (1942).

A detector for the products of acid war gases is described. The detector consists of a mixture of powdered barium or cadmium sulfate and infusorial earth. This mixture is impregnated with a solution of a coloring reagent. An alcoholic solution of methyl orange neutralized with dehydrated sodium carbonate is used as the indicator solution.

48—CHEMICAL WARFARE

Beland, C. E. Can. Chem. Process Ind. **26**, 272 (1942); CA **36**, 4929 (1942).

Describes reagents for the detection of: 1) chlorine and bromine, 2) phosgene, 3) hydrogen cyanide, 4) mustard gas and 5) lewisite are, respectively: 1) Baubigny or fluorescein reagent, 2) Harrison reagent, 3) cupric-benzidine acetate reagent (Solution I, cupric acetate, Solution II, saturated aqueous solution of benzidine acetate), 4) Schroter reagent and 5) Peronnet reagent. Tests (1), (2) and (5) are specific; (3) is specific in the absence of chlorine, and (4) specific in the absence of carbon monoxide and hydrogen sulfide.

49—THE DETECTION OF TOXIC GASES AND VAPORS IN INDUSTRY

Vallender, R. B. Chem. & Ind. (London) 58, 330-333 (1939).

The tests devised by the Department of Scientific and Industrial Research of Great Britain are discussed. Detector papers were used for hydrogen sulfide, arsine, hydrogen cyanide, sulfur dioxide, and phosgene. Indicator solutions were used for chlorine, carbon disulfide, aniline, benzene, carbon monoxide, and nitrous fumes. Detection of traces of toxic gases by the sense of smell or by the use of small animals is not reliable. Add. Ref.: CA 33, 4907 (1939).

50—TESTS AVAILABLE FOR THE IDENTIFICATION OF SMALL QUANTITIES OF THE WAR GASES

Cox, H. E. Analyst 64, 807-813 (1939).

Details are given for the detection and identification of toxic gases in air. A group identification system is described. Methods are presented for chlorine, phosgene, methyl chloroformate, diphosgene, chloropicrin, benzyl bromide, bromoacetone, ethyl bromoacetate, bromobenzyl cyanide, chloroacetophenone, diphenylchloroarsine (adamsite), diphenyl-cyanarsine, dichlorodiethyl sulfide (mustard gas), chlorovinylarsine (lewisite), ethyl dichloroarsine (dick), methyl dichloroarsine, phenylcarbylamine chloride, and methyl (or ethyl) chlorosulfonate. Add Ref.: CA 34, 541 (1940).

51—IDENTIFICATION OF WAR GASES

Liberalli, Marcelo R. Rev. quim. farm. (Rio de Janeiro) 4, 49-53 (1939).

Reagents for the detection and determination of chlorine, phosgene, chloropicrin, yperite, arsine, halogenated acetones, carbon monoxide, and hydrogen cyanide are given. Add Ref.: CA 33, 7921 (1939).

52—THE DETECTION OF SMALL QUANTITIES OF WAR GASES (DIJKSTRA'S METHOD)

Hoogeveen, A. P. J., translated by Albert Smith. Chem. & Ind. (London) 18, 550-556 (1940).

The work in this reference (based on that in Dijkstra's article in Chem. Weekblad 34, 351-355 (1937) q.v.) is included because directions for the preparation and use of various filter paper tests are extremely detailed, even though they are not necessarily for air analysis. The precision with which the author describes the techniques is best learned by reading either the original (in Dutch) or its translation. A detailed scheme of analysis is presented both for the contaminated surfaces and for drinking water. Below is a partial list of the papers used to determine qualitatively the presence and identity of the substances mentioned. Add. Ref.: CA 34, 7215 (1940).

War Gases	Test Papers Used	Other Reactions
Chlorine	Mercurochrome 220; fuchsin; fluorescein	Beilstein's
Bromine	Fuchsin-bisulfite; fluorescein	Beilstein's
Phosgene	Same as chlorine; p-dimethylaminobenzaldehyde	Beilstein's
Diphosgene	Same as chlorine; p-dimethylaminobenzaldehyde	Beilstein's
Mustard gas	Same as chlorine; gold chloride	Silver
Methyldichloroarsine	Same as bromine	
Ethyldichloroarsine		
Lewisite	Mercuric chloride; silver nitrate	Gutzeit; copper
Phenersazine chloride	Mercuric chloride; silver nitrate	Gutzeit
Bromoacetone	Same as bromine	Silver nitrate
Chloroacetophenone	None	Silver nitrate
Bromobenzylcyanide	Same as bromine and chlorine	Thiocyanate
Chloropicrin	Same as bromine and chlorine	Diphenylamine
Hydrogen cyanide	Benzidine acetate-copper acetate	Thiocyanate
Cyanogen chloride	Same as chlorine	Thiocyanate
Cyanogen bromide	Same as bromine	Thiocyanate
Diphenylchloroarsine	Mercuric chloride; silver nitrate	Gutzeit, mercury
Diphenylcyanoarsine	Mercuric chloride; silver nitrate	Gutzeit, mercury

53—IDENTIFICATION OF WAR GASES

Sharman, C. F. Chem. & Ind. (London) **18**, 741-742 (1940).

An incandescent filament is used to burn organic agents such as lewisite, mustard gas, and phosgene. Tests for the products of the combustion then are made with specially prepared papers. Lewisite and mustard gas produce a blue color with starch iodate paper; other halogen-containing organic compounds are identified by color reactions after pyrolysis. Add. Ref.: CA **35**, 820 (1941).

54—THE DETECTION OF WAR CHEMICALS

Leikin, M., Khim. Oborona **1940**, No. 9, 20-21; Chem. Zentr. **1941**, I. 1124; CA **37**, 477 (1943).

The authors provide a summary of reactions for the detection of bromoxylene, mono- and tri-chloroacetophenone, sym. dichloroacetophenone, phosgene, diphosgene, chlorine, yperite, chloropicrin, hydrogen cyanide, bromobenzyl cyanide, arsines, lewisite, and adamsite.

55—APPARATUS FOR DETERMINING POISONOUS GASES IN THE AIR DOWN TO CONCENTRATIONS WHERE THEY HAVE NO IRRITATING EFFECT

Gross, Gustav and Gerhard Budan (to Charlotte Gross nee Wagner and Gerhard Budan). Ger. (Pat. No.) 716,641, Dec. 24, 1941 (Cl. 421. 4.06); CA **38**, 2418 (1944).

The reagents required are sealed in fragile glass spheres or ampules.

56—TESTING FOR WAR GASES AND VAPORS

Deutsches Reich, represented by the Oberkommando des Heeres. Ger. (Pat. No.) 712,082, Sept. 11, 1941 (Cl. 421. 4.06); CA **37**, 4334 (1943).

The contaminated air is washed with a circulating solution which is able to absorb the poisonous gas. Part of the circulating solution is removed and replaced with fresh solution.

57—A PORTABLE FIELD COLORIMETER FOR INDUSTRIAL HYGIENE USE

Thomas, T. R. and Leslie Silverman. Ind. Med. **11**, Ind. Hyg. Sect. **3**, 188-190 (1942); J. Ind. Hyg. Toxicol. **24**, Abstract Section 125 (1942).

A portable photoelectric colorimeter is described by the authors. A rapid response and reading circuit is employed which enables the analyst to make colorimetric or nephelometric determinations in the field. The colorimeter tubes are used as absorber tubes and an adjustable set of filters is provided. Add. Ref.: CA **36**, 4221 (1942).

58—APPARATUS FOR DETECTION OF NOXIOUS GASES IN THE AIR

Brigham, Cecil E. and Derek S. B. Shannon (to Standard Telephones and Cables Ltd.) Brit. (Pat. No.) 545,698, June 9, 1942; CA **37**, 1904 (1943).

59—AN APPARATUS FOR THE CHEMICAL INVESTIGATION OF THE AIR IN STABLES (GIESSEN PROCEDURE)

Schwarzmaier, Eberhard. Z. Infektionskrankh., parasit. Krankh. Hyg. Haustiere **58**, 199-204 (1942); CA **37**, 3977 (1943)

A practical, portable and sturdy apparatus is constructed according to the procedure of Traub (Ibid. 45, 1, (1934) for the determination of ammonia hydrogen sulfide and carbon dioxide in stable air.

60—THE ANALYSIS OF ATMOSPHERIC SAMPLES OF EXPLOSIVE CHEMICALS

Goldman, Frederick H. J. Ind. Hyg. Toxicol. **24**, 121-122 (1942).

The general methods for analysis of explosives in air are given for diphenylamine (absorption in sulfuric acid, treatment with ferric ammonium sulfate to form a purple color); nitric acid (diphenylamine proposed as a reagent for this acid); mercury fulminate (spectroscopic technique); nitroglycerine (absorbed in alcohol and treated with phenoldisulfonic acid; analysis of the nitrogen content of a hydrolyzed solution proved insensitive); pentaerythritol tetranitrate (PETN) (same as for nitroglycerine); dimethylaniline (collected in alcohol and treated with nitrous acid to form the nitroso compound); 2,4,6-trinitrophenylmethylnitramine (collected in dilute sulfuric acid, made alkaline, and the resulting color compared with standards); mononitrotoluene, mono-oil (collected in nitrating acid and titrated with titanium chloride); dinitrotoluene (DNT) (collected in alcohol and make alkaline, the initial violet color compared with known solutions); and trinitrotoluene (TNT) (collected in alcohol and made alkaline, the initial color allowed to fade, and the resulting color compared with standards). Hydroxyamines are introduced for color development and their possible uses in nitro aromatic analysis discussed in detail. When acetone is used to absorb the sample the TNT and DNT may be differentiated in the same solution, due to the fading of the DNT complex. If there is no fading, DNT is not present in the sample. Add. Ref.: CA **36**, 5349 (1942).

61—THE PREPARATION OF WAR GAS IDENTIFICATION SETS

Hickey, F. C., O. P. and J. J. Hanley. J. Chem. Education **20**, 286 (1943).

The sense of smell is the most rapid and convenient method of identifying war gases if no interfering odors are present. The so called "sniff set" is patterned after that developed by the Chemical Warfare Service and contains six bottles for use in identification work.

62—VAPOR DETECTOR TUBES AND DETECTOR KIT FOR SOME CHEMICAL AGENTS USED IN GAS WARFARE

Fenton, Paul F. J. Chem. Education **20**, 564-565 (1943).

The U. S. Army M-4 HS Vapor Detection Kit was modified so that chloropicrin, phosgene, and lewisite could be determined by simple reactions on the silica gel in the tubes. After adsorbtion of the air samples the tubes may be treated with a series of reagents for identification of the contaminant, but more reliable results are obtained when a new tube is used for each gas. Add. Ref.: CA **38**, 898 (1944).

63—TESTING TOXIC ATMOSPHERES
Bernz, N. R. Heating, Piping, Air Conditioning **15**, 236-237 (1943); CA **37**, 6053 (1943).
A review. Six references.

Compound	Odor	Test Used
Mustard gas	Garlic or horseradish	Iodoplatinate
Lewisite	Geranium	Freshly prepared Ilosvay paper
Phosgene	Musty hay or pumpkin	Harrison paper
Chloropicrin	Sweetish, anise	Dimethylaniline test paper
Chlorine	Characteristic	Starch-iodide; fluorescein
Bromobenzylcyanide	Sour fruit	Silver nitrate-silica gel
Chloroacetophenone	Apple blossoms	Silver nitrate-silica gel
Adamsite	None	Silver nitrate-silica gel
Nitrogen mustard	Ammoniacal, fishy, to odorless	Not listed

Add. Ref.: CA **37**, 4821 (1943).

64—CHEMICAL IDENTIFICATION OF WAR GASES
Claflin, A. W. and F. C. Hickey. J. Chem. Education **20**, 351-357 (1943).
The authors present detailed procedures for identifying mustard gas, lewisite, phosgene, diphosgene, chloropicrin, chlorine, bromobenzylcyanide, chloroacetophenone, adamsite, and nitrogen mustard. They describe also the appearance, odor, physiological effects, first aid treatment for, and test kit assembly for the gases. Four test papers in the discussion are: mercuric chloride, starch-iodide, Harrison's reagent paper (dimethylaminobenzaldehydediphenylamine), and fluorescein bromide. Solutions which form or change color also are used. The reactions used for the substances listed are tabulated below.

65—DETERMINATION OF VOLATILE SOLVENTS IN AIR, BLOOD AND ORGANS
Fabre, Rene. Ann. pharm. franc. **2**, 108-115 (1944); CA **40**, 5086 (1946).
Carbon disulfide is the only solvent discussed from a detector standpoint; all other procedures mentioned are laboratory techniques.

66—IDENTIFICATION OF GAS WARFARE AGENTS
Zais, Arnold M. J. Chem. Education **21**, 489-490 (1944).
The scheme of analysis given for gas warfare agents is based on the plan of separation used with the M-4 kit and is suitable for field-use. The confirmatory tests are those of Claflin and Hickey (J. Chem. Education **20**, 351-357 (1943). The system is divided into eight tests and five confirmatory reactions, and includes nitrogen mustard, mustard, phosgene, bromobenzyl cyanide, chloropicrin, lewisite, adamsite, chlorine and chloroacetophenone. The reactions are carried out on plain silica gel, on impregnated silica gel, and on filter paper strips. Add. Ref.: CA **39**, 135 (1945).

67—DETECTION OF WAR GASES. Hyrocyanic Acid and Chloropicrin

Fenton, Paul F. J. Chem. Education **21**, 92 (1944). The author, with tests discussed in an earlier article (see above), uses the same tube to test successively for chloropicrin; if this is negative, for phosgene; and if this is negative, for hydrogen cyanide. A special silica gel detector tube for chloropicrin also is described. Add. Ref.: CA **38**, 1811 (1934).

68—DETECTION OF WAR GASES
Fenton, Paul F. J. Chem. Education **21**, 488-489 (1944).
To overcome objections to the procedures described in previous reports (see above), the author proposes a new method of handling field detectors for war gases. Instead of using a new tube for each reaction he transfers the silica gel, through which contaminated air has been aspirated, to depressions in a spot plate. The identification reactions are applied in sequence for adamsite (on the distal cotton plug from the silica gel tube), chlorine (this should be done first to forestall loss of the chlorine), lewisite, chloropicrin, phosgene, hydrogen cyanide, and mustard gas. Add. Ref.: CA **39**, 135 (1945).

69—DETECTION OF GASES IN AIR OR IN OTHER GASES
Biggs, Norman B. Gas World **122**, 430-432 (1945);

Gas J. **245**, 724-725 (1945); CA **39**, 2941 (1945). The author outlines a series of tests which can be used by engineers or chemists for the detection of manufactured gas, carbon monoxide, sulfur dioxide, carbon disulfide, hydrogen sulfide, benzene, and toluene vapors, hydrogen cyanide, nitrous oxide, and oxygen in air or other gases.

70—INDUSTRIAL AIR SAMPLING AND ANALYSIS

Silverman, Leslie. Ind. Hyg. Foundation (4400 Fifth Avenue, Pittsburgh 13, Pa.), Chem. and Toxicol. Ser., Bull. No. **1**, 72 pp (1947).

The author considers techniques for sampling and analyzing air, including test paper and flame test methods, and discusses odors and their measurement. He explains the calibration of sampling instruments and mentions commercial sources of air sampling and analytical apparatus. Add. Ref.: CA **42**, 3286 (1948).

71—AN APPRAISAL OF PRESENT DAY FIELD INSTRUMENTS

Setterlind, Alfred N. Am. Ind. Hyg. Assoc. Quart. **9**, 35-45 (1948).

The author discusses commercially available instruments from the standpoint of their faults and limitations rather than their virtues, with emphasis on portability, reliability, and sensitivity. Included in the descriptions are standard impingers, flowmeters, motor controls, chlorinated hydrocarbon samplers, mercury-vapor detectors, carbon monoxide indicators, benzene indicators, and colorimetric filter paper tests. Add. Ref.: CA **44**, 1285 (1950).

72—GAS ANALYSIS

Nash, Leonard K. Anal. Chem. **22**, 108-121 (1950). The author presents a review of general methods and equipment, together with special methods for specific gases, including oxygen, ozone, the carbon oxides, nitrogen and sulfur compounds, halogens and hydrocarbons, hydrogen, phosphine, mercury, etc. 359 references.

73—DETECTION OF SOLVENT VAPORS IN AIR

Draegerwerk, Heinrich u. Bernhard Draeger. Ger. (Pat. No.) 1,015,242, Sept. 5, 1957 (Cl.42.1); CA **54**, 12442 (1960).

A method for the detection of some solvent vapors is provided.

74—SAMPLING AND ANALYSIS OF AIR POLLUTANTS

Cralley, Lester V. Proc. Air Pollution Smoke Prevention Assoc. Am. **1950**, 107-115; CA **45**, 6329 1951).

A review, with 55 references.

75—MICRO ANALYSIS OF GASES — I

Malissa, I. H. Mikrochemie ver. Mikrochim. Acta **38**, 213-217 (1951), CA **45**, 9417 (1951).

The author describes an apparatus which can be used to determine gases liberated from solution. The results obtained are reproducible because the conditions of the experiment are always the same.

76—MICRO-ANALYSIS OF GASES — II

Malissa, H., A. Musil, and R. Kriebich. Mikrochemie ver. Mikrochim. Acta **38**, 385-402 (1951); CA **46**, 2441 (1952).

Using the apparatus described in the previous reference, the authors studied the best tests for ammonia, hydrogen sulfide, and the hydrides of arsenic, antimony, and phosphorus. Rarely did the sensitivity agree well with previously published claims. With the exception of ammonia, the results show that with this apparatus, a marked improvement has been made in the method of making the tests.

77—MICRO-ANALYSIS OF GASES — III

Musil, A., H. Malissa, and R. Kreibich. Mikrochemie ver. Mikrochim. Acta **38**, 403-412 (1951); CA **46**, 2441 (1952).

The authors describe a procedure which allows the successive determination of ammonia, arsenic, and antimony in the presence of one another. This method is not always adequate for the detection of antimony in the presence of arsenic. The detection of ammonia is accomplished by treating first with a neutral solution consisting of manganous nitrate and silver nitrate; a black spot of manganese dioxide is formed. Compounds which contain trivalent arsenic are reduced by aluminum in a sodium hydroxide solution while pentavalent arsenic compounds are not. Following the ammonia test, the treatment results in a lemon yellow spot of silver-arsenic-nitrate complex. Antimony produces a black spot on the aluminum.

78—RAPID METHOD OF QUANTITATIVE GAS ANALYSIS BY MEANS OF DETECTOR TUBES

Kitagawa, Tetsuzo. Kagaku no Ryoiki (J. Japan. Chem.) **6**, 386-397 (1952); CA **46**, 11013 (1952).

A review, including Kitagawa's own results.

79—LIMITS OF ALLOWABLE CONCENTRATIONS OF ATMOSPHERIC POLLUTANTS. Book I

Ryazanov, V. A., Editor, translated by B. S. Levine. (U. S. Dept. of Commerce, Office of Technical Services, Washington, D. C., 1952).

The book discusses various committee reports on the principles of establishing hygienic standards for air pollution control. Also discussed are the accepted procedures and techniques for collecting and analyzing air samples. The methods for carbon disulfide and for soot, in air, can be applied as detector techniques or field methods. Detailed laboratory procedures are described for sulfur dioxide, chlorine, hydrogen sulfide, oxides of nitrogen, carbon monoxide, mercury, and lead, in air.

80—GAS-ANALYZING AND GAS-DETECTING APPARATUS IN INDUSTRIAL-SANITARY CHEMISTRY

Derevyanko, D. G. Novosti Med. **1952**, No. 26, 65-68; CA **49**, 13564 (1955).

A critical review.

81—RAPID METHODS FOR THE DETERMINATION OF INJURIOUS SUBSTANCES IN THE AIR

Zhitkova, A. S. Novosti Med. **1952**, No. 26, 58-61. Tables are given for the specific identification of chlorine, hydrogen fluoride, hydrogen sulfide, carbon disulfide, ammonia, acetylene, aniline, sulfur dioxide, sulfur trioxide, formaldehyde, acetone, hydrogen cyanide, chromic acid, carbon monoxide, and arsine. Add. Ref.: CA **49**, 12197 (1955).

82—FIELD EQUIPMENT FOR THE COLLECTION AND EVALUATION OF TOXIC AND RADIOACTIVE CONTAMINANTS

Harris, W. B., H. D. Levine, and M. Eisenbud. Arch. Ind. Hyg. Occupational Med. **7**, 490-502 (1953); CA **47**, 12007 (1953).

The author describes a sampling pump, a 6-v. sampler, filter holder, filter paper, cascade impactor, high volume air sampler, aerotec unit, beta filter paper meter, and radon sampler, suitable for atmospheric studies. *This is included because of the versatility of the pump and the filter paper holder.*

83—DETERMINATION OF ATMOSPHERIC CONTAMINANTS

Clayton, George D. Am. Gas Assoc., Proc. 35th Ann. Conv. **1953**, 892-923; CA **48**, 14060 (1954).

Methods and equipment for the sampling and analysis of atmosphere contaminants are described.

84—WEAPONS AGAINST AIR POLLUTION

Hartz, Nelson W. Safety Maintenance and Production **106**, No. 5, 44-45 (1953); CA **48**, 12348 (1954).

The author discusses several methods for determining gaseous contaminants in air.

85—ESTIMATION OF TOXIC GASES IN AIR

Fukuyama, Tomitaro, Tokuro Sato, Aiko Watanabe and Mieko Yamada. Bull. Inst. Pub. (Tokyo) **3**, No. 1, 9 (1953) (English summary); CA **49**, 14236 (1955).

The authors review the most practical methods for the detection and determination of hydrogen cyanide, ammonia, aniline, nitric oxide, and pyridine in air.

86—INDIVIDUAL PROTECTIVE AND DETECTION EQUIPMENT

Dept. of the Army Technical Manual, TM 3-290; Dept. of the Air Force Technical Order, TO 39C-10C-1, pp. 56-80, Sept. 1953.

Several detector kits are described in the manual, together with their use, application, and restrictions. The M7A1 and the M7 detector crayons are sensitive to vesicants and, applied to surfaces which are or may become contaminated, change color from pink to blue. The crayons are affected by several other chemicals including bleach and high concentrations of acids. The crayons are used also for the detection of G-agents, which cause the pink crayons to turn yellow. The M-5 liquid vesicant detector paint is painted on the surface; when the paint comes in contact with the vesicant the color changes from olive-green to red. This is not affected by the vapor but only by droplets of the vesicant. M-6 detector paper, olive-green on one side and used for distribution out-of-doors, turns red with droplets of the vesicant and is stable for three months in the open. The M9A2 chemical agent detector kit is a compact unit for detecting and identifying chemical agents. It will reveal dangerous concentrations of chemical agents by color changes in tubes through which contaminated air has been drawn with a hand pump. Chemical agents which can be detected with the kit are mustard gas (H), nitrogen mustard (HN), lewisite (L), dichloroethylarsine (ED), hydrogen cyanide (AC), phosgene (CG), cyanogen chloride (CK), and G-agents. Most of the tubes used for the detection of these agents have silica gel impregnated with sensitive reagents. One tube, containing unimpregnated silica gel used for G-agents and cyanogen chloride, is treated later with a reagent solution for color development. Lewisite, dichloroethyl arsine, and nitrogen mustard are detected with a specially prepared tube and finally treated with a chemical agent to develop the color. Mustard gas is detected in a specially designated tube with a heating pad surrounding the active area, which is activated by an exothermic reaction. Several other kits are described for use by chemical laboratory teams for the identification of chemical agents and smokes.

87—ESTIMATION OF THE CONCENTRATION OF SLIGHTLY DISSOCIABLE GASES

Nogari, Kinzo. Japan (Pat. No.) 6345, Dec. 9, 1953; CA **48**, 12618 (1954).

Carbon dioxide, ammonia, hydrogen sulfide, or sulfuric acid vapor can be determined by utilizing a series of indicators which show concentration differences on the basis of pH differences.

88—THE LINEAR COLORIMETRIC METHOD FOR THE DETERMINATION OF GASES AND VAPORS IN INDUSTRIAL HEALTH INVESTIGATIONS

Filyanskaya, E. D. Trudy Nauch. Sessii Vsesoyuz. Nauch.-Issledovatel. Inst. Okhrany Truda **1954** (1955). No. 1, 198-204; Referat. Zhur., Met. 1957, Abstr. No. 1648; Ref. Zhur., Khim., **1956**, Abstr. No. 75, 347; AA **4**, 3147 (1957).

The authors state that the determination of airborne contaminants can be carried out by utilizing an indicator that changes color when contaminated air is drawn through it. A different type indicator is needed for each contaminant. The indicating reagent is usually impregnated on silica gel. A study was made to determine the influence of the specific surface of the silica gel and the concentration of a solution of lead acetate on the length of the stained column and its boundary. The influence of varying the drying temperature of the silica gel, moisture variations and additional other ions to the impregnated silica gel are studied. The contaminant used in this study was hydrogen sulfide. The study shows that when the specific surface of the silica gel is decreased by drying, the length of the colored column is decreased and the color intensity and boundary sharpness are decreased. When the silica gel granules are heavily coated with the indicator reagent an intense color and sharp boundary are found. The introduction of chloride ion into the reagent produces a longer colored column. Indicator tubes are recommended for the determination of hydrogen sulfide, chlorine, ammonia, gasoline vapor, benzene, toluene, and nitrogen oxides in air.

89—METHODS AND INSTRUMENTATION FOR AIR SAMPLING

Dieringer, L. F., and W. T. Ingram. Instruments and Automation **27**, 1086-1089 (1954); AA **1**, 2861 (1954).

The authors review sampling methods for particulate matter and gases. Advances in sampling methods made possible by photoelectric devices and chemical instrumentation are described.

90—ANALYTICAL PROCEDURE FOR THE DETECTION OF GASES

Guatelli, Manuel A. Rev. asoc. bioquim. arg. **18**, 3-40 (1954).

The author discusses the detection, determination, and toxicity of each of the following gases: hydrogen cyanide, cyanogen, sulfur dioxide, hydrogen sulfide, chlorine, bromine, oxides of nitrogen, ozone, hydrogen fluoride, carbon dioxide, sulfur trioxide, carbon monoxide, hydrogen, carbon disulfide, ammonia, aniline, piperidine, hydrogen chloride, phosgene, methyl chloride, methyl bromide, and Freon. He presents also a scheme of analysis. Add. Ref.; CA **48**, 8124 (1954).

91—ANALYSIS OF MEDICALLY IMPORTANT GASES USING SPOT TESTS

Massmann, W. Arch. Gewerbepathol. Gewerbehyg. **13**, 262-275 (1954).

The author discusses in detail the techniques for evaluating and testing detectors used to analyze air for arsine, hydrogen sulfide, and sulfur dioxide. Add. Ref.: IHD **19**, 599 (1955).

92—LIMITS OF ALLOWABLE CONCENTRATIONS OF ATMOSPHERIC POLLUTANTS. Book 2.

Ryazanov, V. A., Editor, translated by B. S. Levine. (U. S. Dept. of Commerce, Office of Technical Services, Washington, D. C., 1955).

Strictly laboratory procedures are described for fluorine, sulfuric acid, sulfur dioxide and sulfuric acid mixtures, arsine and phosphine mixtures, phenol, lead, mercury, manganese, hydrocarbons, and benzene. Methods for chlorine and sulfur dioxide are applicable to field determination as well. The basis for establishing a limit of air pollution concentration is discussed for each of the above agents.

93—DETERMINATION OF TOXIC GAS COMPONENTS IN AIR BY THE DEICH STOP-METHOD

Krause, E. Chem. Tech. (Berlin) **7**, 552-555 (1955); AA **3**, 1893 (1956); CA **50**, 12750 (1956).

The author proposes a method for determining traces of hydrogen sulfide, sulfur dioxide, chlorine, ammonia, and hydrogen chloride.

94—DETECTION OF CERTAIN IONS IN 10^{-10} - to 10^{-15} -GRAM PARTICLES

Seely, Ben K. Anal. Chem. **27**, 93-95 (1955).

The modified spot test methods described in this paper depend on microscopic observation of chemical reactions in the surface of a gelatin medium sensitized with a mercurous salt. The author discusses in detail procedures for the identification of copper, cobalt, nickel, ferrous and ferric ions, sodium, potassium, iodides, and carbonates, in particulate matter. Particles are collected on the surface of a 0.3 mm thick gelatin-glycerol medium on a microscope slide. The medium may be sensitized by dissolving 1 part of the specific reagent in 9 parts of the gelatin; or the particles may be collected on the surface of unsensitized gelatin, and the reagent applied to the particles by diffusion through a plastic film covering the sample. In either procedure the specific reagent reacts with the particle to form a characteristic color or halo which can be identified microscopically.

Substance	Reagent	Color
Iodides	Mercurous fluosilicate	Strong yellow halo
Copper	Rubeanic acid + ammonium	Intense green or green-black halo
Cobalt	acetate in ethylene	Yellow or yellow-brown halo
Nickel	glycol monoethyl ether	Intense blue or blue-violet halo
Ferrous ion	2,2'-bipyridine	Deep red, transparent halo
Ferrous ion	Potass. ferricyanide	Turnbull's blue halo
Ferric ion	Potass. ferrocyanide	Prussian blue halo
Sodium	Fluosilicic acid	Feathery-crystal halo
Potassium	Fluosilicic acid	Halo of small cubic crystals
Carbonates	Nickel dimethylglyoxime equilibrium soln.	Red needle-like crystals
Carbonates	Conc. hydrochloric acid	Carbon dioxide bubbles

Add. Ref.: CA **49**, 3731 (1955).

95—SAMPLING AND ANALYZING AIR FOR CONTAMINANTS

Silverman, Leslie. Air Conditioning, Heating, and Ventilating **52**, No. 8, 88-100 (1955).

Granules of inert material impregnated with palladium sulfate and molybedenum turn yellowish green to dark green with 10 to 10,000 ppm of carbon monoxide; test papers impregnated with 0.5% palladium chloride turn gray to black with 25 to 1,000 ppm. Aromatic hydrocarbons, carbon monoxide, hydrogen cyanide, hydrogen sulfide, and sulfur dioxide are determined by adsorption onto granules of inert material impregnated with suitable reagents. Ammonia, arsine, carbon dioxide, carbon monoxide, chlorine, hydrogen cyanide, hydrogen sulfide, mercury, methyl bromide, phosgene, phosphine, stibine, and sulfur dioxide are detected with test papers. A unit for ozone sampling, impinger units, and other common devices used in industrial health work are illustrated and described, together with factors influencing their use, and precautions to be observed with them. Add. Ref.: CA **49**, 14390 (1955).

96—PRODUCTION OF APPROVED INSTRUMENTS FOR DETERMINATION OF AIR CONTAMINATION

Kudachkov, N. A. Gazovaya Prom. **5**, 29 (1956).
The All-Union Scientific Research Institute of Labor Safety of the All-Union Central Council of Trade Unions in Leningrad in 1956 recommended a universal portable gas analyzer of the inspector type (UG-1) for the rapid estimation in air of hydrogen sulfide, chlorine, ammonia, gasoline, benzene, toluene, and oxides of nitrogen. The operating principle is based on color changes in an indicator tube (not discussed) under the action of gases and vapors drawn through the tube. The length of the colored column is proportional to the concentration of the contaminant in the air. The suggested sampling time is one to five minutes (rate not given), and the accuracy is 10 to 15%. The ranges of sensitivity are:

Hydrogen sulfide	0.002	to	0.35	mg/liter
Chlorine	0.002	to	0.25	mg/liter
Ammonia	0.002	to	0.30	mg/liter
Gasoline vapor	0.2	to	30.0	mg/liter
Benzene vapor	0.1	to	2.0	mg/liter

Add. Ref.: CA **50**, 13333 (1956).

97—NEW METHODS IN GAS ANALYSIS. I. MEASUREMENT OF TENSIONS BY MICRO-CHEMICAL MEANS (VAPOR SPACE ANALYSIS)

Schulek, E., E. Pungor, and J. Trompler. Mikrochim. Acta **1956**, 1005-1022 (in German).

The basic principles of gas analysis are reviewed and a new device described for taking gas samples with exactness. The procedure is illustrated by analyses of methanol and ethanol.

98—A COLOUR REAGENT FOR CATIONS

Harrop, D. and E. F. G. Herington. Analyst **81**, 499-500 (1956).

Rubeanic acid and trisodium pentacyanoamminoferrate react to form a rubeanic acid-pentacyanide complex which gives, with many heavy metal ions, characteristically colored salts insoluble in acetic acid. Filter paper showed the following coored spots after being sprayed with reagent and washed with 0.2 N acetic acid:

Periodic Group

I A: Sodium, no color.

I B: Copper, brown black; silver, grayish brown; gold, green.

II A: Magnesium, no color; calcium, no color.

II B: Zinc, brick red; cadmium, blue; bivalent mercury, green grey; monovalent mercury, grayish brown.

III A: Aluminum, no color; thallium, pale gray; the rare earths, lanthanum, cerium, praseodymium, neodymium, samarium, gadolinium, and holmium, very pale blue.

IV A: Tin, quadrivalent, pale red brown; bivalent tin, red brown; lead, purplish gray.

IV B: Titanium, brown; zirconium, red purple; thallium, red purple.

V A: Antimony, no color; bismuth, brown.

V B: Ortho-vanadate, no color; niobium, no color; tantalum, no color.

VI B: Chromium, no color; molybdate, very pale brown; tungstate, no color; uranyl, brown.

VII B: Manganese, blue.

VIII : Iron, green; cobalt, brown green; nickel, blue; rhodium, no color; palladium, yellow brown; iridium hexachloride, no color; chloroplatinate, no color.

Filter paper collections of dust might react with the above reagent if the papers first were treated to dissolve the dust. Add. Ref.: CA **51**, 934 (1957).

99—POLLUTION
Avy, A. P. Pollution air et ses mefaits, Conf. soc. pathol. comparee, Paris **1956**, 87-112 (Pub. 1957); CA **51**, 13276 (1957).

The author states that sampling can be simplified by determining the most common pollutants such as particulates, sulfur dioxide, carbon dioxide and lead. Some values obtained by several investigators are given.

100—SAMPLING AND ANALYZING AIR FOR CONTAMINANTS IN WORK PLACES
Silverman, Leslie. Encyclopedia of Instrumentation for Industrial Hygiene, pp. 7-25 (Univ. of Michigan, Inst. of Industrial Health, Ann Arbor, Mich., 1956).

The author reviews techniques for sampling and analyzing air. Direct-reacting chemical devices for gases and vapors are tabulated. Impregnated granules of inert material are used for the determination of aromatic hydrocarbons, carbon monoxide, hydrogen cyanide, hydrogen sulfide, and sulfur dioxide. Test papers are used for the detection of ammonia, arsine, carbon dioxide, carbon monoxide, chlorine, hydrogen cyanide, hydrogen sulfide, mercury, methyl bromide, phosgene, phosphine, stibine, and sulfur dioxide. Several common devices used in industrial health work are described, together with factors influencing their use, and precautions to be observed with them.

101—MICRO-DETERMINATION OF ELEMENTAL FLUORINE
Peregud, E. A. and B. S. Boikina. Zhur. Anal. Khim. **12**, 513-515 (1957); J. Anal. Chem. U.S.S.R. **12**, 531-533 (1957) (English translation).

Coarse silica gel, sieved so that particles from 260 to 300 microns were retained, was washed with 6N hydrochloric acid by boiling, then washed with water, calcined at 750° C., and treated with the active agent. Two methods are outlined for the detection of fluorine in air, one using fluorescein, the other employing methyl red. The sensitivity of the latter method is 0.35 μg fluorine in 2 ml. Add. Refs.: CA **52**, 1852; 18073 (1958); AA **5**, 1201 (1958).

102—NO TITLE
Kozlyaeva, T. N., and I. G. Vorokhobin. Trans. Phys. Chem. Lab. of the All-Union Inst. of Occupational Hygiene and Diseases in Leningrad, p. 101 (1951). Publication not available. However, the method of preparing granules for detector tubes describes in this article is repeated in that above.

103—FIELD TYPE COLORIMETRIC TESTERS FOR GASES AND PARTICULATE MATTER
McConnaughey, Paul W. Presented at the annual meeting of the American Industrial Hygiene Association, Atlantic City, N. J., 1958. (Author's abstract). See Section II for details of each detector.

The author presents some recent developments in colorimetric analysis and presents analytical methods for some toxic substances. Analytical methods are given for arsine, carbon monoxide, hydrogen fluoride, nitrogen dioxide, chlorine, mercury vapor, and lead. The techniques used require almost no training for their field use by inexperienced personnel.

104—RAPID SEMI-MICRO METHODS FOR CHEMICAL AND INDUSTRIAL HYGIENE CONTROL OF TECHNICAL OPERATIONS
Iwanoff, T. Chem. Tech. (Berlin) **10**, 35-40 (1958); AA **5**,3536 (1958).

The author describes methods for the determination of some industrial toxicants. Rapid methods for aniline vapor, nitrous and nitric oxides, hydrogen cyanide, benzene, mineral oil vapors, and carbon monoxide in air are described and particular methods are recommended.

105—DETECTION OF ALCOLOH IN AIR
Draegerwerk, Heinrich u. Bernhard Draeger. Ger. (Pat. No.) 932,750, Sept. 8, 1955 (Cl. 42.**1**, 406); CA **53**, 5024 (1959).

Detector tubes for the determination of alcohol use small rods of porous sintered material as the reagent carrier.

106—FIELD TESTING FOR AIR CONTAMINANTS
McConnaughey, Paul W. Safety Maintenance **116**, 44-46 (1958); IHD **23**, 115 (1959).

Relatively inexperienced personnel can detect and measure many toxic airborne substances in the field. Simple and rapid methods and equipment are available. Prepared chemical reagents are available for detecting and analyzing, semi-quantitatively, some of these toxic materials. The required reagents are supplied in glass tubes whose tips are broken off when preparing for the test. Color changes which indicate the concentration of a toxic material are usually compared against a standard color chart or by the length of the color change in the indicator tube. The author briefly describes detectors for lead dust and fume, arsine, hydrogen fluoride, hydrogen sulfide, mercury vapor, and nitrogen dioxide. Some gases and vapors, such as hydrogen sulfide, sulfur dioxide and aromatic hydrocarbons require reagents that are stable for short periods of time. These, however, can be easily prepared from components which are stored separately and mixed only when needed.

107—AIR POLLUTION

Kay, Kingsley. Anal. Chem. (Applied Reviews, Part II) **31**, 633-645 (1959).

In the author's discussion of the newer methods of air pollution analysis, the use of detectors and field unit analytical techniques is mentioned for each contaminant. Ten new detector procedures for this year are discussed.

108—REPORT ON THE DRAEGER GAS DETECTOR

American Conference of Governmental Industrial Hygienists (A.C.G.I.H.). Transactions of the Twenty-first Annual Meeting, pp. 125-127 (1959).

A summarized report offered to the convention of the A.C.G.I.H. was approved. A new instrument on the market is well-constructed. It has a lightweight pump of approximately 100 cubic centimeters volume per stroke, to overcome one of the major objections to the detector tube, which required as many as fifty strokes to detect low concentrations. A counting device was suggested. (See the following individual compounds listed separately: mercury, toluene, nitrous gases, trichloroethylene and other halogenated hydrocarbons, carbon monoxide, benzene, hydrocarbons, and alcohol.)

109—AN ALARM FOR THE DETECTION OF TOXIC INDUSTRIAL GASES

Kinnear, A. M. Chem. & Ind. (London) **1959**, 361-363; AA **6**, 5073 (1959).

Air is drawn through filter paper tape which is illuminated at the point where sample is taken. The contaminant reacts with the reagent impregnated into the paper and forms a colored product which reduces the amount of reflected light reaching the photocell which trips the alarm. A reagent pump built into the system can be used to impregnate the paper with up to three separate reagents. It is also possible to utilize dry, untreated, or previously impregnated tapes. The limits of detection are about 0.3 ppm of hydrogen, sulfide, 0.5 ppm of hydrogen cyanide, 0.9 ppm of phosgene, 0.1 ppm of chlorine and 1.5 ppm of sulfur dioxide.

110—INDUSTRIAL HYGIENE INSTRUMENTS (A REVIEW OF COMMERCIALLY-AVAILABLE EQUIPMENT)

Cook, Warren A. National Safety News **79**, 32-33, 101-109 (1959).

The author discusses the use of several different types of instruments in the field of industrial health and safety. Grab sample devices are mentioned and their application to rapid detection of poisonous gases and vapors is outlined. Of the three commercial detector sources described, two are American: Mine Safety Appliances Company (Uni-jet), and Union Industrial Equipment Company, while the third is German, Draegerwerk. One of the advantages of direct-reading devices is that operations may be changed and the evaluation of the change may be made immediately.

111—A SPOT TEST ANALYSIS OF THE GROUP III CATIONS

Marion, Stephen P. and Isaac Zlochower. J. Chem. Educ. **36**, 379-380 (1959).

The authors use spot tests with both liquid reagents and impregnated, dried reagent papers, to detect nickel, iron, cobalt, aluminum, manganese, chromium, and zinc. Add. Ref.: CA **54**, 2093 (1960).

112—PORTABLE GAS ANALYSIS INSTRUMENTS. DAVIS TOXIC GAS DETECTOR KIT (MODELS NF AND F)

Davis Emergency Equipment Company, Inc. (Davis Instrument Division), Newark, N. J.

Two instruments with tubes for the detection of toxic gases and vapor in the air are described. The Model NF is designed with an aspirator bulb pump and a set of detector tubes for halogenated hydrocarbons. The Model F kit has a pyrolysis unit and accessary equipment, and is suitable for the determination of forty-six gases and vapors. The length of the stain in the detector tube is measured and compared with standard curves for the compound being tested.

113—U.S.S.R LITERATURE ON AIR POLLUTION, RELATED OCCUPATIONAL DISEASES. A SURVEY. VOL. 4

Levine, B. S. (U.S. Dept. of Commerce, OTS No. 60-21913, Washington 25, D. C., 1960).

Some of the pieces of apparatus mentioned, as well as several of the analytical methods, are applicable to field detection, notably those for dimethylaniline and nitrogen oxides in air.

114—DETECTOR FOR TOXIC SUBSTANCES IN AIR

Draegerwerk, Heinrich u. Bernhard Draeger (by Edgar Koch). Ger. (Pat. No.) 1,013,098, Aug. 1, 1957 (Cl. 42.**1**); CA **54**, 12442 (1960).

(No description given in the abstract.)

115—STUDIES ON SPOT PAPERS

Ackermann, Gerhard. Mikrochim. Acta **1959**, 357-369 (in German); CA **54**, 24097 (1960).

Author describes a series of physical and chemical tests made on 69 varieties of filter paper with respect to their use in spot test analysis. Drop surface, the paper surface which 1 drop (50 μl) of 0.25 N potassium chromate solution wets, was measured. Iron and copper impurities in the papers and exchange capacity of the papers were determined. Sensitivity was determined for the sodium rhodizonate spot test for divalent lead ion, dipicrylamine test for potassium ion, and ilver nitrate test for chromate ion. Papers of high exchange capacity had greater sensitivity for lead ion detection, and those which were thicker and thus had smaller drop surface showed higher sensitivity for the detection of chromate ion.

116—RESEARCH IN CHEMICAL COMPOSITION OF SOME FORMS OF ATMOSPHERIC PARTICLES

Antisari, O. Vittori. Chicago Univ., Dept. Meteorol., Tech. Note **5**, 48 pp. (1956); CA **54**, 25422 (1960).

Procedures were developed for identifying the chemical composition and size of airborne particles. The basic technique involves the capture of the particles in a specially treated gel. Reagents in the gel produce Liesegang rings. Identification of the particles is made by 1 or more of 3 factors: 1) the character of the pattern of the precipitate, 2) the color of the precipitate, or 3) its change of color. Tests were developed for particles containing the following substances: chlorides soluble iodide, soluble sulfide, soluble ferrocyanide, soluble sulfates, nitrates, potassium ion, soluble silver, fluorine, lead, and all heavy metals. Details are given for the preparation of the gels to be used for specific tests, and techniques for the capture of particles are discussed . . . Cf. Fuel Abstr. **24**, Abstr. No. 5629 (1958).

117—ANALYTICAL METHODS FOR HARMFUL IMPURITIES IN THE WORKER'S ENVIRONMENT

Kobayashi, Yoshitaka. Kogyo Kagaku Zasshi **61**, 509-514 (1958); CA **55**, 10764 (1961).

Various chemical and physical methods for the determination of harmful materials used in chemical industry are reviewed.

118—GAS-MASK ATTACHMENT FOR IDENTIFYING TOXIC GASES

Draegerwerk, Heinrich und Bernhard Draeger. Ger. (Pat. No.) 1,087,376 (Cl. 42.**1**). Appl. May 2, 1959; CA **56**, 3778 (1962).

The authors describe a transparent attachment to the mask filter which allows an indicator paper to be placed in the air passage. Nonstable indicators are used in solution and are contained in a fragile vial which can be broken by finger pressure thus spreading the indicator on paper or other material.

119—CALIBRATION AND EVALUATION OF GAS DETECTING TUBES

Kusnetz, Howard L., Bernard E. Saltzman, and Marshall B. LaNier. Am. Ind. Hyg. Assoc. J. **21**, 361-373 (1960).

The authors present theoretical and practical principles for the calibration of direct reading colorimetric gas detecting devices. Because current gas-detecting tubes, in general, are semi-quantitative devices useful in screening or preliminary survey work, their use should be restricted to qualified industrial hygienists who are aware of the toxicity of contaminants and of the tube performances. Tubes and auxiliary equipment should be calibrated before use if possible. Results of tests are presented for the following specific gases: arsine, carbon monoxide, nitrogen dioxide, stribine, phosgene, chlorine, chlorine dioxide, and mercury vapor.

120—GAS ANALYSIS

Hobbs, A. P. Anal. Chem., Anal. Reviews **32**, No. 5, 54R-63R (1960).

Several advances in detector tubes and paper techniques are mentioned, including those for hydrogen cyanide, phosgene, arsenic halide, acetaldehyde, phosphine, and lewisite. 300 references.

121—THE USE OF DETECTORS AND TEST KITS IN INDUSTRIAL HYGIENE INVESTIGATIONS

Gisclard, J. Brennan. A.M.A. Arch. Ind. Health **21**, 250-260 (1960).

A discussion of portable, easily-operated samplers and detecting kits for air contaminants, including their advantages and limitations. Instances of actual application of test kits are described and future applications indicated. Add. Refs.: A.P.C.A. Abstr. **5**, 3069 (1960); CA **54**, 12439 (1960).

122—THE RAPID MEASUREMENT OF TOXIC GASES AND VAPORS

Kitagawa, Tetsuzo. Abstracts of papers presented at the 13th International Congress on Occupational Health, New York (July, 1960).

"For the measurement of toxic gases and vapors in industrial environments, the method must be rapid and simple in operation, require only a small air sample, and have high accuracy and selectivity. The equipment must be portable, and it must be possible to record the results. The most suitable method is that using detector tubes, whose color change shows the concentration of gas. Detector tubes, however, have been so inaccurate that they might be considered semi-quantitative rather than quantitative. The writer has developed a length measuring method with detector tubes by making corrections for the inside diameter of tubes and for temperature and by simplifying correction method, thus obtaining considerably increased accuracy. Besides the length measuring method, volumetric and colorimetric methods with detector tubes have also been used . . . " (Transcript of paper distributed by the author.) Add. Ref.: Ind. Hyg. News Report **3**, No. 11, Nov., 1960.

123—SIMPLE METHODS FOR MICRODETERMINATION OF INDUSTRIAL TOXICS IN AIR

Zurlo, N. and L. Metrico. La Medicina del Lavoro (Industrial Medicine) (Milan) (English translation) **51**, 241-358 (1960).

The article includes numerous analytical methods, each described in detail, together with many field methods. The authors discuss 79 different industrially important chemical compounds, and give 2 or more analytical procedures for each one. Most of the procedures are already described under the individual compounds in our book.

124—AUTOMATIC RECORDING GAS ANALYZER BASED ON A LINE-COLOR METHOD

Derevyanko, D. G. and Yu G. Zverev. Sb. Nauchn. Rabot. Inst. Okhrany Tr. Vses. Tsentr. Soveta Prof. Soyuzov **1961**, No. 2, 106-113; CA **58**, 5 (1963).

An automatic recording gas analyzer (AGS-1) operates by periodically pressing between 2 flat glass plates a reagent treated indicator tape. "In the upper motionless plate is a longitudinal groove (width 1 mm, depth 0.25 mm), the ends of which are connected with inflow and outflow tubes. When the 2 plates are pressed together, a known volume of the sample gas is pumped through the groove and over the surface of the tape. If a constituent of the sample reacts with the tape it produces a colored line whose length is a function of its concentration. After the gas sample has been drawn through, the plates separate automatically and the indicator tape moves 3 mm. The length of 1 cycle is 3 minutes. There is a system of coordinates on the indicator tape so that the concentration of the gas at various times can be determined by the length of the colored lines. . . . The design of the apparatus, determination of gas permeability of paper for indicator tapes, calibration curves, and preparation of tapes, are described in detail." Add. Ref.: Ref. Zh., Khim. **1962**, Abstr. No. 71183.

125—PREPARATION AND ANALYSIS OF CALIBRATED LOW CONCENTRATIONS OF SIXTEEN TOXIC GASES: AMMONIA, ARSINE, BROMINE, CARBON DIOXIDE, CARBON MONOXIDE, CHLORINE, CHLORINE DIOXIDE, ETHYLENE OXIDE, HYDROGEN CHLORIDE, HYDROGEN CYANIDE, HYDROGEN FLUORIDE, MONOETHANOLAMINE, NITRIC OXIDE, NITROGEN DIOXIDE, PHOSGENE, AND STIBINE.

Saltzman, Bernard E. Anal. Chem. **33**, 1100-1112 (1961).

Evaluation of detecting devices and instruments requires accurately known low concentrations of toxic gases. The article discusses the general problems and techniques of the preparation and analysis of calibrated low concentrations of toxic gases in air, as well as specific details for each gas indicated. Add. Ref.: CA **55**, 27724 (1961).

126—DETERMINATION OF TOXIC SUBSTANCES IN THE ATMOSPHERE OF INDUSTRIAL PLANTS IN CZECHOSLOVAKIA

Vasak, V. Ann. Occup. Hyg. **3**, 122-123 (1961).

At least two analytical methods are recommended for routine evaluation of air samples. The author states that all Czech hygiene stations are equipped with detector tubes, and implies that the detectors are used routinely for control purposes.

127—GAS TITRATION OF AIR CONTAMINANTS

Huffman, D. D. Paper presented at Am. Ind. Hyg. Assoc. meeting, Detroit, Mich. (1961).

A table of procedures for 14 different contaminants is included, and some sample calculations are given.

128—AIR POLLUTION

Lodge, James P., Jr. Anal. Chem., Anal. Reviews **33**, No. 5, 3R-13R (1961).

A review of analytical methods, including field studies, for determinations of air pollution. 390 references.

129—RAPID METHODS FOR THE DETERMINATION OF TOXIC SUBSTANCES IN THE AIR

Peregud, E. A., M. S. Bykhovskaia, and E. V. Gernet. Moscow, Goskhimizdat (1962) 272 pp.; A.P.C.A. Abstr. **8**, No. 9, 5035 (1963).

The book includes methods for sampling air containing one or more toxicants, methods for determining the toxicants, and a discussion of gas analyzers. The authors give some 45 colorimetric methods, for substances such as ammonia, nitrogen oxides, carbon disulfide, hydrogen sulfide, sulfur dioxide, ozone, etc.

130—DETERMINATION OF VERY SMALL AMOUNTS OF ACIDS IN AIR

Peregud, E. A., E. S. Stepanenko, and B. S. Boikina. J. Anal. Chem. of U.S.S.R. (English translation of Zh. Analit. Khim.) **17**, No. 6, 760-761 (1962).

Small amounts of hydrofluoric acid, hydrochloric acid, and sulfuric acid in air can be determined colorimetrically by reacting the acid with bromide-bromate in the presence of fluorescein, to form red tetrabromofluorescein. The glass indicator tubes are 45 mm long by 2.5 mm i.d. and contain a 40 mm column of the indicator powder held in place in the tube with a cotton plug at either end. The indicator powder is 0.2 to 0.25 mm mesh silica gel, boiled twice with 6 N hydrochloric acid, washed free of chloride ion, dried calcined at 750° for 2 hours, and impregnated with a solution containing 30 g of potassium bromide, 2 g of potassium bromate, and 1 g of potassium carbonate in 100 ml of water, to which 0.1 g of fluorescein previously dissolved in 1 ml of 10% potassium hydroxide is added. The length of the red colored zone in the indicator is proportional to the acid concentration of the air. Add. Ref.: CA **58**, 3887 (1963).

131—DETECTION OF GASES IN AIR

Anon. Dust Topics, 4-8, July-Aug. and Sept.-Oct. 1961. Published by Gelman Instrument Co., Chelsea, Mich.

The article discusses sensitized papers for the detection and determination of gaseous contaminants in air. Detection of toxic gases by chemically treated wet or dry filter papers, which change color in the presence of specific gases, is faster and simpler than by standard chemical methods. The detector paper must be treated with an indicating reagent, then exposed to the contaminated air in a sampling procedure; and the color change produced by the contaminant must be measurable, visually or photometrically. Dry detector papers usually are more satisfactory than wet papers. In gas sampling, wet papers replace bubblers or impingers, and, because the air stream evaporates the color-forming solution, the amount of air that can be sampled is limited. Also, because wet papers must be prepared just before use, liquid reagents must be transported and handled. Dry detector papers are pre-impregnated, dried, and ready to use, both for spot checking and for continuous sampling. Many instruments also use sensitized papers for continuously measuring variations in the concentration of airborne gases. Effective detector papers should be specific and sensitive, and should have storage stability and color stability. For accurate, reproducible results with detector papers, air flow should be measured carefully, dust prefilters should be used, and humidity effects should be counteracted with prefilter driers or humidifiers.

132—A TENTATIVE SYSTEMATIC DESCRIPTION OF DETECTOR TUBE REACTIONS

Grosskopf, Karl. Chem. Zeit. - Chem. Apparatur **87**, No. 8, 270-275 (1963).

The author presents a systematic discussion of detector tubes and the problems associated with their manufacture, use, and interpretation. By taking detector tube readings as a function of the flow velocity of the test gas, or of its volume flow, which is proportional to the flow velocity, he classifies the numerous available detector tubes into 6 groups with characteristic properties. He shows that knowledge of the group characteristics is helpful in the practical application of the tubes.

133—PRACTICES IN THE FIELD USE OF DETECTOR TUBES

LaNier, Marshall B. and Howard L. Kusnetz. Arch. Environ. Health (A.M.A.) **6**, No. 3, 418-421 (1963). From a survey of a cross section of governmental and commercial industrial hygiene agencies, the authors draw the following conclusions about the use of detector tubes: Most industrial hygiene agencies recognize that the tubes are intended for screening purposes, and do so use them, even, for convenience, when detector tubes are not the preferred method for sampling. More than half of those who replied to the authors' questionnaires prefer detector tubes in which stain length indicates concentration. Users rarely calibrate detector tubes, but rely unduly on manufacturer's calibrations. Nontrained people take samples and interpret results, and even qualified industrial hygienists interpret detector tube results without previous knowledge of true calibration values. Nevertheless, detector tubes are useful both to the industrial hygienist and to those not trained in industrial hygiene investigations and interpretations. Therefore, to prevent dangerous industrial situations from going unheeded, and also to prevent manufacturers from being burdened with unnecessary controls, detectors must be maximally reliable. An interprofessional joint committee should recommend minimum performance standards for detector tubes, including standards of quality control, reproducibility of results, limits of sensitivity, reliability, and uniform interpretation. The group could help manufacturers meet the standards without raising the cost of the tubes prohibitively, and manufacturers then could certify that their products not only meet the minimum standards, but can be used with a known limit of reliability. Add. Ref.: D.O.H. Activities, No. 2, 5-6 (April, 1963).

SECTION II
List of Detectors by Compound

Acetic Acid

1—DETERMINATION OF ACETIC ACID IN AIR
Miller, Franklin, Richard Scherberger, Henry Brockmyre, and David W. Fassett. Am. Ind. Hyg. Assoc. Quart. **17**, 221-224 (1956).

A 1-1 glycerine-water solution containing silicone antifoam and methyl purple turns from green to bright purple at the endpoint during an air titration of acetic acid; this was confirmed by laboratory titrations. Add. Ref.: IHD **20**, 1063 (1956).

2—MICROCHEMICAL NOTES. XV
Rosenthaler, L. Mikrochemie **23**, 194-197 (1937); CA **32**, 1609 (1938).

The authors describe a sensitive test for acetic acid where calcium acetate is converted into acetone and the resulting vapors tested with o-nitrobenzaldehyde. The method may be applied to detectors although it is not a field test at present.

Acetone

1—RAPID DETERMINATION OF ACETONE IN AIR
Bulycheva, A. I. Gigiena i Sanit. **13**, 30 (1948); CA **43**, 8974 (1949).

The author describes a colorimetric determination for acetone which is based upon the reaction with hydroxylamine hydrochloride and bromophenol blue. The error is less than 16% using 10 to 15 minute air samples.

2—GAS ANALYSIS BY MEANS OF DETECTOR TUBES. IV. RAPID METHOD FOR THE DETERMINATION OF ACETONE VAPOR
Kobayashi, Yoshitaka. J. Chem. Soc. Japan, Ind. Chem. Sect. **56**, 174-175 (1953); CA **48**, 9271 (1954).

The detector tube for the determination consists of a column of 40 to 60 mesh silica-gel granules which is impregnated with a dichromate solution made acid with sulfuric acid. In the presence of acetone the orange yellow detection column changes to a chocolate color. The concentration of acetone is determined by measuring the length of the chocolate stain. Calibration factors are provided for various temperatures at which the determinations are made. Among the interferences found are methyl alcohol, ethyl alcohol, benzene, ether, sulfur dioxide, hydrogen sulfide.

3—ESTIMATION OF TOXIC GASES IN AIR. VIII. ACETONE
Fukuyama, Tomitaro, Tokuro Sato, and Aiko Watanabe. Bull. Inst. Public Health (Tokyo) **5**, 2-7 (1956) (English summary); AA **4**, 3470 (1957).

The authors describe an improved salicylaldehyde method for acetone. Air is bubbled through a 1% sodium bisulfite solution at a rate of 100 ml per minute. Five ml of sample is mixed with 5 ml dilute potassium hydroxide and warmed to 30° C for 10 minutes. One ml of salicylaldehyde is added and the mixture is heated in a water bath for 15 minutes. The sample is immediately cooled, diluted to 15 ml with distilled water and the color intensity determined at the end of about 20 minutes. Add. Ref.: CA **50**, 11172 (1956).

4—A RAPID METHOD FOR THE DETERMINATION OF ACETONE VAPOR IN ACETYLENE BY MEANS OF DETECTOR TUBES
Kobayashi, Yoshitaka. Yuki Gosei Kagaku Kyokaishi **16**, 194-197 (1958); CA **52**, 8849 (1958).

Acetone vapor colors orange-yellow to intense brown silica gel which has been impregnated with potassium dichromate solution acidulated with sulfuric acid. Corrections for temperature, the internal diameter of the glass tubes containing the silica gel, column length-concentration ratios, etc., are given.

Acetylene

1—COLORIMETRIC DETERMINATION OF ACETYLENE
Weaver, E. R. J. Am. Chem. Soc. **38**, 352-361 (1916).

An ammoniacal solution of cuprous chloride containing gelatin and ethyl alcohol is used. Acetylene produces a red color, which is compared colorimetrically with a standard. The method is sensitive to 0.03 mg acetylene. Add. Ref.: CA **10**, 731 (1916).

2—INDICATOR PAPER FOR THE DETECTION OF ACETYLENE
Deniges, G. Bull. soc. pharm. Bordeaux **1921**, No. 2; Repert. pharm. **33**, 232 (1921); CA **16**, 395 (1922).

An indicator paper—for acetylene is prepared by dissolving 50 g of ammonium chloride, 25 g copper sulfate and 0.55 cc hydrochloric acid in enough water to make 250 cc. When testing for acetylene 5 cc of the prepared solution is placed in a test tube containing 0.3 g of copper turnings and boiled until the solution is colorless. One cc of water is added and the solution is cooled. Pieces of filter paper are dipped in the liquid and the test conducted while the paper is moist. In the presence of acetylene the paper takes on a red coloration.

3—ANALYSIS OF ETHYLENE FOR ANESTHETIC USE

Busi, M. and C. Collina. Atti soc. ital. progresso sci. **19**, 195-199 (1931).

Five percent ammoniacal silver nitrate is used for the detection of acetylene in ethylene. Add. Ref.: CA **26**, 1707 (1932).

4—DETECTION OF VERY SMALL QUANTITIES OF ACETYLENE

Pietsch, E. and A. Kotowski. Z. angew. Chem. **44**, 309-312 (1931); CA **25**, 2939 (1931).

To prepare the reagent dissolve 1 g of blue vitriol in 8 ml of 10% ammonium hydroxide, add slowly 3 g hydroxylamine hydrochloride, and dilute to 50 ml with water. When air is bubbled through this solution at 1.7 to 1.9 liters per hour under normal pressure, the detectable limit is $3.7 \times 10^{-4}\%$ or 1.7×10^{-5} g of acetylene in 4 liters of gas. The sensitivity may be increased by adding small, fibrous-edged squares of filter paper to adsorb the copper acetylide and thus make the precipitate more visible. The authors refer to E. Czako, Z. angew. Chem. **44**, 388 (1931).

5—ADSORPTION OF CUPROUS SALTS FROM ILOSVAY'S REAGENT IN PRECIPITATING CUPROUS ACETYLIDE

Novotny, D. F. Collection Czechoslov. Chem. Communications **6**, 514-527 (1934); CA **29**, 2878 (1935).

The analyses must be made in an inert atmosphere using the sulfate ion instead of the chloride ion. The gas is diluted to 10% and adsorbed in Ilosvay's reagent prepared from sulfate.

6—THE DETECTION OF TOXIC GASES AND VAPORS

Leroux, Lucien. Rev. hyg. et med. prevent. **57**, 81-112 (1935).

Acetylene with Ilosvay reagent forms red-colored cuprous acetylide. The sensitivity of the reaction is 5 parts per million; hydrogen sulfide and nitrous gas interfere. To prepare the Ilosvay reagent, dissolve 2 g copper nitrate in 10 ml cold distilled water, add 8 g hydroxylamine hydrochloride, and when this is dissolved, cautiously add 10 ml of 20% ammonium hydroxide. Then add 6 ml of freshly prepared 2% gelatin, mix, and dilute the solution to 100 ml with distilled water. A more sensitive test also is discussed. In a round bottom flask place 1 part crystalline copper sulfate, 1 part copper turnings, 2 parts sodium chloride, and 10 parts distilled water. Acidify with several drops of hydrochloric acid; bring to a boil and boil until just decolorized; cool; add ammonium hydroxide. The sensitivity of this test is 1 part per 200,000. The color formed is red-brown. Add. Ref.: CA **29**, 3627 (1935).

7—COLORIMETRIC METHOD FOR THE ESTIMATION OF SMALL QUANTITIES OF ACETYLENE IN AIR

Coulson-Smith, C. and A. P. Seyberg. Analyst **67**, 39-41 (1942).

The reaction is based on the formation of copper acetylide in an ammoniacal solution. The density is compared with the depth of color of a standard reference consisting of ferric alum and thiocyanate. The accuracy is 0.01% with 0.02 to 0.25% acetylene by volume in 100 ml of air. Add. Ref.: CA **36**, 5444 (1942).

8—ACETYLENE. DETECTION AND ESTIMATION

Jacobs, Morris B. "The Analytical Chemistry of Industrial Poisons, Hazards, and Solvents." (Interscience Publishers, Inc., New York, N.Y., 1944), p. 397.

Acetylene reacts in a manner analogous to that of ethylene. It will react with chlorine, bromine, potassium permanganate and with hydrogen chloride. It forms, with an ammoniacal cuprous chloride or silver salt solution, a dark red precipitate of cuprous or silver acetylide which when dry is explosive. The author cites two references in detailing the Ilosvay test, viz.: Ilosvay, Ber. **32**, 2698 (1899), and Treadwell and Hal, Analytical Chemistry, Vol. 2, New York (1915). To make the Ilosvay reagent place 1 g cupric nitrate pentohydrate or the chloride or sulfate salt in a 50 ml volumetric flask and dissolve the compounds in a little water. Add 4 ml concentrated ammonium hydroxide and 3 g hydroxylamine hydrochloride. Shake until the mixture is colorless, then dilute to volume. To test for acetylene, place 20 ml of the Ilosvay reagent in a 500 to 3000 ml glass-stoppered cylinder or separatory funnel, and either measure the volume of gas passed in or add the gas until the reagent is pink. Stopper the vessel and shake frequently for 1 hour. A red precipitate indicates acetylene. The gas also may be passed through a large bulb tube containing glass wool wet with the reagent. The precipitate may be used for quantitative determination of the acetylene content in a laboratory procedure.

9—A COLOR SCALE FOR THE COLORIMETRIC DETERMINATION OF ACETYLENE

Strizhevskii, I. I. and M. D. Chekhovich. Zevodskaya Lab. **11**, 480-482, (1945); CA **40**, 1428 (1946).

Standards can be prepared from cobalt nitrate and chromium nitrate to match the color of the colloidal copper acetylide solutions. These solutions can be kept indefinitely. Nine references.

10—DETERMINATION OF TRACES OF ACETYLENE IN LIQUID OXYGEN IN RECTIFYING COLUMNS

McKeon, H. P. and Henry D. Eddy. Ind. Eng. Chem., Anal. Ed. **18**, 133-136 (1946); CA **40**, 1756 (1946).

The authors provide full details for the analysis of acetylene in liquid oxygen in rectifying columns.

11—DETERMINATION OF TRACES OF ACETYLENE IN AIR

Geissman, T. A., Samuel Kaufman, and David Y. Dollman. Anal. Chem. **19**, 919-921 (1947).

The method essentially involves the use of a grab sample and the formation of cuprous acetylide. The red color is measured photometrically. Add. Ref.: CA **42**, 60 (1948).

12—NEW METHODS OF DETERMINING ACETYLENE IN GASEOUS MIXTURES IN AIR

Strizhevski, I. I. Zavodskaya Lab. **14**, 24-33 (1948); CA **43**, 971 (1949).

The author provides a review with 38 references.

13—ANALYTICAL CONTROL OF AIR-FRACTIONATION (LIQUEFACTION) PLANTS

Machemer, Hans. Chemie-Ing.-Tech. **21**, 58-60 (1949); CA **43**, 4972 (1949).

The procedures for the rapid determination of acetylene, crabon monoxide and hydrocarbons are given. 20 references.

14—DETERMINATION OF ACETYLENE IN THE ATMOSPHERE OF INDUSTRIAL ESTABLISHMENTS

Zhitkova, A. S. and S. I. Kut'in. Zavedskaya Lab. **15**, 674-676 (1949); CA **44**, 485 (1950).

The authors describe the preparation of an absorbing solution which will yield a reproducible color of cuprous acetylide for the determination of acetylene. The solution is suitable for determining 0.01 to 0.4 mg acetylene per liter in 1 to 5 ml samples.

15—ESTIMATION OF ACETYLENE IN AIR

Purser, B. J. Analyst **74**, 237-239 (1949); CA **43**, 6943 (1949).

The air sample is collected in a bubbler containing methyl ether cooled in dry ice. The acetylene is determined with ammoniacal cuprous chloride and gum ghatti. The color produced is measured in a Spekker absorptiometer. This method can be used to determine 0.67 ppm of acetylene by volume.

16—A METHOD OF DETECTING THE SPONTANEOUS COMBUSTION OF COAL AT ITS EARLY STAGE. II

Kitagawa, Tetsuzo. J. Mining Inst. Japan **68**, 525-528 (1952); CA **48**, 5463 (1954).

The author states that spontaneous combustion in coal mines can be foreseen by analyzing for acetylene because spontaneous combustion is related to the concentration of acetylene in the air.

17—A NEW COLOR REACTION OF ACETYLENE

Tilenschi, Silviu. Acad. rep. populare Romane, Filiala Cluj, Studii cercetari stiint. **3**, No. 3/4, 99-102 (1952); CA **50**, 11174 (1956).

The author describes a new colorimetric reaction for the determination of acetylene. A copper sulfate pentohydrate solution is reduced with hydroxylamine hydrochloride and ammonia. The pH of this solution is adjusted to 5.3 with sulfuric acid. In the presence of acetylene this reagent assumes a blue coloration which can be used for both qualitative and quantitative analysis of acetylene.

18—GAS ANALYSIS BY MEANS OF DETECTOR TUBES. III. RAPID DETERMINATION OF LOW CONCENTRATIONS OF ETHYLENE AND ACETYLENE

Kitagawa, Tetsuzo and Yoshitaka Kobayashi. J. Chem. Soc. Japan, Ind. Chem. Sect. **56**, 56-58 (1953); CA **48**, 8128 (1954).

The analytical reagent is prepared by impregnating silica gel with a mixture of ammonium molybdate and palladium sulfate. The yellow color of the reagent changes to blue in the presence of ethylene and to a yellowish green with acetylene. A semi-quantitative method of analysis for the two gases is described.

19—DETERMINATION OF ACETYLENE IN AIR

Purser, B. J. Analyst **78**, 732 (1953); CA **48**, 1894 (1954).

The author presents improvement on his procedure, described above.

20—DETERMINATION OF ACETYLENE AND ALDEHYDE IN ETHYLENE OXIDE

Reid, V. W. and D. G. Salmon. Analyst **80**, 602-604 (1955).

The method of Geissman (see above) is applied to the analysis of acetylene in ethylene oxide. Add. Ref.: CA **49**, 13836 (1955).

21—CHROMATOGRAPHIC ANALYSIS OF ACETYLENE AND DIACETYLENE IN THE PRESENCE OF MONOSUBSTITUTED ACETYLENES

Nebbia, Luisa and Basilio Pagani. Chimica e industria (Milan) **37**, 200-201 (1955); CA **49**, 11503 (1955).

Acetylene and diacetylene are deposited near the head of a column consisting of 96 parts of alumina and 4 parts of cuprous chloride. These two materials must be in ammoniacal aqueous or alcoholic aqueous solution for optimum results. Other acetylenes will deposit in lower portions of the column. Semiquantitative analysis can be made by relating band widths to concentration. The limit of detection is in the neighborhood of 0.1 to 0.5 mg of acetylene.

22—DETERMINATION OF A SMALL AMOUNT OF ACETYLENE IN LIQUID OXYGEN

Yasui, Eizo and Hiroshi Suzuki. Koatsu Gasu Kyokaishi **21**, 316-325 (1957); CA **52**, 5207 (1958).

The authors present a review of the subject with 34 references.

23—DETERMINATION OF SMALL AMOUNTS OF ACETYLENE IN AIR WITH SILICA GEL TREATED WITH LIQUID OXYGEN

Yasui, Eizo and Hiroshi Suzuki. J. Chem. Soc. Japan, Ind. Chem. Sect. **61**, (2), 176-179 (1958); AA **5**, 4326 (1958).

Silica gel immersed in liquid oxygen is the carrier of the acetylene. Most of the oxygen is then removed by a current of nitrogen, and the remaining liquid oxygen and acetylene react with Ilosvay reagent. The error is 5 to 10%.

24—DETERMINATIONS OF ACETYLENE IN LOW CONCENTRATIONS FOR AIR POLLUTION CONTROL

Anon. J. Wash. Acad. Sci. **48**, 307-308 (Oct. 1958); IHD **23**, 426 (1959).

The author presents a rapid, accurate colorimetric method for the detection of small quantities of acetylene in air. Concentrations of acetylene on the order of 10 ppb can be determined by this method and, since the equipment required is simple and portable, the method is applicable to field air pollution studies. The acetylene is first concentrated by adsorption on silica gel. The silica gel surface is then treated with a solution of ammoniacal cuprous chloride and the concentration of the gas is proportional to the depth of color produced. The concentration is determined by comparing the sample with a series of standards containing known concentrations of acetylene. The authors data shows that the method can identify quantities of acetylene as low as 0.01 μg in 12 ml of air at a volume concentration of 1 ppm.

25—DETERMINATION OF ACETYLENE IN AIR IN CONCENTRATIONS FROM TEN PARTS PER BILLION TO TEN PARTS PER MILLION

Hughes, Ernest E. and Ralph Gorden, Jr. Anal. Chem. **31**, 94-98 (1959).

Acetylene is adsorbed from an air stream on a column of silica gel 10 mm long by 2 mm diameter, cooled to —78° C. After warming to room temperature the silica gel is impregnated with a freshly prepared solution of ammoniacal cuprous chloride. For the exact preparation of the silica gel the authors refer to Martin Shepherd, "Rapid Determination of Small Amounts of Carbon Monoxide. Preliminary Report on the NBS Colorimetric Indicating Gel," Anal. Chem. **19**, 77-81 (1947).

See Section One
For reference number 81.

Acrolein

1—DETERMINATION OF ACROLEIN AND OF FORMALDEHYDE IN THE AIR

Uzdina, I. L. Hig. Truda **15**, No. 3, 63-66 (1937); Chimie & industrie **40**, 260; CA **33**, 89 (1939).

Acrolein is determined in alcoholic solution by adding hydrogen peroxide and hydrochloric acid to the solution, mixing, and adding phloroglucinol. The concentration of acrolein is determined from the pink coloration produced. Formaldehyde produces a yellow color under the same conditions and if both substances are present a yellowish pink coloration results. It is possible to determine both materials simultaneously by using mixed standards.

2—DETERMINATION OF ACROLEIN IN THE AIR OF INDUSTRIAL PLANTS

Berezova, M. K. Hig. i Sanit. (U.S.S.R.) **1940**, No. 10, 31-37; CA **36**, 6949 (1942).

The author gives three colorimetric methods for the determination of acrolein. These reagents are: 1) 1% solution of benzidine in concentrated acetic acid, 2) 1% pyrogallol in either concentrated acetic acid or concentrated hydrochloric acid, 3) 1% solution of pure phenol ethyl alcohol plus concentrated sulfuric acid. Reagent (2) must be freshly prepared. The results obtained with the 3 methods are tabulated. 10 references.

3—DETERMINATION OF ACROLEIN IN AIR

Senderikhina, D. P. Gigiena i. Sanit. **12**, No. 3, 17-19 (1947); CA **43**, 1289 (1949).

The air containing the acrolein is scrubbed through 5 ml of water and 0.5 ml of Schiff's reagent is added. The color produced is stable after 25 minutes and the color is compared with a set of standard acrolein or formaldehyde solutions. The lower limit of detection is 0.5 μg per 5 ml.

Acrylonitrile

1—DETERMINATION OF ACRYLONITRILE VAPOR BY MEANS OF DETECTOR TUBES

Kobayashi, Yoshitaka. Yuki Gosei Kagaku Kyokai Shi **14**, 673-675 (1956); CA **51**, 7240 (1957).

The author describes the preparation of an indicating tube for the determination of acrylonitrile. The reagent consists of silica gel coated with a solution of sulfuric acid, chromic acid and water sealed in a glass tube. To carry out the determination the tips are broken from the tube and 100 cc of air are aspirated through it in 200 minutes. The concentration of acrylonitrile is determined by the length of the dark green colored stain produced. The useful range is 1 to 120 mg of acrylonitrile per 1000 cc of air. Oxygen, nitrogen, carbon dioxide, ethane, methane, carbon tetrachloride, and hydrogen cyanide do not interfere, but reducing substances such as hydrogen sulfide, sulfur dioxide, propane, ethylene, alcohols, aldehydes, and ketones color the silica gel and interfere with the result. When acetylene is present in air, the silica gel is colored light brown but causes no hindrance.

Adamsite
(Diphenylaminechloroarsine)

1—THE DETECTION OF TOXIC GASES AND VAPORS
Leroux, Lucien. Rev. hyg. et med. prevent. **57**, 81-112 (1935).

Adamsite produces a blue color in sulfuric acid containing a trace of nitric acid. Because of the impossibility of separating all the arsines, in general, except by laboratory procedures, it is difficult at present to identify them exactly in the field. However, all the arsine compounds may be broken down with nascent hydrogen to give arsine (q.v.). The material to be analyzed may be collected by placing a piece of filter paper over the cartridge of a respirator. Add. Ref.: CA **29**, 3627 (1935).

2—TESTS AVAILABLE FOR THE IDENTIFICATION OF SMALL QUANTITIES OF THE WAR GASES
Cox, H. E. Analyst **64**, 807-813 (1939).
Identification by the Gutzeit test after decomposition with nitric and sulfuric acids. Add. Ref.: CA **34**, 541 (1940).

3—THE ANALYTICAL CHEMISTRY OF INDUSTRIAL POISONS, HAZARDS AND SOLVENTS
Jacobs, Morris B. (Interscience Publishers, Inc., New York, N.Y. 1941), p. 608.
Dust sampled into an impinger containing sulfuric acid will color the acid red if adamsite is present. The red color will turn to blue if a trace of nitrate is added.

4—DETECTION OF WAR GASES
Fenton, Paul F. J. Chem. Education **21**, 488-489 (1944).
The distal cotton plug of the silica gel sampling tube (see Ibid., Section I) is eluted with alcohol and treated with 0.1 N potassium dichromate acidified with sulfuric acid. A greenish-blue color indicates adamsite. The author tried the test only on diphenylamine because he could not obtain any adamsite. Add. Ref.: CA **39** , 135 (1945).
See Section One
Reference Numbers 54, 64, and 66.

Aldehydes

1—USE OF SPOT TESTS FOR THE EXAMINATION OF PHARMACEUTICALS. VIII. DETECTION OF ALDEHYDE WITH A PERMANENT TEST PAPER
Frehden, O. and K. Fuerst. Mikrochemie **26**, 39-40 (1939); CA **33**, 3526 (1939).

The test paper is prepared by dissolving 0.8 g of malachite green and 3 g sodium sulfite, to this is added 3 more grams of sulfite and the resulting solution is filtered. Strips of filter paper are dipped into the solution and air dried. When an aldehyde contacts the impregnated paper malachite green is reformed. In order for the test to be successful the test solution used must be neutral and the test paper white. Approximately 20 aldehydes were tested by this method and concentration in the range of 0.02 to 0.3 could be detected.

2—COLORIMETRIC DETERMINATION OF FUMARALDEHYDE AND 2, 3-UNSATURATED ALDEHYDES
Breusch, F. L. and E. Ulusoy. Hoppe-Seyler's Z. physiol. Chem. **291**, 64-67 (1952); CA **48**, 12211 (1954).

The method depends upon the fact that when an aldehyde contacts a solution of p-aminophenol in trichloroacetic acid a yellowish green color is produced. This color can be measured photoelectrically. The concentration of trichloroacetic acid must be known because the color increases linearly with the acid concentration. The color produced is stable for 2 hours and is also produced by fumaraldehyde and other 2,3-unsaturated aldehydes, cinnamaldehyde, and furfural. Acrolein gives a color which fades rapidly. Saturated aldehydes, acetones, alcohols, mesityl oxide, and 2,3-unsaturated ketones do not react.

3—COLOR REACTIONS OF ALDEHYDES
Rosenthaler, L. and G. Vegezzi. Mitt. Lebensm. Hyg. **45**, 178-182 (1954); CA **48**, 13543 (1954).
The authors investigated the colorimetric reactions of a number of aldehydes with Schiff's reagent, diazobenzenesulfonic acid, phenylhydrazine plus diazobenzenesulfonic acid (formazan reaction), and m-phenylenediamine. The formazan and m-phenylenediamine yielded the best results.

4—DETECTION OF AROMATIC ALDEHYDES
Sawicki, Eugene, Thomas Stanley, and Thomas Hauser. Chemist-Analyst **47**, 31-32 (1958).
The authors describe a method which has been developed for the detection of polynuclear aromatic aldehydes. One ml of a 5% fluoranthene in chloroform solution is mixed with the suspected aromatic aldehyde also contained in chloroform. Added to this solution is 0.8 ml trifluoroacetic-acid anhydride. The mixture is allowed to stand for 5 minutes and then diluted to 10 ml with trifluoroacetic acid. The color obtained is stable for approximately 24 hours. Add. Ref.: CA **52**, 16124 (1958).

5—DETECTION AND ESTIMATION OF LOW CONCENTRATIONS OF ALDEHYDE IN AIR

Hughes, Ernest E. and Sharon G. Lias. Anal. Chem. **32**, 707-708 (1960).

Aldehyde is adsorbed from an air stream on purified silica gel, which is contained in glass tubes 5 mm in internal diameter and 7 cm long. The tubes, filled about half full, are plugged with a wad of cotton at the outlet end only. The air sample is drawn with a syringe or pump through the gel with the tube vertical, after which the remainder of the tube is filled carefully with clean silica gel and closed with a second cotton plug. The gel added after exposure filters out the dark oxidation products of the developing reagent, which interfere with the color detection. The tube is dipped into developing reagent (saturated solution of p-phenylenediamine in water, mixed with 3% hydrogen peroxide in the ratio of 1:2 just before use) inlet end down. A dark band from impurities in the reagent appears at the inlet end of the tube, but adlehyde catalyzes oxidation of the p-phenylenediamine and produces a second dark band, colored from pale purple-brown to deep purple-brown or black, at the boundary of the two layers of gel, the depth of color on the gel being measured by the quantity of aldehyde adsorbed. Standard tubes can be prepared. As little as 0.0001 ppm can be detected in less than 10 liters of sample, with a flow rate as high as 0.7 liter per minute. Nitriles, aldehyde ammonia, oximes, and aldehyde bisulfite compounds interfere; ketones do not. Pure gum rubber tubing should be used for connections in the apparatus, because certain kinds of plastic tubing contain detectable quantities of aldehyde. Add. Ref.: IHD **24**, 596 (1960).

6—SENSITIVE NEW TEST FOR ALIPHATIC, AROMATIC, AND HETEROCYCLIC ALDEHYDES

Sawicki, Eugene and Thomas W. Stanley. Mikrochim. Acta **4**, 510-517 (1960).

A sensitive new spot test for aliphatic, aromatic, and heterocyclic adlehyde is given, with limits of identification for over 70 aldehydes. All the aldehydes tested give a blue or green color except chloral and hexadecanal. For the spot paper procedure add 1 ml of test solution (in water or in dimethylformamide) to 0.03 ml of 1% aqueous 2-hydrazino-benzothiazole. After 1 to 2 minutes add 0.03 ml of 1% aqueous solution of p-nitrobenzene-diazonium fluoborate; after 1 to 2 minutes add 0.03 ml of 10% aqueous potassium hydroxide (or ammonia fumes). If aldehydes are present, a blue to green stain surrounded by a dark red stain appears on the paper immediately. Blanks show only the dark red stain which changes to brownish yellow within 2 minutes. The blue or green stain is stable and its intensity is proportional to the concentration of the aldehyde.

7—SPOT TEST DETECTION AND COLORIMETRIC DETERMINATION OF ALIPHATIC ALDEHYDES WITH 2-HYDRAZINOBENZOTHIAZOLE. APPLICATION TO AIR POLLUTION

Sawicki, Eugene and Thomas R. Hauser. Anal. Chem. **32**, 1434-1436 (1960).

All the modifications of a versatile new procedure for the detection and determination of alipathic aldehydes are especially sensitive for formaldehyde. On the spot plate 0.01 μg of formaldehyde, 0.3 μg of acetaldehyde, and 0.3 μg of propionaldehyde can be detected; on paper 0.05 μg of formaldehyde, 1 μg of acetaldehyde, and 1 μg of propionaldehyde are detectable, and with proper standards, the amount of formaldehyde can be estimated. A tube containing silica gel impregnated with 2-hydrazino-benzothiazole solution can detect or estimate formaldehyde in the air or in auto exhaust gases. In all the modifications a brilliant blue color is easily seen.

8—THE 3-METHYL-2-BENZOTHIAZOLONE HYDRAZONE TEST. SENSITIVE NEW METHODS FOR THE DETECTION, RAPID ESTIMATION, and DETERMINATION OF ALIPHATIC ALDEHYDES

Sawicki, Eugene, Thomas R. Hauser, Thomas W. Stanley, and Walter Elbert. Anal. Chem. **33**, 93-96 (1961).

Versatile spot plate, paper, silica gel, and colorimetric modifications of a sensitive new analytical method can detect, estimate, and determine water-soluble aliphatic aldehydes, with the formation of an intensely brilliant blue dye. The silica gel procedure especially is both simple and sensitive, and can be applied to the analysis of auto exhaust fumes and polluted air. Two simple methods for synthesizing the reagent, 3-methyl-2-benzothiazolone, are described.

9—SPECIFIC SPOT TESTS FOR ALDEHYDES

Kashmi, M. H., A. A. Oyoz, H. Ahmed. Anal. Chem. 36(10), 2029 (1964) CA **61**, 11311 (1964).

One drop of the aldehyde solution is placed on a spot plate. A few drops of 0.5% NaCLO₂ and 2 drops of 0.1 HCl are added and the solution is stirred. A yellow color indcates the presence of an aldehyde.

10—SPOT TESTS FOR AROMATIC AND A,B-UNSATURATED ALDEHYDES

Feegle, Fritz and E. Libergott. Anal. Chem. (36) (1), 132-3 (1964) CA **60**, 8614 (1964).

The authors present a method for the detection of aromatic aldehydes which depends upon the formation of an orange color when they are reacted with thiobarbituric acid. Maximum sensitivity is obtained when the reactants are heated in phosphoric acid.

Alkali

1—DETERMINATION OF SMALL QUANTITIES OF ALKALI IN THE AIR

Luzina, G. S. Zavodskaya Lab. **16**, 1402 (1950); CA **45**, 10135 (1951).

The method recommended by the author for the determination of alkali in air is to bubble the air through water followed by an acid titration in the presence of methyl red indicator.

Amines

1—NEW REACTION OF RESORCINOL AND ITS APPLICATION TO THE DETECTION OF THE NITROPRUSSIATE ION AND AMMONIA

Caseneuve, M. Bull. soc. pharm. Bordeaux **61**, 153-155 (1923); CA **18**, 208 (1924).

One drop of a reagent (2 g sodium nitroprussiate, 1 g resorcinol in sufficient water to effect solution) is placed on a spot plate. The reagent turns green or bluish green in atmospheres containing ammonia and volatile amines.

2—ACTION OF ULTRA-VIOLET RAYS UPON PYRIDINE. I. A NEW TEST FOR SEVERAL PRIMARY AROMATIC AMINES AND PYRIDINE

Freytag, Hans and Walter Neudert. J. prakt. Chem. **135**, 15-35 (1932); CA **27**, 724 (1933).

Filter papers impregnated with pyridine yield a yellow color under ultra-violet light. The filter papers show various colorations with aromatic amine salts.

3—DETECTION OF CERTAIN CHLORINATED TERTIARY ALIPHATIC AMINES

Cruikshank, A.J., H. A. Bewick, J. E. Currah, and F. E. Beamish. Anal. Chem. **19**, 849-850 (1947).

Five papers were studied for the detection of specific tertiary aliphatic amines. The vapor detectors were prepared by immersing Whatman No. 1 filter papers in a solution made by adding 3.5 g potassium iodide and 2.5 g calcium chloride hexahydrate to a solution of 2.5 g bismuth subnitrate in 9 ml concentrated hydrochloric acid and 10 ml of glycerol. The papers, blotted momentarily on absorbent paper, then dried in an oven for 1 hour at 60° C, were stable. They were exposed to the air to absorb moisture before use, then tested by passing through them, through a circular opening 0.5 cm in diameter, an air-gas mixture at 500 ml per minute. The sensitivity for bis (2-chloroethyl) methylamine was 25 μg in 1000 ml of mixture. (Bis(2-chloroethyl)methylamine in air gave a red color on paper impregnated with nickel dimethylglyoxime, with a sensitivity of 19 μg. Four additional papers were prepared for detecting various amines either in solution or in the pure state. Add Ref.: CA **42**, 60 (1948).

4—THE DETECTION AND DIFFERENTIATION OF SOME AROMATIC AMINES

Barakat, M. Z., N. Wahba, and M. M. El-Sadr. Analyst **79**, 715-717 (1954).

The authors use aqueous N-bromosuccinimide to distinguish between primary, secondary, and tertiary aromatic amines. Cyclic triketones (ninhydrin, perinaphthindanetrione hydrate, m-nitroperinaphthindanetrione hydrate, and alloxan) can detect, and differentiate between, various aromatic amines. *These reagents might detect amines in air.* Add. Ref.: CA **49**, 1486 (1955).

5—FERRIC THIOCYANATE PAPER AS AN ANALYTICAL REAGENT IN THE ANALYSIS OF AIR

Deckert, Walter. Z. anal. Chem. **150**, (6), 421-425 (1956); CA **50**, 10608 (1956).

The author presents detailed directions for the preparation of test papers from potassium thiocyanate and ferric alum solutions. These test papers can be used for the detection and analyses of basic gases in the atmosphere such as ammonia, amines, and ethylene oxides.

Ibid. AA **3**, 3206 (1956).

Impregnate S & S No. 2403 chromatographic paper with a mixture of 96 ml of 40% potassium thiocyanate solution and 4 ml of 10% ferric ammonium sulfate solution for 1 to 2 seconds. Dry the paper in moist, ammonia-free air at not more than 20° C. Ammonia in the air being tested will decolorize the paper. Although the technique is primarily chromatographic, it is useful also to detect acid gases in the air because they will recolorize the bleached ferric thiocyanate paper.

6—PAPER ELECTROPHORESIS OF AROMATIC AMINES. p-NITROBENZENEDIAZONIUM FLUOBORATE, A NEW COLOR REAGENT FOR AROMATIC AMINES

Hanot, C. Bull. soc. chim. Belges **66**, 76-92 (1957) (in English); CA **51**, 7935 (1957).

p-Nitrobenzenediazonium fluoborate reacts with microgram quantities of aromatic and aryl amines in neutral or acid solution, to form colors *which might be used for filter paper detectors.*

7—DETECTION OF PRIMARY AROMATIC AMINES

Sawicki, Eugene, Thomas W. Stanley, and Thomas R. Hauser. Chemist-Analyst **48**, 30-31 (1959).

To test for polynuclear aromatic amines, place 1 drop of the sample (in dimethylsulfoxide) on a white porcelain spot plate, add 1 drop of 0.25% diazonium reagent, wait 5 minutes, then add 1 drop of 10% aqueous tetraethylammonium hydroxide solution with stirring. A violet color indicates a positive reaction. To prepare the diazonium reagent dissolve 19.7 g of 4-aminoazobenzene in a mimimum amount of dimethyformamide and add 49 ml of concentrated hydrochloric acid. Then add dropwise, with stirring, 7.6 g of sodium nitrite dissolved in a minimum amount of water while keeping the mixture between 0 and 5° C. Stir for 10 minutes, add 1.0 g of urea, and filter cold. To the filtered solution add 12.1 g of sodium fluoborate dissolved in a minimum amount of water. Filter off the diazonium fluoborate and wash thoroughly with water, then with methanol, and finally with ether. Add. Refs.: Anal. Chem., Anal. Reviews **33**, No. 5, 3R-13R (1961); CA **53**, 18759 (1959).

8—A TEST FOR THE DETECTION OF AROMATIC AMINES

Hearn, W. E. and R. Kinghorn. Analyst **85**, 766-768 (1960).

The authors describe reactions of aromatic amines with ammonium ceric nitrate reagent, which serves to distinguish aromatic amines from other nitrogen-containing compounds. The test also can characterize a particular amine and can distinguish between isomers, e. g., the color reactions of o-, m-, and p-toluidine. The authors list 33 amines and the color each gives with the reagent.

9—DETECTING AMMONIA AND AMINE VAPOR

Williams, Dale D. (to U. S. Dept. of the Navy). U. S. (Pat. No.) 3,025,142, March 13, 1962, Appl. Oct. 30, 1959; CA **56**, 13202 (1962).

Detect less than 1 ppm of gaseous ammonia and/or amines colorimetrically by passage through silica gel-ninhydrin, followed by heating to produce the characteristic blue color. The concentrations of the gases are directly proportional to the band widths produced. Distinguish the ammonia from the amine by passing the sample through boric acid which selectively filters out the amine. At the unfiltered end the concentration is the total ammonia + amine. At the boric acid filtered end, the concentration is that of the ammonia; the amine concentration is the difference between the two. After both tube ends have been exposed for equal times, heat the tube to 95 to 100° for 2 minutes. Cool to room temperature and note the band widths. Read results in ppm from a calibration chart.

Ammonia

1—SIMPLE METHODS FOR THE DETERMINATION OF GASEOUS IMPURITIES IN THE AIR OF FACTORIES

Hahn, Martin, Gesundh. Ing. **31**, 693-697 (1910); CA **4**, 1074 (1910).

Colorimetric methods are described for the determination of ammonia. Ammonia is determined by the Nessler test and the depth of color produced is compared with a standard color scale.

2—NEW REACTION OF RESORCINOL AND ITS APPLICATION TO THE DETECTION OF THE NITROPRUSSIATE ION AND AMMONIA

Caseneuve, M. Bull. soc. pharm. Bordeaux **61**, 153-155 (1923); CA **18**, 208 (1924).

The author describes a test for ammonia gas and volatile amines. The color forming reagent consists of two grams of sodium nitroprussiate and one gram of resorcinol dissolved in water. The detection of ammonia involves exposure, on a white spot plate, of one drop of reagent to the air. A bluish green coloration indicates the presence of ammonia. Other volatile amines produce the same reaction.

3—A NEW AND SENSITIVE TEST FOR AMMONIA

Makris, Konstantin G. Z. anal. Chem. **81**, 212-214 (1930); CA **24**, 4731 (1930).

A freshly prepared mixture of 2 cc of 20% silver nitrate solution mixed with 1 cc of a 5% tannin solution provides a sensitive reagent for the detection of ammonia. One drop of the mixture is placed on a watch glass and 0.1 cc of the test solution is contacted with the reagent. If ammonia is present a silver ring will appear rapidly. An alternate procedure is to impregnate a wad of cotton with the reagent and bring it close to a solution containing ammonia. Heat the ammonia containing solution and a silver deposit will form on the cotton if at least .005 g of ammonia is present.

4—CHEMICAL DETECTION OF RESPIRATORY POISONS

Smolczyk, E. and H. Cobler. Gasmaske **2**, 27-33 (1930); Wasser u. Abwasser **28**, 95 (1930).

Paper impregnated with phenolphthalein will change color immediately in air when 100 ppm of ammonia is present. Litmus paper will change in one second at this concentration. A concentration of 10 ppm will require 5 and 6.5 seconds for phenolphthalein or litmus papers to turn, respectively. Add. Ref.: CA **26**, 1214 (1932).

5—NEW COLORIMETRIC DETERMINATION OF AMMONIA

Makris, Konstantin G. .Z anal. Chem. **84**, 217-220 (1931); CA **25**, 4200 (1931).

Essentially the same as a previous article by the same author (see above).

6—DETECTION OF AMMONIA IN AIR

Korenman, I. M. Z. anal. Chem. **90**, 115-118 (1932). Aniline, sulfanilic acid, benzidine, phenylhydrazine, "ursol D.W.", "ursol D. S.", alhpa- and beta-naphthylamine, para-aminobenzearsonic acid salt and p-nitraniline were diazotized by sodium nitrite and hydrochloric acid. The products formed were sensitive agents for the detection of ammonia. Filter paper impregnated with one of the diazotized amines will detect fractions of a milligram of ammonia. Add. Ref.: CA **27**, 43 (1933).

7—A RAPID METHOD FOR DETERMINING AMMONIA IN STABLES.

Meurice, R. and G. Demortier. Bull. inst. agron. sta. recherches Gembloux **4**, 28-30 (1935); CA **29**, 5039 (1935).

A drop of Nessler's reagent turns from yellow to brown in the presence of ammonia. Time is used to make the technique quanitative.

8—THE DETECTION OF TOXIC GASES AND VAPORS

Leroux, Lucien. Rev. hyg. et med. prevent. **57**, 81-112 (1935).

Two tests are discussed, one using alpha-naphthylamine filter paper and the other a silver-tannin reagent on cotton wadding. The sensitivity of the former is 0.07 mg ammonia per liter and the latter will detect 0.001 mg. Filter paper strips are prepared as shown by Korenman (above) and are stable for about one week. The following references are cited by this author: Korenman, I. M. Z. anal. Chem. **90**, 115 (1932); Makris, K. G. THE PROBLEMS OF AIR POLLUTION IN PARIS, Masson, Paris 1933, p. 219. Add. Ref. CA **29**, 3627 (1935).

9—SOME METHODS FOR THE DETECTION AND ESTIMATION OF POISONOUS GASES AND VAPORS IN THE AIR. (A PRACTICAL MANUAL FOR THE INDUSTRIAL HYGIENIST)

Zhitkova, A. S., translated by J. B. Ficklen (Service to Industry, Box 133, West Hartford, Conn., 1936) pp 72-75.

Ammonia will turn litmus paper blue when exposed to a contaminated atmosphere, and solutions containing ammonia will react with Nessler's reagent to form an orange-brown color. The color is dependent on the concentration of ammonia. Fuchsin-hydrochloric acid paper is used for the detection of ammonia also.

10—THE USE OF INDICATORS FOR THE DETECTION OF POISONOUS GASES AND VAPORS

Heering, D. Gasmaske **8**, 88-89 (1936).

Red litmus paper turns blue and phenolphthalein paper turns red with ammonia at concentrations of 0.071 mg/liter. Add. Ref.: CA **30**, 7059 (1936).

11—DETERMINING SMALL QUANTITIES OF ADSORBABLE GAS OR VAPOR IN AIR OR OTHER GASES.

Schroeter, August Gustav-Adolf. U. S. (Pat. No.) 2,103,187 (to Otto H. Draeger) December 21, 1937; May 24, 1933 in Germany.

Silica gel impregnated with cobaltous sulfate (1:100 in water) is placed in a 1 to 2 cm tube; when ammonia-contaminated air is drawn through the tube the pink color changes to blue. Add. Ref.: CA **32**, 1214 (1938).

12—RAPID METHODS FOR THE DETERMINATION OF NOXIOUS GASES IN THE AIR OF INDUSTRIAL PLANTS. DETERMINATION OF AMMONIA.

Khrustaleva, V. A. and M. V. Yakovenko. Sbornik Trudov Tsentral. Sanit.-Higienicheskoi Lab. Otdela Zdravookhraneniya Moskov. Soveta Deputatov Trudyashchikhsya **1940**, No. 3, 5-14; CA **37**, 5925 (1943).

The authors present detailed directions for aspirating air through Nessler's reagent and the comparison of the resulting color with that of standards.

13—TEST FOR AMMONIA

Draegerwerk Heinrich u. Bernhard Draeger; Ger. (Pat. No.) 718,767, February 26, 1942 (Cl. 421. N. 06); CA **37**, 1674 (1943).

Ammonia can be detected with a concentrated solution of copper salts saturated with ammonium salts.

14—DETECTION OF CERTAIN CHLORINATED TERTIARY ALIPHATIC AMINES

Cruikshank, A. J., H. A. Bewick, J. E. Currah and F. E. Beamish. Anal. Chem. **19**, 849-850 (1947).

In addition to the tertiary aliphatic amines a detector paper for ammonia is described. Whatman No. 1 filter papers are immersed in a solution prepared by mixing 7 ml of cobalt solution (10 mg cobalt nitrate hexahydrate in 90 ml water), 10.7 ml bismuth solution, 10 g bismuth subnitrate in 90 ml water and 30 ml hydrochloric acid), 12 ml thiocyanate solution (5 g sodium thiocyanate in 95 ml water), and 5 ml glycerol. The papers are then blotted and dried for one hour in an oven at 60° C. The green color of the paper turns pink with ammonia. Add. Ref.: CA **42**, 60 (1948).

15—AMMONIA DETECTOR

Kitagawa, Tetsuzo. Japan (Pat. No.) 177,024; November 26, 1948; CA **45**, 4974 (1951).

Silica gel impregnated salts of iron, copper, cobalt or nickel can be used to colorimetrically evaluate the concentration of ammonia in air.

16—DETECTION OF NITROGEN IN ORGANIC COMPOUNDS

Brown, Lawrence E. and Carroll L. Hoffpauir. Anal. Chem. **23**, 1035-1036 (1951).

The authors used a strip of filter paper impregnated with a zinc-8-quinolinol complex to detect nitrogen in organic compounds. The samples were pyrolysed in a tube with xylene oxide and the wet filter paper absorbed the ammonia formed. The paper was examined under fluorescent light. Add. Ref.: CA **45**, 9421 (1951).

17—APPLICATION OF PARRI'S REACTION TO THE DETECTION OF AMMONIA IN AIR

Castagnou, R. and R. Quilichini. Bull. soc. pharm. Bordeaux **90**, 202-204 (1952); CA **47**, 11659 (1953).

The authors present a modification of the "Parri" reaction as an indicator for ammonia. The following procedure is used to prepare the indicator: 0.5 g of phenobarbital and 1 g of cobalt chloride is dissolved in 50 ml of methyl alcohol. One drop of this solution is placed on Whatman paper and allowed to dry. This stable reagent paper will detect subtoxic quantities of ammonia in air.

18—A SIMPLE DEVICE FOR AIR ANALYSIS

Gisclard, J. B. et al. Am. Ind. Hyg. Assn. Quart. **14**, 23-25 (1953).

Ammonia is absorbed in 0.0001 N sulfuric acid (1 ml = 0.0017 mg ammonia) in a micro bubbler with methyl purple as the indicator. The air titration is carried out by using a syringe as the pump and air is drawn through the solution until a color change from purple to green is noted. The volume of air is used to calculate the ammonia concentration in the air. Add. Ref.: IHD **17**, 517 (1953).

19—ANALYSIS OF MEDICALLY IMPORTANT GASES USING SPOT TESTS

Massman, W. Arch. Gewerbepathol. Gewerbehyg. **13**, 262-275 (1954).

Filter papers sensitive to ammonia are prepared by impregnating the papers with diazotized amines such as aniline, benzidine etc. Fractions of a mg of ammonia can be detected with this technique. Korenman is referred to (above). Add Ref.: IHD **19**, 599 (1955).

20—ANALYTICAL PROCEDURE FOR THE DETECTION OF GASES

Guatelli, Manuel A. Rev. asoc. bioquim. arg. **18**, 3-40 (1954).

To detect the present M.A.C. in air for ammonia, paper impregnated with a 1% alcoholic solution of phenolphthalein will turn red in 5 to 5.6 seconds in an atmosphere of 10 ppm and in one second in 100 ppm. The use of Nessler's reagent in filter papers is also discussed. Add. Ref.: CA **48**, 8124 (1954).

21—FERRIC THIOCYANATE PAPER AS AN ANALYTICAL REAGENT IN THE ANALYSIS OF AIR

Deckert, Walter. Z. anal. Chem. **150**, 421-425 (1956); CA **50**, 10608 (1956).

The author presents detailed directions for the preparation of test papers from potassium thiocyanate and ferric alum solutions. These test papers can be used for the detection and analysis of basic gases, such as ammonia, amines and ethylene oxide. S & S No. 2043 chromatographic paper is impregnated with 96 ml of 40% potassium thiocyanate and 4 ml of 10% ferric ammonium sulfate. The paper is

dried at not more than 20° C. in the absence of ammonia. If ammonia is present in the air being tested, it will bleach the paper.

22—TUBE FOR DETECTION AND DETERMINATION OF AMMONIA VAPOR IN AIR OR OTHER GASES

Auergesellschaft Akt.-Ges. (by Hermann Heidrich). Ger. (Pat. No.) 961,036, March 28, 1957 (Cl. 42.1); CA **54**, 176 (1960).

Silica gel impregnated with a neutral solution of nickel dimethylglyoxime is dried and placed in a detector tube. The colorless grained layer becomes golden yellow when ammonia-containing gases are passed through it. The color strength is proportional to the concentration.

23—RAPID METHOD FOR THE DETERMINATION OF LOW CONCENTRATIONS OF AMMONIA AND CARBON DIOXIDE IN AIR BY MEANS OF DETECTOR TUBES

Kobayashi, Yoshitaka. Kogyo Kagaku Zasshi **61**, 525-527 (1958); CA **55**, 10764 (1961).

Tubes containing acrylic resin powders impregnated with alcoholic thymol blue solution are detectors for 0.002 to 0.07% of ammonia in air. The air (100 ml) is sampled at a rate of 1 ml per second. The length of the yellowish stain in the tube is proportional to the concentration of the ammonia producing it, within ± 5%. Chlorine or amines interfere but carbon dioxide does not.

24—THE DETERMINATION OF MONOETHANOLAMINE AND AMMONIA IN AIR

Williams, D. D. and R. R. Miller. Anal. Chem. **34**, 225-227 (1962).

A method for the routine determination of parts per million quantities of ammonia and/or monoethanolamine (MEA) vapor in air uses the reagent ninhydrin, which, supported on silica gel in a glass tube, reacts equally well with both contaminants. Orthoboric acid serves as a selective filter to remove MEA from the sampled air. Consecutive sampling through the tube in opposite directions permits the simultaneous determination of either of both contaminants. The tubes are 4-inch lengths of glass tubing drawn out and sealed at one end. An end-holding plug of properly sized polyurethane foam or glass wool is inserted and positioned at this end of the tube, being careful to leave a flat interface. In order, a 20 mm layer of impregnated silica gel, a separator plug, a 10 mm layer of 30 to 60 mesh calcium carbonate, another separator plug, a 10 mm layer of 30 to 60 mesh orthoboric acid, and a holding plug are added. The other end of the tube now is drawn out and sealed, being careful to avoid heating the boric acid. The fillings should be tamped enough to ensure firm layers of uniform density. The silica gel is prepared by adding to a weighed quantity (W) of pure white gel (dried at 110° C) 2% (0.02 W) of triketohydrindene hydrate (ninhydrin) dissolved in just enough distilled water to completely wet the gel. Stir, allow to stand 10 minutes, then remove excess water by passing a stream of filtered air or inert gas at a temperature of 20 to 25° C and relative humidity of 50 to 60% over or through the gel until equilibrium is attained. The gel should contain 25 to 30% by weight of water and should be free flowing. The interposition of the calcium carbonate layer prevents the transport of the boric acid to the active gel under ambient temperature fluctuations. The shelf life of the tubes is at least 18 months, especially if they are refrigerated. Add. Ref.: A.P.C.A. Abstr. **7**, No. 10, 4309 (1962).

25—DETECTING AMMONIA AND AMINE VAPOR

Williams, Dale D. (to U. S. Dept. of the Navy). U. S. (Pat. No.) 3,025,142, March 13, 1962, Appl. Oct. 30, 1959; CA **56**, 13202 (1962).

Detect less than 1 ppm of gaseous ammonia and/or amines colorimetrically by passage through silica gel-ninhydrin, followed by heating to produce the characteristic blue color. The concentrations of the gases are directly proportional to the band widths produced. Distinguish the ammonia from the amine by passing the sample through boric acid which selectively filters out the amine. At the unfiltered end the concentration is the total ammonia + amine. At the boric acid filtered end, the concentration is that of the ammonia; the amine concentration is the difference between the two. After both tube ends have been exposed for equal times, heat the tube to 95 to 100° for 2 minutes. Cool to room temperature and note the band widths. Read results in ppm from a calibration chart.

See Section One

For reference numbers 3, 6, 15, 39, 59, 76, 77, 81, 85, 88, 93, 95, 96, 112, 125, 129.

Amyl Acetate

1—COLORIMETRIC METHOD FOR THE ESTIMATION OF AMYL ACETATE VAPORS IN THE AIR

Custance, H. M. and M. Higgins. Analyst **74**, 310-315 (1949); CA **43**, 7377 (1949).

The determination depends upon the color produced when amyl acetate is reacted with sulfuric acid and p-dimethylaminobenzaldehyde in ethyl alcohol solution. Ethyl alcohol is a satisfactory collection medium. The lower limit of detectability is approximately 10 ppm.

Aniline

1—DYNAMIC METHOD FOR THE DETERMINATION OF ANILINE IN THE AIR

Grodsovskij, M. Gigiena truda **4**, 53-67 (1926); Ber. ges. Physiol. exptl. Pharmakol. **39**, 134 (1926); CA **21**, 1946 (1927).

The author describes a method for the detection of aniline in air. The method involves saturating muslin strips with a concentrated solution of aluminum hexachlorate nonahydrate containing a few drops of vanadous chloride. This reagent is oxidized to aniline black if aniline is present. The standard is a similarly treated muslin strip kept in a glass jar containing a known concentration of aniline.

2—SIMPLE METHODS FOR THE DETECTION AND DETERMINATION OF POISONOUS GASES, VAPORS, SMOKES, AND DUSTS IN FACTORY AIR

Weber, Hans H. Zentr. Gewerbehyg. Unfallverhuet. **23**, 177-180 (1936).

Aniline may be detected on cotton strips impregnated with the following reagent: dissolve 23.1 g aluminum hydroxide in 250 g of 30% perchloric acid and shake well; add a few drops of 50% vanadyl chloride solution. Aniline colors the reagent from blue to blue-violet to black. Add. Ref.: CA **32**, 1609 (1938).

3—THE USE OF INDICATORS FOR THE DETERMINATION OF POISONOUS GASES AND VAPORS

Heering, D. Gasmaske **8**, 88-89 (1936).

Aniline reacts with a solution of aluminum chloride and vanadium chloride to give a violet color. Add. Ref.: CA **30**, 7059 (1936).

4—IDENTIFICATION OF WAR GASES

Liberalli, Marcelo Robertson. Rev. quim. farm. (Rio de Janeiro) 4 49-53 (1939).

Aluminum and vanadium chloride are turned violet with aniline. Add Ref.: CA **33**, 7921 (1939) (N. B. - name listed under "Robertson" in CA author index.)

5— DETECTION OF ANILINE VAPOR

Anon. Dept. Sci. & Ind. Research, "Method for the Detection of Toxic Gases in Industry, Leaflet No. 11, 9 pp. (1939).

To test for aniline vapor in the atmosphere pass a sample of air through a small bubbler containing dilute hydrochloric acid. If sufficient aniline be present the aniline chloride formed will give to bleaching powder a purple color, which changes quickly to a dirty red. There will be a trace of color if only a small amount of aniline is in the air. The test is more sensitive if, after the bleaching powder, the solution be made slightly ammoniacal and a little phenol solution added; as little as 1 part of aniline in 100,000 parts of air then will give a permanent deep blue color. Add. Ref.: Chem & Ind. (London) **58**, 1070 (1939); CA **34**, 19 (1940).

6—THE DETECTION OF TOXIC GASES AND VAPORS IN INDUSTRY

Vallender, R. B. Chem. & Ind. (London) **58**, 330-333 (1939).

The usual bleaching powder test is insensitive to 1 part in 100,000; however, if the sample is taken in an acid solution and a few "drops" of bleaching powder added, followed by an ammoniacal solution of phenol, an intense blue color is readily observed. Add. Ref.: CA **33**, 4907 (1939).

7—SIMPLIFIED DETERMINATION OF ANILINE IN AIR

Alekseeva, M. V. Gigiena i Sanit. **13**, No. 11, 30 (1948); CA **43**, 8979 (1949).

Chloramine-T is used as the reagent instead of the usual standard hypochlorite solution.

8—RAPID DETERMINATION OF ANILINE IN INDUSTRIAL ESTABLISHMENTS

Bulycheva, A. I. Zavodskaya Lab. **14**, 1208-1209 (1948); IHD **15**, 627 (1951).

A colorimetric reaction of aniline treated with Chloramine-T in alkaline solution in the presence of phenol is described. The resulting blue color obtained appears in approximately 20 minutes and is stable for 2 to 3 days. Air containing the aniline is bubbled through water and treated with the prepared reagent. The sample coloration is compared visually with a set of calibration standards. Samples containing quantities of aniline as small as 0.01 to 0.2 mg/l can be determined. Add. Ref.: CA **44**, 10603 (1950).

9—RAPID DETECTION OF ANILINE VAPORS IN AIR

Riehl, Wilbur A. and Karl F. Hager. Anal. Chem. **27**, 1768-1769 (1955).

Paper impregnated with 4μ (by volume) furfural in glacial acetic acid readily turns from white to pink or red with aniline in a range from 5 to 150 ppm. The reagent is stable for at least one month at room temperature, when stored in the specially adapted tubes. Interference from other amines is minimal. Add. Ref.: IHD **19**, 1415 (1955); CA **50**, 2370 (1956).

10—DETECTION AND DETERMINATION OF ANILINE VAPORS IN THE AIR

Centralny Instytut Ochrony Pracy (by Stefan Zawadzki. Pol. (Pat. No.) 41,005, May 15, 1958; CA **54**, 7440 (1960).

The air is aspirated through an indicator tube which contains silica gel saturated with a mixture of furfural and glacial acetic acid. The amount of aniline can be estimated from the length of the red colored section of silica gel. Silica gel of 0.4 to 0.7 mm grain size and absorption capacity of 40 to 60% in relation to benzene and dried at 180° is treated with a 2 to 6% solution of furfural in acetic acid. The silica gel is then filtered off and dried at 60

to 100° for 20 minutes. The length of the indicator tube is 100 mm and the diameter is 6.0 mm. The sensitivity is 0.005 mg of aniline in 1 liter of air.

11—NEW METHOD FOR THE DETECTION OF ANILINE IN SANITARY HYGIENE INVESTIGATIONS

Belikov, V. G. Gigiena Truda i Professional. Zabolevaniya **3**, No. 5, 53-54 (1959); CA **54**, 7944 (1960).

Filter paper moistened with a 1% solution of sodium nitroprusside can be used for the detection of aniline. The paper turns blue or greenish—blue in the presence of aniline.

12—AN INDICATOR TUBE FOR THE RAPID DETERMINATION OF ANILINE IN THE ATMOSPHERE

Bulycheva, A. I. and P. A. Mel'nikova. Fiz.-Khim. Methody Issled. Vozdushn. Sredy, Vses. Tsentr. Nauchn.-Issled. Inst. Okhrany Truda **1961**, 56-64; CA **56**, 13200 (1962).

Mix 2 ml of a 1% alcoholic solution of p-dimethylaminobenzaldehyde with 1 ml of 1% aqueous hydrochloric acid solution and 2 ml of distilled water. Add 3.5 ml of the mixture to 7 g of dry porcelain powder (granular fineness 247 to 280μ); mix and after 10 minutes dry for 1 hour at 50° $\pm$ not more than 2° (the drying temperature influences the sensitivity). Fill a glass tube 90 to 91 mm long and 2.5 to 2.6 mm inside diameter with a 70 mm column of the indicator powder and stopper both ends of the tube with cotton. The tubes are usable for 1 month if stored vertically in a closed container. Pass 250 ml of air contaminated with aniline through the tube in 7 or 8 minutes and compare the length of the yellow colored column with a standard scale, prepared with 0.003 to 0.09 mg of aniline per liter of air.

13—SPOT TEST DETECTION AND COLORIMETRIC DETERMINATION OF ANILINE, NAPHTHYLAMINE AND ANTHRAMINE DERIVATIVES WITH 4-AZOBENZENEDIAZONIUM FLUOBORATE

Sawicki, Eugene, James L. Noe, and Francis T. Fox. Talanta **8**, 257-264 (1961).

For a spot paper procedure, the authors placed on paper 1 drop of a 2-methoxyethanol test solution, then added 2 drops of 0.1% 4-azobenzenediazonium fluoborate. Next, they treated the spot with a jet of steam for 30 seconds, then with either a jet of hydrogen chloride gas or a drop of concentrated hydrochloric acid. They include a table giving colors and limits of identification. *This probably is not applicable at the present time for field detection.*

See Section One

For reference numbers 81, 85, 90, 104.

Antimony

See Section One

For reference number 77.

Aromatic Hydrocarbons

1—METHODS FOR THE DETECTION OF TOXIC GASES IN INDUSTRY. BENZENE VAPOR

Anon. Dept. of Scientific and Industrial Research, London, England. Leaflet No. 4 (1938) 7 pp.; Ibid., 2nd Edition (1955) 5 pp.

Benzene produces an orange-brown color with formaldehyde-sulfuric acid reagent. The reagent is prepared by adding 0.5 ml of 40% formaldehyde to a bubbler and diluting to 10 ml with concentrated sulfuric acid. Air is bubbled through the solution with a hand pump and the color formed is compared with that of standards made from sodium nitroprusside. With 18 strokes the sensitivity is 1 part in 10,000. Naphthas, toluene, and xylene react only qualitatively. Naphthalene interferes by producing a black film on the surface of the reagent. Thiophene and unsaturated hydrocarbons also interfere, but can be detected by bubbling the air through sulfuric acid alone. Add. Refs.: CA **33**, 4159 (1939); IHD **20**, 1066 (1956).

2—DETERMINATION OF BENZENE IN AIR BY MEANS OF THE DRAEGER-SCHROETER GAS DETECTOR

Gemeinhardt, K. Draeger-Hefte No. **194**, 3752-3753 (1938); CA **32**, 2645 (1938).

The method described requires 10 minutes for the detection of benzene vapor concentration which are only one fiftieth of the concentration that can be tolerated for one hour.

3—BENZENE DETECTION WITH THE DRAEGER-SCHROETER APPARATUS

Gemeinhardt, K. Petroleum Z. **34**, No. 15, Motorenbetrieb u. Maschinen-Schmierung **9**, No. 4, 2-3 (1938); CA **32**, 8624 (1938).

Same as above.

4—THE DETECTION OF TOXIC GASES AND VAPORS IN INDUSTRY

Vallender, R. B. Chem. & Ind. (London) **58**, 330-333 (1939).

Air containing 1 part benzene in 10,000 will turn a concentrated sulfuric acid solution containing a few drops of formalin reddish-brown. The color then is compared with that of standards made from dilute sodium nitroprusside solutions. Add. Ref.: CA **33**, 4907 (1939).

5—SOLVENTS AND THINNERS USED IN PAINT AND VARNISHES FOR ARTICLES OF DAILY USE

Beythien, A. Paint Varnish Production Mgr. **21**, 81-82 (1941); CA **35**, 3836 (1941).

The toxicology is described and methods for the detection of benzene in the air . . . are given.

6—DANGER OF BENZENE HYDROCARBONS IN THE ATMOSPHERE. THEIR DETERMINATION

Roger, Louis. Chimie & industrie **50**, 135-136 (1943); CA **40**, 2907 (1946).

The author describes a method for the determination of benzene and its homologs. The method is based on Deniges' reaction (color produced by benzene and homologs on adsorption in 9.5 cc 66° Bé sulfuric acid and 0.5 cc 40% formaldehyde, Bull. Soc. Pharm. Mordeaux **1900**, 321). Owing to the color standard selected (1% aqueous solution of sodium nitroprusside) the method is applicable only to the determination of pure benzene, as toluene gives a rose-brown coloration and xylene a pink coloration. Roger has developed more stable and more suitable standards which permit determination of all 3 hydrocarbons. The base solutions for preparing the standards are: (1) 1.25% cobalt as chloride, (2) 1.25% nickel as chloride, (3) 0.5% iron as ferric chloride. The standards are prepared by mixing solutions (1), (2), and (3) in the following respective proportions: benzene 9.0:11.0:3.5, toluene 9.3:7.3:1.8, xylene 12.2:11.8:0.

7—RAPID METHOD FOR THE DETERMINATION OF AROMATIC HYDROCARBONS IN AIR

Hubbard, Byron R. and Leslie Silverman. Arch. Ind. Hyg. Occupational Med. **2**, 49-55 (1950).

Benzene and its homologs can be determined in the field by passing air to be tested through tubes containing silica gel impregnated with sulfuric acid and formaldehyde. Benzene produces immediately a reddish-brown color, which changes to light purple; toluene gives pink to lavender, changing to purple; and xylene colors the reagent yellow to pink to purple. The length of the stain is proportional to the concentration of the hydrocarbon. The range of sensitivity is: benzene 0-100 ppm; toluene 0-400 ppm; xylene 0-400 ppm. Thiophene interferes. Add. Ref.: CA **44**, 8285 (1950).

8—DETECTING BENZENE VAPORS IN GASES

Draegerwerk Heinrich und Bernhard Draeger. Ger. (Pat. No.) 823, 805, Dec. 6, 1951 (Cl 421, 402); CA **48**, 7883 (1954).

Gas containing benzene or its homologs can be reacted with nitrous acid in sulfuric acid to produce colored reaction products. This reagent can be used with detector tubes by impregnating silica gel with the same acids plus a complex-forming heavy metal salt such as copper, iron, cobalt or nickel salts which yield nitrite complex compounds which stabilize the reagent. A method for the preparation of the indicator tube is described. The reagent in the finished tube has a pale pink coloration which in the presence of benzene, changes from violet through yellow-brown. The depth of the discolored area is proportional to the concentration of benzene present.

9—GAS ANALYSIS BY MEANS OF GAS DETECTORS. II. RAPID METHOD FOR THE DETERMINATION OF THE MINUTE QUANTITY OF BENZENE IN AIR

Kobayashi, Yoshitaka. J. Chem. Soc. Japan, Ind. Chem. Sect. **55**, 544-546 (1952); CA **48**, 3852 (1954).

The author describes a method for the determination of benzene in air. A glass detector tube is filled with silica gel impregnated with a solution of sulfuric acid and formadlehyde. The benzene concentration is determined by the length of stain produced. The average error in the determination was found to be 5%. Add. Ref.: IHD **18**, 561 (1954).

10—DETECTOR FOR AROMATIC HYDROCARBONS

Westgate, Mark W. and Marjorie R. Christian. Natl. Paint, Varnish Lacquer Assoc., Sci. Sect., Circ. No. **757**, 110-115 (1952); CA **47**, 3049 (1953).

The authors conducted a series of laboratory tests to determine the efficiency of the Mine Safety Appliances Company "Aromatic Hydrocarbon Detector". The results showed that the instrument was able to detect separately benzene, toluene, or xylene in air at or below concentrations found where good industrial hygiene practices are followed. Non-aromatic solvent vapors were found not to interfere with the analyses. Mixtures of the aromatic hydrocarbons gave abnormally high results.

11—SAMPLING AND ANALYZING AIR FOR CONTAMINANTS IN WORK PLACES

Silverman, Leslie. Encyclopedia of Instrumentation for Industrial Hygiene, edited by Yaffe, Charles D., Dohrman H. Byers, and Andrew D. Hosey. (Univ. of Michigan, Inst. of Industrial Health, Ann Arbor, Mich., 1956) pp. 7-25.

Granules impregnated with sulfuric acid and paraformaldehyde turn violet to black with 0 to 100 ppm of benzene and with 0 to 400 ppm of toluene. The stain length is proportional to the concentration of the hydrocarbon. Thiophene interferes.

12—DETERMINATION OF SOLVENT VAPORS IN AIR. III. BENZENE AND TOLUENE

Kobayashi, Yoshitaka. J. Soc. Org. Synthet. Chem., Japan **12**, 319-322 (1954); CA **51**, 952 (1957).

Silica gel is impregnated with sulfuric acid and paraformaldehyde is used for the determination of benzene and toluene. One hundred ml of air is aspirated through the

tube in 200 seconds and a reddish-brown coloration results. The effective range is 1-400 ppm for benzene and 1-1000 ppm for toluene.

13—RAPID METHOD OF BENZENE OR BENZENE HOMOLOGS DETERMINATION WITH THE USE OF INDICATORS

Yavorovskaya, S. F. Khim. Prom. **1956**, 366-367; CA **51**, 3371 (1957).

The author describes a chromatographic method for the determination of benzene and its homologs. Silica gel is impregnated with sulfuric acid and formaldehyde. Air is aspirated through the column; the color produced is orange yellow which changes after 2 to 3 minutes to a violet, gray, brown and violet-brown depending upon the homolog present. The sample column is compared with standards prepared by vaporizing known amounts of benzene, toluene, or xylene in acetone. The results obtained with this method differ little from the results of tests conducted by nitration or catalytic combustion.

14—REPORT ON THE DRAEGER GAS DETECTOR. BENZENE

Transactions of the Twenty-first Annual Meeting of the Am. Conf. of Gov. Ind. Hyg. (1959) pp. 125-127.

The most sensitive benzene tube has an indicated range of 0.05-2 mg per liter which is equivalent to 15.0 to 600 ppm. The study indicates that it is difficult to determine concentrations below 25 ppm but good accuracy can be expected in the range of 50 ppm. At 25 ppm calibration shows that there is relatively good agreement with true values. It has also been noted that the presence of toluene produces an interference.

15—REPORT ON THE DRAEGER GAS RETECTOR. TOLUENE

Transactions of the Twenty-first Annual Meeting of the Am. Conf. of Gov. Ind. Hyg. (1959) pp. 125-127.

The efficiency of the two available detector tubes for benzene and toluene was studied. It was found that considerable variation could be observed when a known concentration of these materials was analyzed with indicator tubes. Generally, the results obtained were higher than true values.

16—MINE SAFETY APPLIANCES COMPANY

Catalog of Industrial Safety Equipment, Catalog 7-B, Section 3, p. 26, "Aromatic Hydrocarbon Detector" (1957); also MSA Bull. No. 0811-6 (1959).

The aromatic hydrocarbon detector is a self-contained aspirator unit. Two silica gels impregnated with active reagents are mixed before use and poured into the sampling tube, through which the air to be tested is drawn. The length of the stain in the silica gel tube is proportional to the concentration of aromatic hydrocarbon in the air. A precalibrated sliding scale on the barrel of the instrument is marked for benzene from 0 to 100 ppm and for toluene and xylene from 0 to 400 ppm.

17—QUANTITATIVE DETECTION OF BENZENE IN AIR AND OTHER GASES

Auergesellschaft Akt.-Ges. (Hermann Heidrich, inventor). Ger. (Pat. No.) 933,711, Sept. 29, 1955 (Cl. 42.**1**.4.06); CA **53**, 5024 (1959).

For the detection of benzene in air or gas mixtures, dissolve 50 g of antimony pentachloride in 150 ml carbon tetrachloride, and charge 100 g of dry silica gel with 60 ml of the solution. Fill and seal the tube, excluding atmospheric moisture. Benzene and its homologs change the colorless substance to yellow or brown-black.

18—REAGENT FOR DETECTION OF HYDROCARBONS

Draegerwerk, Heinrich und Bernhard Draeger. Ger. (Pat. No.) 932,995, Sept. 15, 1955 (Cl. 42.**1**.4.06); CA **53**, 5022 (1959).

Impregnate 100 g of silica gel with a solution of 3 g of selenous acid in 50 g of water at 140°, dry to constant weight, and charge with sulfur trioxide until the entire increase in weight is 40 g. Activate at 180° for 90 minutes. Aliphatic or aromatic hydrocarbons change the color of the preparation to brown or dark brown. The reagent may be used in tubes with gas detection instruments.

19—NEW COLOUR TESTS FOR THE LARGER POLYNUCLEAR AROMATIC HYDROCARBONS

Sawicki, Eugene and Roger Barry. Talanta **2**, 128-134 (1959).

The authors describe the preparation of the following aldehyde-phosphorus pentachloride reagents: furfural; 2-thenaldehyde; 3-nitro-4-dimethylaminobenzaldehyde; 9-anthraldehyde; indole-3-aldehyde. In the procedure 1 ml of the chloroform test solution is added to 1 ml of the aldehyde-phosphorus pentachloride solution, 0.5 ml of phosphorus oxychloride, and trifluoroacetic acid to a final volume of 10 ml. An alternate method: to 1 ml of a 2% solution of 2-naphthaldehyde in chloroform add 0.1 ml of trifluoroacetic anhydride followed by 1 ml of the chloroform test solution. After 5 minutes add 1 ml of phosphorus oychloride and dilute the solution to 10 ml with trifluoroacetic acid. In both methods the adsorption spectrum is determined against a blank of the same reagent-solvent composition. The authors do not mention the method of sample collection. Although this is a laboratory procedure, it is included here because of its potential application to field techniques. Add. Refs.: Anal. Chem., Anal. Reviews **33**, No. 5, 3R-13R (1961); CA **53**, 14843 (1959).

20—DETERMINATION OF BENZENE IN THE PRESENCE OF ITS HOMOLOGS IN THE ATMOSPHERE

Vlasak, Rudolf. Pracovni lekarstvi **11**, 418-422 (1949); CA **54**, 12440 (1960).

A description of a method for the determination of benzene, where the air sample is nitrated and the resulting nitrogen dioxide compound reacted with methyl ethyl ketone in pyridine to produce a violet color, is given. Benzene is adsorbed on silica gel and desorbed with a stream of nitrogen at 100-110°. Adequate sensitivity is achieved.

21—DETECTION OF TOLUENE

Draegerwerk Henrich u. Bernhard Draeger. Ger. (Pat. No.) 1,037,178 (Cl. 42 **1**), Aug. 21, 1958; CA **55**, 3308 (1961).

The authors present a test tube method for detecting benzene and its homologs. The tube contains silica gel impregnated with more than 2.5 g of paraformaldehyde and less than 10 ml sulfuric acid per 100 g of gel.

22—DETECTION OF AROMATIC HYDROCARBON VAPORS IN AIR

Draegerwerk Heinrich und Bernhard Draeger. Ger. (Pat. No.) 1,089,999, Sept. 29, 1960 (Cl. 42.**1**); CA **55**, 14178 (1961).

"The concentration of aromatic hydrocarbon vapors in air is determined by aspirating the air sample through a detector tube containing 1st a snythetic zeolite layer (to remove water) and then a calcium aluminum silicate layer impregnated with 18 ml of sulfuric acid, 1 g of selenium dioxide, and 0.1 g of potassium nitrate per 100 g. The aromatic hydrocarbons are separated chromatographically on the silicate and identified by characteristic colors, e.g., red-violet for toluene and light-brown for benzene. The length of the color zone is a measure of the amount of hydrocarbon present. The range of detection is from 0.1 to 7 mg of toluene per liter of air by using a 1 liter sample.

23—COLORIMETRIC METHOD FOR DETERMINING XYLENE VAPORS IN AIR

Kozlyaeva, T. N. and I. G. Vorokhobin. Sb. Nauchn. Rabot Inst. Okhrany Truda, Vses. Tsentr. Sov. Prof. Soyuzov **1961**, No. 4, 114-120; CA **58**, 870 (1963).

The method is based on color reactions with xylene in an indicator tube. A UG-2 gas analyzer's scales are calibrated in 2 ranges for concentrations of vapors of xylene and its isomers: from 0 to 0.5 mg per liter and from 0 to 2.0 mg per liter. The error is approximately ± 10% of the upper limit of the scale. Add. Ref.: Ref. Zh., Khim. **1962**, Abstr. No. 111354.

See Section One

For reference numbers 23, 69, 88, 96, 100, 104, 112.

Arsenic

1—MERCURIC BROMIDE FOR THE GUTZEIT METHOD FOR ARSENIC

Kemmerer, George and H. H. Schrenk. Ind. Eng. Chem. **18**, 707 (1926); CA **20**, 2800 (1926).

The authors describe a filter paper method for the detection of arsenic.

See Section One
For reference number 77.

Arsenic Halide

See Section One
For reference number 120.

Arsenic Trioxide

1—ABSORPTION OF ARSENIC TRIOXIDE FUMES BY FILTER PAPER

Sedivec, V. Pracovni Lekarstvi **7**, 223-227 (1955); CA **50**, 4712 (1956).

Older methods of determining the concentration of toxic vapors in the atmosphere are modified by introducing absorption on filter paper. Schleicher and Schuell's "Blue ribbon" proved satisfactory as it absorbed 98-100% of the arsenic trioxide fumes. The efficiency of absorption did not depend on the rate of flow of the inspired air. A metal-cap device is described for fixing the filter papers.

Arsine

1—DETECTION OF TRACES OF ARSINE IN ATMOSPHERIC AIR

Herbert, A. and F. Heim. Bull. soc. chim. I (4), 573-575 (1907); CA **2**, 37 (1908).

The air sample to be analyzed is led through a Gautier wash apparatus which contains a hydrochloric acid solution of cuprous chloride. This reagent absorbs any hydrogen sulfide, phosphine or stibine present but does not absorb arsine. The air containing the arsine is passed through a U-tube, one arm being filled with glass wool, to remove cuprous chloride while the other arm contains a strip of filter paper moistened with a 5% mercuric chloride solution. The presence of arsine is indicated by a yellow coloration of the filter paper. This method is capable of detecting 1 part arsine per 100,000 parts of air.

2—SENSITIVE TEST FOR THE HYDRIDES OF ARSENIC, ANTIMONY, AND PHOSPHORUS BY MEANS OF GOLD CHLORIDE

Zimmerman, W. Apoth. Ztg. **36**, 26 (1921); J. Chem. Soc. **120**, II, 276 (1921); CA **15**, 2691 (1921).

A filter paper strip is impregnated with sodium aurichloride can be used to detect the presence of the hydrides of arsine, stibine and phosphorus if organic matter has first been destroyed. If any of the hydrides are present the reagent assumes a violet color. Hydrogen sulfide interferes with the determination and must be absent.

3—THE MICRO-DETECTION OF GASES AND VAPORS

Blank, Eugene W. J. Chem. Education **11**, 523-525 (1934).

Mercuric bromide is used for the determination of arsine. Add. Ref.: CA **28**, 6392 (1934).

4—DETECTION OF TOXIC GASES AND VAPORS

Leroux, Lucien. Rev. hyg. et med. prevent. **57**, 81-112 (1935).

Arsine in the atmosphere turns mercuric chloride test paper from yellow to brown within 10 to 20 minutes, giving warning that the arsine concentration is hazardous. The test papers are impregnated with a warm, saturated solution of mercuric chloride and dried at 60 to 70° C. Silver is precipitated from silver nitrate paper by the passage through the test paper of 200 ml of air containing a 1:50,000 dilution of arsine, or by 1000 ml of air with a 1:200,000 dilution of arsine. Impregnate the test paper with a solution of 1.70 g silver nitrate per liter and dry at 60 to 70°C. Arsine with Deniges reagent gives color changes from yellow to brown. The Deniges reagent consists of mercuric chloride 13.55 g, potassium iodide 36 g, and water sufficient to make 1 liter. Antimony, phosphorus and sulfur compounds produce analogous results unless previously washed out. Aliphatic arsines react by hydrolysis with amyl alcohol solutions of methyl orange (0.050 g methyl orange dissolved in 100 ml amyl alcohol) to form a red color. Dichlorodiethyl sulfide reacts similarly. The author cites the following references: Treadwell, F. P. Chimie analytique (transl. by M. Boll). Paris, Dunod, t. II (1920) p. 194; Gluhmann. Arbeitschutz No. 10, 219 (1932); Izard, Des Cilleuls, De Kermarrec. La guerre aerochimique et les populations civiles. Paris, Lavauzelle (1933), p. 239; Bruere, Paul. Exercises pratiques sur la protection contre les gas de combat. Paris, Vigot (1933), 18-25. Add. Ref.: CA **29**, 3627 (1935).

5—PROBLEMS OF PASSIVE DEFENSE AGAINST THE DANGER OF CHEMICAL GAS ATTACKS

Harsovescu, C. Antigaz (Bucharest) **9**, no. 9/10, 22-34 (1935); Chem. Zentr. **1936**, I, 4240.

A method, using copper iodide and based on the work of Paul Bruere ("Practical Methods for the Protection from War Gases," Paris, Vigot, 1933, p. 18-25) is described for the detection of organic arsines. Arsines of the aromatic series (e.g. adamsite) form a blue color (due to the impurity of diphenylamine in the adamsite) with sulfuric acid containing a trace of nitric acid. Detection in the field is difficult and laboratory techniques are described. The material may be collected in the field by placing a strip of filter paper in the cartridge of a gas mask; the residual gas can then be tested for in the laboratory. Add. Ref.: CA **31**, 7141 (1937).

6—THE USE OF INDICATORS FOR THE DETECTION OF POISONOUS GASES AND VAPORS

Heering, D. Gasmaske **8**, 88-89, (1936).

Mercuric bromide paper will turn yellow-brown, and mercuric cadmium iodide paper light brown, with 0.01 mg per liter of arsine. Silver nitrate paper changes from yellow with blue-black edges to complete blackness according to the concentration of arsine present. Stibine and phosphine react similarly. Add. Ref.: CA **30**, 7059 (1936).

7—SIMPLE METHODS FOR THE DETECTION AND DETERMINATION OF POISONOUS GASES, VAPORS, SMOKES, AND DUSTS IN FACTORY AIR

Weber, Hans. H. Zentr. Gewerbehyg. Unfallverhuet. **23**, 177-180 (1936).

Filter paper treated with 5% mercuric chloride and dried turns yellow-brown with 0.1 mg arsine in 10 minutes. Hydrogen sulfide, phosphine, and stibine interfere. Another method uses paper impregnated with mercuric-cadmium-iodide. It is not sensitive to hydrogen sulfide, but turns dark brown with 0.075 mg per liter of arsine, and light brown with 0.005 mg per liter. Phosphine turns the paper orange. Add. Ref.: CA **32**, 1609 (1938).

8—SOME METHODS FOR THE DETECTION AND ESTIMATION OF POISONOUS GASES AND VAPORS IN THE AIR (A PRACTICAL MANUAL FOR THE INDUSTRIAL HYGIENIST)

Zhitkova, A. S., translated by J. B. Ficklen. (Service to Industry, Box 133, West Hartford, Conn., 1936), pp. 92-98.

S and S No. 598 papers are immersed in 10% silver nitrate solution, then air-dried. Exposed to an atmosphere containing arsine, a grey to black precipitate of metallic silver appears, the degree of blackening being proportional to the concentration of the arsine. The sensitivity of the method is 0.2 to 20. ppm. Although silver nitrate paper is twenty times more sensitive than mercury papers, it is less stable.

9—MODERN METHODS OF DETECTION AND DETERMINATION OF INDUSTRIAL GASES IN THE ATMOSPHERE

Leclerc, E. and R. Haux. Rev. universelle mines **12**, 293-298 (1936).

Arsine colors mercuric chloride paper ranging from yellow to brown, depending on the concentration of the arsine; if the paper turns brown in from 10 to 20 minutes the amount of arsine in the air is hazardous. A precipitate of silver is formed from silver nitrate after passage through the reagent of 200 ml of air with a dilution of 1:50,000 of arsine. Deniges' mercuric iodide reagent is colored to yellow through brown depending on the concentration of the arsine reacting with it. Other reagents recommended by Deniges to test for arsine are ammonium molybdate and stannous chloride. Add. Ref.: CA **30**, 6672 (1936).

10—IDENTIFICATION OF WAR GASES

Liberalli, Marcelo Robertson. Rev. quim. farm. (Rio de Janeiro) **4**, 49-53 (1939).

The most useful reagents for the identification and detection of arsine are discussed and that of Bougault is recommended. Add. Ref.: CA **33**, 7921 (1939).

11—METHODS FOR DETECTION OF TOXIC GASES IN INDUSTRY. ARSINE

Anon. Dept. of Scientific and Industrial Research. (H. M. Stationery Office, London, England) Leaflet No. 9, 6 pp. (1939, reprinted 1951).

Postlip No. 633, extra-thick white filter paper is immersed in a 5% mercuric chloride solution, drained until damp-dry, dried in warm air, and stored until ready for use. The paper is placed in a special holder and adapted to a hand-operated pump which has a capacity of 126 ml per stroke. The yellow to brown color produced by any arsine present is compared with a standard stain chart. The concentration of arsine is calculated from the number of strokes used to obtain a desired color. *Filter papers (Whatman No. 41) prepared as described above were used in a 1·1/8" filter head and air with arsine drawn through the paper by a Gast pump at 1 liter per minute. The resulting stains were compared with a watercolor series which had been calibrated with known concentrations of arsine. The results were within the limits of the curve but it was difficult to interpret a specific concentration.* Add. Ref.: CA **34**, 1935 (1940).

12—THE DETECTION OF TOXIC GASES AND VAPORS IN INDUSTRY

Vallender, R. B. Chem. & Ind. (London) **58**, 330-333 (1939).

The detection of toxic gases by odor and animal experimentation is not reliable; actual measurement is mandatory. The arsine technique devised by the Department of Scientific and Industrial Research (London, England) is discussed (see above). Add. Ref.: CA **33**, 4907 (1939).

13—COLORIMETRIC DETERMINATION OF ARSENIC

Vasak, Vladimir and Vaclav Sedivec. Chem. Listy **46**, 341-344 (1952).

Arsine develops a red-violet color, suitable for colorimetric estimation, with a pyridine solution of silver diethldithiocarbamate, which is sensitive to 0.5 μg of arsenic. Hydrogen sulfide must be removed first with lead acetate paper. Stibine develops a different color; phosphine does not interfere. The author gives the procedure for the determination of arsenic in biological materials, and suggests the use of this reagent for air analysis. *The reagent is difficult to prepare in an extremely pure form and is unstable.* Add. Ref.: CA **47**, 67 (1953).

14—DETERMINATION OF TRACES OF ARSENIC BY MEANS OF GOLD CHLORIDE

St. Mokranjac, M. and B. Rasajski. Acta Pharm. Jugoslav. **2**, 9-13 (1952); CA **47**, 440 (1953).

Arsine, containing between 0.05 and 15 μg arsenic, reacts with gold chloride to produce a violet stain. 14 x 14 mm square papers are impregnated with 3 drops of a 1% alcoholic gold chloride solution for 0.05 to 1 μg, and 17 x 17 mm squares with 4 drops of gold chloride solution for 0.5 to 15 μg. These are proposed as more sensitive although less stable than the mercury or silver papers in the Gutzeit method for arsenic. *Gold chloride has been used successfully at the Los Alamos Scientific Laboratory, but for field work the papers must be freshly prepared before use.*

15—ANALYTICAL PROCEDURE FOR THE DETECTION OF GASES

Guatelli, Manuel A. Rev. asoc. bioquim. arg. **18**, 3-40 (1954).

A 3.5 cm diameter paper is impregnated with 5% mercuric chloride. The paper is blackened by arsine the sensitivity being 0.013 mg arsine per liter of air. Add. Ref.: CA **48**, 8124 (1954).

16—ANALYSIS OF MEDICALLY IMPORTANT GASES USING SPOT TESTS

Massmann, W. Arch. Gewerbepathol. Gewerbehyg. **13**, 262-275 (1954).

S and S 1573 filter paper is moistened on both sides with 1% silver nitrate solution, then blotted. The filter paper is placed in a special holder (5 mm diameter surface exposure) and attached to a special apparatus consisting of a series of four simple bubblers. The air sample is drawn through the first two bubblers, each containing 5% hydrochloric acid, then through the next two bubblers in which is 15% lead acetate, and finally through the filter paper at a rate of 0.5 liter per minute. The black stain produced by arsine in the air is fixed by soaking the paper in a 2.5% sodium thiosulfate solution for 5 to 10 minutes. After drying the stain on the paper it is compared with stains from known concentrations of arsine. The sensitivity of this method is 0.03 ppm; phosphine and stibine interfere. Add. Ref.: IHD **19**, 599 (1955).

17—A RAPID DETERMINATION OF A SMALL AMOUNT OF ARSINE IN THE ATMOSPHERE BY MEANS OF A DETECTOR TUBE

Kobayashi, Yoshitaka. J. Chem. Soc. Japan, Ind. Chem. Sect. **59**, (8), 889-891 (1956); AA **4**, 1689 (1957).

The author describes in detail the preparation of an indicating tube for the determination of arsine. A 100 ml air sample is passed through the detector tube at a constant rate of 60 ml per minute. The length of the stain produced is measured. An empirical table is used for the calculation of the arsine content. Corrections for factors affecting the length of stain i.e., temperature, tube diameter etc., are also made from empirical tables. Phosphine and hydrogen selenide, and hydrogen sulfide interfere with the determination. The hydrogen sulfide interference is eliminated by absorbing it in a tube of copper sulfate pentahydrate which is placed in front of the arsine detecting tube.

18—RAPID METHOD FOR THE DETERMINATION OF LOW CONCENTRATION OF ARSINE BY DETECTOR TUBE

Kobayashi, Yoshitaka. Kogyo Kagaku Zasshi **59**, 889-891 (1956); CA **52**, 8837 (1958).

Arsine contained in air in various concentrations up to 150 ppm was determined by use of a silica gel column in 2-mm-diameter glass tube, which was prepared by soaking the gel into mercuric chloride solution and drying with 0.3% mercuric chloride to the gel. The amount of moisture in the sealed detecting tube was also made constant. The working curves expressing the relation between the length of color change column (dark brown) and the concentration of arsine were given together with correction curves on temperature, diameter of glass tube, etc. Apart from hydrogen sulfide, most of the common gases did not affect the accuracy of the determination. *This article appears to be another version of the preceding.*

19—FIELD TYPE COLORIMETRIC TESTERS FOR GASES AND PARTICULATE MATTER

McConnaughey, Paul W. Presented at the annual meeting of the American Industrial Hygiene Association, Atlantic City, N. J., 1958.

Arsine, sampled from a known air volume with a specially designed hand pump, is adsorbed on a paper freshly impregnated with silver nitrate solution. After sampling, a drop of developer reagent (a dilute solution of ammonium hydroxide) is added to the center of the test disc, then the brown or black metallic silver test stain is compared with stains produced by known concentrations of arsine. Hydrogen sulfide must be removed on a prefilter impregnated with lead acetate and glycerine. The sensitivity is in the range of the allowable limit, 0.05 ppm. *This instrument is available commercially from Mine Safety Appliances Company (see below).*

20—ARSINE DETECTOR KIT

Mine Safety Appliances Company, 201 N. Braddock, Pittsburgh, Pa. Bull. 0811-0811-7 (1959).

The arsine detector kit consists of a 500 ml displacement pump with an attached filter head and prefilter cover. The two comparison stains correspond to 0.05 and 0.2 ppm arsine with two strokes of the pump. The paper is treated with an absorbing reagent; then, after sampling, the color is developed with a second reagent. Interference from sulfur dioxide and hydrogen sulfide up to 100 ppm can be prevented by absorbing these gases in a prefilter.

21—TESTING TUBE FOR THE QUANTITATIVE DETERMINATION OF ARSINE

Auergesellschaft Akt.-Ges (by Hermann Heidrich). Ger. (Pat. No.) 1,016,963, Oct. 3, 1957 (Cl. 42.1); CA **54**, 16948 (1960).

The detector tube contains a filler material soaked with silver nitrate solution and a layer of carrier material soaked with a salt of a heavy metal to absorb hydrogen sulfide from the gas stream tested.

See Section One

For reference numbers 3, 33, 54.

Benzyl Bromide and Xylyl Bromide

1—TESTS AVAILABLE FOR THE IDENTIFICATION OF SMALL QUANTITIES OF THE WAR GASES

Cox, H. E. Analyst **64**, 807-813 (1939).

Silver bromide is precipitated when either gas is passed through a solution of silver acetate in alcohol. Add. Ref.: CA **34**, 541 (1940).

See Section One

For reference numbers 16, 41, 42, 119, 125.

Boranes

1—A SPOT TEST FOR ESTIMATING CONCENTRATIONS OF BORON HYDRIDE VAPORS IN AIR

Etherington, T. L. and L. V. McCarthy. Arch. Ind. Hyg. Occupational Med. **5**, 447-450 (1952).

Filter paper impregnated with 5% silver nitrate solution

in n-amylamine turns yellow to brown in the presence of borane. The sensitivity is 1 μg with the maximum color intensity at 10 μg. The color formation is independent of the air flow rate but the latter should not exceed 4 liters or a total time lapse of 10 minutes. Penta- and decaborane respond similarly. Add. Refs.: CA **46**, 10488 (1952); IHD **16**, 683 (1952).

2—DETERMINATION OF BORON HALIDES IN AIR

Horton, Charles A. and Carroll S. Weil. National Nuclear Energy Series, Div. VI, Vol. 1, Book 3, 2328-2334 (1953); CA **47**, 10705 (1953).

A description of a spot testing method for the determination of boron hydrides in air is given. The boron halide vapor is collected on turmeric-impregnated filter paper. The color produced is compared with color standards. The accuracy of the method depends on the analyst's ability to differentiate between shades and intensities of color.

3—DETECTION OF BORANES

Hill, William H. (to Callery Chem. Co.) U. S. (Pat. No.) 2,848,307, Aug. 19, 1958; CA **53**, 12098 (1959).

The author describes a quantitative method for microgram quantities of borane.

Bromine

1—DETECTION OF CHLORINE AND BROMINE IN AIR, GAS MIXTURES AND SOLUTIONS BY THE FORMATION OF IRIS BLUE

Eichler, Hermann. Z. anal. Chem. **99**, 272-275 (1934); CA **29**, 1359 (1935).

A solution of resorufin can be utilized for the determination of chlorine and bromine. Resorufin, in the presence of alkali carbonates shows an intense yellow-red fluorescence. Upon addition of bromine or chlorine this fluorescence disappears.

2—THE DETECTION OF TOXIC GASES AND VAPORS

Leroux, Lucien. Rev. hyg. et med. prevent. **57**, 81-112 1935).

Paper treated with a 1 g per liter solution of dimethylphenylenediamine is colored violet by bromine; the color disappears in the presence of hydrochloric acid. Add. Ref.: CA **29**, 3627 (1935).

3—THE USE OF INDICATORS FOR THE DETECTION OF POISONOUS GASES AND VAPORS

Heering, D. Gasmaske **8**, 88-89 (1936).

Schiff's reagent turns blue-violet in an atmosphere of bromine. Add. Ref.: CA **30**, 7059 (1936).

4—MODERN METHODS OF DETECTION AND DETERMINATION OF INDUSTRIAL GASES IN THE ATMOSPHERE

Leclerc, E. and R. Haux. Rev. universelle mines **12**, 293-298 (1936).

Dimethylphenylenediamine paper is colored violet with bromine, but is bleached by hydrogen chloride. The reference cited is L. Leroux (see above). Add. Ref.: CA **30**, 6672 (1936).

5—NEW REAGENT FOR CHLORINE AND OXIDIZING AGENTS

Noriega del Aguila, M. Prim. congr. peruano quim. (Actas y trab.) **1938**, 999-1000; Chimie & industrie **43**, 469 (1940); CA **34**, 4355 (1940).

A procedure for the detection of chlorine, bromine or nitrogen oxides is presented. These gases and vapors can be detected in air by passing the sample through a 10% alcoholic pyramidone solution which has been acidified with acetic acid. A violet to violet-red color is produced if any of the three compounds are present. Filter paper strips can be impregnated with the same solution and the test carried out by air drying the paper in the air being tested.

6—A NEW TYPE OF AUTOMATIC DEVICE FOR SIGNALING THE PRESENCE OF GASES IN AIR

Romankov, P. G. and V. A. Grigor. Trudy Leningrad. Tekhnol. Inst. im. Leningradskogo Soveta **1946**, No. 12, 175-183; CA **44**, 5652 (1950).

The authors describe a method for the automatic determination of bromine and other gases in air. The air sample is led through a pyrolysis chamber and then around an indicator film. Light passes through the film and impinges on a photocell. Changes in the photocell readings actuates a signaling device.

7—STUDIES ON GAS ANALYSIS BY MEANS OF DETECTORS. I. RAPID MICRODETERMINATION OF BROMINE IN AIR

Kitagawa, Tetsuzo and Yoshitaka Kobayashi. J. Chem. Soc. Japan, Ind. Chem. Sect. **55**, 191-194 (1952); CA **47**, 11074 (1953).

A bromine detector consisting of a glass tube containing silica gel impregnated with o-tolidine-hydrochloride is described. In the presence of bromine the silica gel is colored and the quantity of bromine present can be detected. One to two hundred μg can be detected in 2 minutes with an average error of 5%. Add. Ref.: IHD **18**, 560 (1954).

8—ANALYTICAL PROCEDURE FOR THE DETECTION OF GASES

Guatelli, Manual A. Rev. asoc. bioquim, arg. **18**, 3-40 (1954).

Odor permits the detection of bromine in air, but a rapid and sensitive detector consists of a paper using the Deniges-Chelle reaction. The color produced is a bromo derivative of rosanilin; a similar change is observed when eosin is used, or an alcoholic solution of fluorescein which has been made ammoniacal. Add. Ref.: CA **48**, 8124 (1954).

9—MODIFIED SPOT TEST FOR BROMIDE

Somerville, W. C. and A. D. Campbell. Mikrochim. Ichnoanal. Acta 1963 (5-6), 991-2 CA **60**, 4775, 1964.

A modification of the fluorescein spot test for bromine is described. Three drops of the test solution are placed on a spot plate and 1 drop of 2M AcOH, along with an excess of $CaCO_3$, and 1 drop of a saturated aqueous solution of fluorescein are added. One drop of 1% aqueous solution of chloramine T is added. A pink color indicates the presence of Br^-. Limit of detection is 0.1 g.

See Section One

For reference numbers 15, 35, 48, 52, 112.

Bromoacetone
Bromomethylethylketone

1—TESTS AVAILABLE FO RTHE IDENTIFICATION OF SMALL QUANTITIES OF THE WAR GASES

Cox, H. E. Analyst **64**, 807-813 (1939).

Dissolve either vapor in warm, alcoholic, 0.5 N potassium hydroxide solution, and add a few drops of sodium nitroprusside solution. Bromoacetone produces a red color, intensified by acetic acid, while bromomethylethylketone gives an orange color. Add. Ref.: CA **34**, 541 (1940).

2—IDENTIFICATION OF WAR GASES

Liberalli, Marcelo Robertson. Rev. quim. farm. (Rio de Janeiro) **4**, 49-53 (1939).

Halogenated acetone (bromoacetone, chloroacetone) may be identified by the sodium nitroprusside reaction, in which colored derivatives are formed. Add. Ref.: CA **33**, 7921 (1939).

See Section One

For reference number 52.

Bromobenzylcyanide

1—TESTS AVAILABLE FOR THE IDENTIFICATION OF SMALL QUANTITIES OF THE WAR GASES

Cox, H. E. Analyst **64**, 807-813 (1939).

Bromobenzylcyanide can be detected by its non-specific

reaction with Sudan red. A filter paper impregnated with a solution of the dye produces a blood-red color when contacted by bromobenzylcyanide. The author does not consider this test very satisfactory. Add. Ref.: CA **34**, 541 (1940).

See Section One
For reference numbers 52, 54, 64, 66.

Bromoxylene

See Section One
For reference number 54.

Butyl Nitrate

1—RAPID DETERMINATION OF BUTYL NITRATE IN AIR

Parfenova, K. G. Uchenye Zapiski Ukrain. Nauch.-Issledovatel. Inst. Gigiena Truda i Profzabolevanii **27**, 131-132 (1958); APCA Abstracts **V**, No. 11, 3024 (1960).

A rapid method for the determination of butyl nitrate in air is described. The air sample is aspirated through silica gel impregnated with Griess reagent at a rate of 25 ml per minute. The concentration of butyl nitrate is determined by comparison of the red color produced with a series of standards. The standards (2.5 to 100 μg per liter) are prepared by saturating silica gel with solutions of various concentrations. The sensitivity of the method is 2.5 μg per liter. The apparatus proposed for the analysis consists of a rubber bulb in a metal case which has a metal capillary and a moveable scale. Add. Refs.: Central Intelligence Agency, Sci. Inf. Rept. U. S. Dept. Comm., OTS, Wash. 25, D. C. (Dec. 4, 1959), p. 59. Transl. abstr. in: Referat. zhur. Khim. (Moscow) No. 18, abstr. No. 6-882, p. 273 (Sept. 25, 1959).

Cadmium

1—NEW REAGENT PAPERS FOR POROSITY TESTING AND FOR THE DETERMINATION OF METALS

Kutzelnigg, Arthur. Metalloberflaeche **5**, B 113-115 (1951); CA **46**, 56 (1952).

Dithizone absorbed on filter paper gives an orange color with cadmium. The paper should be moistened with an organic solvent.

2—NEW SENSITIVE SPOT REACTION FOR CADMIUM

Anger, V. Mikrochim. Acta **1959**, 473-475 (in German); CA **56**, 9391 (1962).

Add ammonium thiocyanate and sodium sulfite to an ammoniacal solution of cadmium and copper, acidify the solution with acetic acid or dilute sulfuric acid, and warm. Place 1 drop of this solution on a filter paper and add 1 drop of reagent solution. Cadmium gives a malachite green ring. Detection limits are 0.5 μg cadmium in the presence of up to 50 μg of copper.

See Section One
For reference numbers 55, 98.

Calcium

1—SPOT TEST FOR CALCIUM WITH GLYOXAL BIS (2 HYDROXYANIL)

Deguchi, Masakazu., K. Yamamoto. Kagaku Keisatsu Kenkyusho Kokoku **16** (1) 58-9 (1963); CA **60** 1098 (1964).

A spot test for calcium is described utilizing glyoxal bis (2-hydroxyanil). A drop of sample solution is placed on filter paper and a drop of 0.5% alkaline solution of the reagent and one drop of 10% NaOH are added. The appearance of a red spot indicates the presence of calcium. The limit of identification is 0.02 g.

Carbazoles

1—SPOT TEST DETECTION AND SPECTROPHOTO-METRIC CHARACTERIZATION AND DETERMINATION OF CARBAZOLES, AZO DYES, STILBENES, AND SCHIFF BASES. APPLICATION OF 3-METHYL-2-BENZO-THIAZOLONE HYDRAZONE, p-NITROSOPHENOL, AND FLUOROMETRIC METHODS TO THE DETERMINATION OF CARBAZOLE IN AIR

Sawicki, Eugene, Thomas R. Hauser, Thomas W. Stanley, Walter Elbert, and Frank T. Fox. Anal. Chem. **33**, 1574-1579 (1961). .

For the spot plate test add 1 drop of 0.5% solution of p-nitrosophenol in sulfuric acid to 1 drop of methanolic or acetic acid test solution. Carbazole produces a green color, limit of identification 0.4 μg. Add 1 drop of water; in the presence of carbazole the green turns to blue, identification limit 2 μg. In both cases the blank is yellow. For a filter paper test, use H. Reeve Angel and Co.'s glass fiber paper No. 934-AH. To 2 drops of 0.5% p-nitrosophenol in sulfuric acid add 1 drop of methanolic test solution. Read after 1 minute. Carbazole produces a bright blue-green, identification limit 0.6 μg. The blank is yellow. The identification limit for N-methyl- and N-ethyl-carbazole is approximately 1 μg. *The reactions might be applied to field detectors.* Add. Ref.: CA **56**, 3774 (1962).

Carbon Dioxide

1—SIMPLE METHODS FOR THE DETERMINATION OF GASEOUS IMPURITIES IN THE AIR OF FACTORIES

Hahn, Martin. Gesundh. Ing. **31**, 693-697 (1910); CA **4**, 1074 (1910).

Colorimetric methods for the determination of carbon dioxide are described. One excellent test described is a modification of the Lunge-Zeckendorf method.

2—THE DETERMINATION AND ESTIMATION OF EXCEEDINGLY MINUTE QUANTITIES OF CARBON DIOXIDE

McCoy, Herbert N. and Shiro Tashiro. Orig. Com. 8th Intern. Congr. Appl. Chem. **I**, 361; CA 6, **3243** (1912).

The authors describe a method for the determination of carbon dioxide that is sensitive to 1×10^{-7} grams. The reagent used is barium hydroxide.

3—APPARATUS FOR DETERMINING CARBON DIOXIDE IN THE AIR

Kobayashi, M. Japan (Pat. No. 30,227, Oct. 25, 1916; CA **11**, 1580 (1917).

A method for the determination of carbon dioxide in air is described. A piece of phenolphthalein paper is exposed to lime water and a pink coloration occurs on the paper. Carbon dioxide decolorizes the reagent paper and a rough determination of the carbon dioxide content can be obtained.

4—COLORIMETRIC METHOD FOR THE DETERMINATION OF THE CARBON DIOXIDE PERCENTAGE IN AIR

Higgins, H. L. and W. M. Marriott. J. Am. Chem. Soc. **39**, 68-71 (1917); CA **11**, 241 (1917).

The authors present the theory and the analytical technique for the determination of carbon dioxide in air. When a current of air containing carbon dioxide is passed through a solution of sodium bicarbonate until the solution is saturated with carbon dioxide at existing atmospheric pressures, the hydrogen ion concentrations of the solution will depend

on the relative amounts of sodium bicarbonate and carbon dioxide present, and this depends on the pressure of carbon dioxide in the air. The hydrogen ion concentration of the solution is determined by adding a solution of phenolphthalein and comparing the resulting color with that of standards made from monobasic potassium phosphate and dibasic sodium phosphate solutions in different proportions. Details are presented for the preparation of solutions so that their numbers are parts per 10,000 when used with one sodium bicarbonate solution and parts per 1,000 when used with a second sodium bicarbonate solution. The accuracy is about 5% of the total carbon dioxide present. The method is not appricable in the presence of acid or ammonia fumes.

5—THE DETERMINATION OF CARBONIC ACID IN AIR

Bieler, A. Chem.-Ztg. **47**, 893 (1923); CA **18**, 954 (1924).

Carbonic acid in air is determined by bubbling the air, at a rate of from 50-100 cc per minute, through 10 cc of 0.02 N sodium carbonate colored with phenolphthalein, and calculating the volume of air from the observed volume of water that runs out of the aspirator.

6—TEST PAPER FOR GAS ANALYSIS

Atkinson, L. B. Brit. (Pat. No.) 248,807, Oct. 13, 1924; CA **21**, 722 (1927).

A test paper for the determination of ,carbon dioxide is described. The paper is impregnated with an indicator such as thymol blue or phenolphthalein. A portion of paper is dipped into an alkali solution which is allowed to diffuse into a portion of the paper so that a part of the paper remains dry. The test is conducted by noting the time required for the color to change.

7—NOTE ON THE DETECTION OF CARBON DIOXIDE

Elteste, G. Z. angew. Chem. **41**, 1858 (1928); CA **22**, 4409 (1928).

The detection of carbon dioxide from a leaky bomb or from a small quantity of carbonate is difficult because the air always contains some carbon dioxide. This difficulty can be overcome if a filter paper is wet with 0.1 N barium hydroxide containing 1 cc of 1% phenolphthalein per 10 cc, it will, while wet be bleached by more carbon dioxide than the air contains. If the paper is then allowed to stand in air the color will slowly return.

8—A COLORIMETRIC METHOD FOR THE DETERMINATION OF CARBON DIOXIDE

Emmert, E. M. J. Assoc. Official Agr. Chem. **14**, 386-389 (1931); CA **25**, 5875 (1931).

The authors describe a method for the determination of carbon dioxide which is based on the decrease in color produced when carbon dioxide is shaken with the sodium salt of phenolphthalein. Other acidic or basic materials must not be allowed to enter the flask with the carbon dioxide; this is accomplished by bubbling the gas through 1% sulfuric acid. An error of 0.1-0.2 mg carbon dioxide may be expected from the air enclosed in the shaking flasks; it is not significant in large amounts of carbon dioxide, but is in amounts of 2-5 mg.

9—ANALYSIS OF ETHYLENE FOR ANESTHETIC USE

Busi, M. and C. Collina. Atti soc. ital. progresso sci. **19**, 195-199 (1931).

The ethylene is placed in a 500 ml Van Slyke chamber and 5 ml of saturated barium hydroxide is added. If carbon dioxide is present a turbidity will be observed. Add. Ref.: CA **26**, 1707 (1932).

10—DETECTION AND ESTIMATION OF CARBON DIOXIDE AND CARBON MONOXIDE IN AIR

Hughes, T. W. Chem. Eng. Mining Rev. **24**, 179-181 (1932); CA **26**, 2394 (1932).

The author presents a review of known methods.

11—SEMI-MICROMETHOD FOR DETERMINING CARBON DIOXIDE IN AIR

Winkler, L. W. Z. anal. Chem. **92**, 23-31 (1933); CA **27**, 2112 (1933).

A method for the determination of carbon dioxide is presented. The determination depends on the fact that carbon dioxide dissolves more readily in ethyl alcohol at room temperature than in water. Carbon dioxide in the presence of alcohol reacts much more rapidly with sodium carbonate and the bicarbonate formed is neutral to phenolphthalein. The determination is carried out by adding sodium carbonate solution to a 4 liter bottle containing ethyl alcohol and phenolphthalein until the solution is alkaline to phenolphthalein.

12—ACCURACY OF THE SEMI-MICRO METHOD FOR DETERMINING CARBON DIOXIDE IN AIR

Winkler, L. W. Z. anal. Chem. **92**, 245-247 (1933); CA **27**, 2397 (1933).

The method recently described by Winkler (see above) is shown to be accurate.

13—COLORIMETRIC DETERMINATION OF CARBON DIOXIDE IN AIR BY THE AID OF A PHOTOELECTRIC CELL

Fegler, J. and T. Modzelewski. Compt. rend. soc. biol. **116**, 248-250 (1934); CA **28**, 5005 (1934).

The authors describe in detail a method for the determination of carbon dioxide. The air sample is passed through a large horizontal glass tube. At one point a solution of thymol blue-bromothymol blue mixture, made dark green by the addition of a little potassium hydroxide, is allowed to drip from a capillary tube sealed in the upper side of the air tube. A side tube sealed in directly below collects

the indicator solution as it drops through the air current and passes it between a light source and a Weston photoelectric cell. For concentrations of carbon dioxide less than 4% the apparatus can be adjusted so that the galvanometer reading is directly proportional to the carbon dioxide content. Higher concentrations require a calibration curve.

14—DETECTION OF TOXIC GASES AND VAPORS

Leroux, Lucien. Rev. hyg. et. med. prevent. **57**, 81-112 (1935).

Same as Guatelli reference (see below). Add. Ref.: CA **29**, 3627 (1935).

15—A RAPID AND PRACTICAL METHOD FOR THE DETERMINATION OF CARBON DIOXIDE AND THE DETECTION OF CARBON MONOXIDE IN THE AIR BY MEANS OF A VERY SIMPLE APPARATUS

Mihaeloff, S. Ann. hyg. publ. ind. sociale **1935**, 22-27; CA **29**, 7223 (1935).

The determination of carbon dioxide is accomplished by bubbling the air sample through 1 cc of 0.001 N sodium carbonate solution containing phenolphthalein and noting the volume of air required to decolorize the indicator. The same apparatus can be used for the detection of carbon monoxide using palladium chloride as the reagent.

16—DETERMINATION OF TRACES OF IMPURITIES IN COMMERCIAL GASES, PARTICULARLY OXYGEN

Grant, J. Ind. Gases **16**, 138-141 (1935); CA **31**, 6133 (1937).

The author describes a method for the determination of trace amounts of carbon dioxide.

17—SEMIAUTOMATIC DETERMINATION OF CARBON DIOXIDE IN THE ATMOSPHERE AND IN COMBUSTION GASES

Chovin, P. and L. Gion. 15me Congr. chim. ind. Bruxelles, Sept. 1935) **1936**, 276-280; CA **30**, 5464 (1936).

The apparatus described atomizes a solution of rosaniline decolorized by hydrazine using the gas to be analyzed. If the conditions under which atomization takes place are well defined and kept constant, the color acquired by the reagent can yield an accurate measurement of the carbon dioxide content of the sample. A photoelectric comparator is used to make the color comparisons. The various operations required for carrying out the determination are carried automatically by the manipulation of a single cock. By combining with a suitable combustion furnace (to burn carbon monoxide to carbon dioxide), the apparatus can be used for determining carbon monoxide. By means of special reagents for other gases, the latter can be determined or detected with the same apparatus.

18—MODERN METHODS OF DETECTION AND DETERMINATION OF INDUSTRIAL GASES IN THE ATMOSPHERE.

Leclerc, E. and R. Haux. Rev. universelle mines **12**, 293-298 (1936).

One part of carbon dioxide in 1000 parts of air will make a barium hydroxide solution heavily turbid in 10 minutes. The carbonate formed may be titrated with nitric acid using two indicators—phenolphthalein, then bromothymol blue. Air to be tested also may be drawn into an alkaline solution and the changes in pH of the solution measured. Various automatic instruments have been devised to apply these methods, e.g., a photoelectric cell to detect color changes in an alkaline solution containing bromothymol blue indicator. Add. Ref.: CA **30**, 6672 (1936).

19—NEW RAPID METHOD FOR DETERMINING CARBON DIOXIDE IN AIR

Ivanov, Nicholas. Ann. fals. **29**, 488-490 (1936); CA **31**, 971 (1937).

A simple and rapid method for the determination of carbon dioxide is presented. The method involves filling a prescription bottle with carbon dioxide free air. This can be accomplished by passing the air through soda lime. The prescription bottle is filled ¾ full with 0.1 N barium hydroxide containing 0.1% barium chloride. The number of syringefuls of pure air, i.e., air assumed to contain 0.035% carbon doxide by volume, that will yield a perceptible turbidity is noted. The number of syringefuls of test air required to produce the same turbidity is also noted.

20—DETERMINATION OF CARBON DIOXIDE IN AIR

Maricq, Louis. J. pharm. Belg. **18**, 37-43 (1936); CA **30**, 8069 (1936).

Glass vials containing 0.01 N, 0.1 N, and 0.25 N barium hydroxide solutions plus 0.1 g of thymol blue dissolved in 5 cc of alcohol per liter of solution, are prepared. Air samples are collected in 500 cc flasks in which one or more vials have been placed. The flasks are sealed, the vials broken and the resulting color changes are noted. The flask showing a green end point is used. Tables are provided which show the equivalents of the various dilutions, the absolute values of the results and the time that must be allowed for the change to take place.

21—A METHOD OF DETECTING AND DETERMINING CARBON OXIDE AND DIOXIDE AND TOXIC VAPORS IN AIR

Demesse, J. Bull. acad. med. **118**, 771-774 (1937); CA **32**, 4831 (1938).

The author describes two types of apparatus for the determination of carborn oxide and dioxide. The air sample is contacted with a 0.001 or 0.0001 N solution of sodium bicarbonate containing bromothymol blue. The color changes caused by the pH shift are evaluated by a table.

22—PORTABLE DETECTOR FOR SMALL CONCENTRATIONS OF CARBON DIOXIDE

Williamson, John G. Gas **15**, No. 8, 33 (1939); CA **33**, 7153 (1939).

The method described involves drawing an air sample with a bicycle pump, through a measured volume of 0.0004 N strontium hydroxide containing phenolphthalein, with until the solution is decolorized. The number of pump strokes is counted and a calibration chart is used to determine the percentage of carbon dioxide

23—AN ALKALIMETER

Hall, W. Heinlen. Ind. Eng. Chem., Anal. Ed. **11**, 462-463 (1939).

In a new, light, compact, simple, and speedy alkalimeter for the indirect determination of carbon dioxide, stopcocks are eliminated and a solid desiccant replaces sulfuric acid. Add. Ref.: CA **33**, 7153 (1939).

24—RAPID AND CONVENIENT COLORIMETRIC METHOD FOR DETERMINING THE CARBON DIOXIDE TENSION OF AIR

Boeri, Enzo. Bull. soc. ital. biol. sper **18**, 284-285 (1943); CA **41**, 1176 (1947).

A method for determining carbon dioxide tension in air is presented. The method involves the preparation of a 0.005 N sodium hydroxide and 0.3 N sodium chloride solution colored with an appropriate pH indicator. The air sample is bubbled through the solution until no further change in color occurs. The pH of the solution is then determined by comparing it with a series of pH color standards, and the carbon dioxide tension of the air is calculated from this pH value. A correction for temperature is important.

25—STOP-WATCH, DROP METHOD FOR THE APPROXIMATE DETERMINATION OF CARBON DIOXIDE IN AIR

Reinau, Erich and Ad. Johaentges. Bodenkunde u. Pflanzenernaehr. **36**, 121-130 (1945); CA **41**, 5054 (1947).

Add 5 drops of an indicator consisting of 1% phenolphthalein and 1% bromothymol blue in butyl alcohol to 5 ml of 0.005 N barium hydroxide. Impregnate filter papers with 5 drops of the indicator. When exposed to an atmosphere containing carbon dioxide the following pattern of colors results: 1) a radiating dark blue blot; 2) a violet circle with a dark gren border; 3) the violet circle becomes surrounded with a light green border which turns yellow on the outside; 4) the inner circle gradually becomes pale violet with a blue and yellow border; and 5) the violet disappears but a blue circle with a yellow border remains The reaction is complete after the last trace of violet disappears. The concentration of carbon dioxide in the atmosphere is calculated on the basis of the time required to reach the endpoint. Eleven to thirteen minutes usually is required for complete reaction out of doors, and 4 to 6 minutes in an occupied room.

26—COLORIMETRIC METHOD FOR DETERMINATION OF TRACES OF CARBON DIOXIDE IN AIR

Spector, Norman A. and Barnett F. Dodge. Anal. Chem. **19**, 55-58 (1947).

A Lumetron photoelectric colorimeter is used to measure the bleaching of color of a sodium hydroxide solution containing phenolphthalein if the alkali has absorbed carbon dioxide. Add. Ref.: CA **41**, 1576 (1947).

27—TEST PAPERS FOR HIGH CONCENTRATIONS OF CARBON DIOXIDE

Industrial Hygiene Manual. Loss Prevention Dept., Liberty Mutual Insurance Co., Boston, Mass. (1951). Personal communication from C. H. Williams.

Whatman No. 1 filter paper is treated with a saturated solution of strontium hydroxide octahydrate containing phenolphthalein. The filter paper detectors are used wet and are prepared just before use. If the paper is still pink or reddish after 5 minutes' exposure to the atmosphere the carbon dioxide concentration is less than 4%, but if the paper is white the environment is unsafe and should not be entered.

28—ANALYTICAL PROCEDURE FOR THE DETECTION OF GASES

Guatelli, Manual A. Rev. asoc. bioquim. arg. **18**, 3-40 (1954).

A barium water solution, used to determine the quality of the air for breathing, is prepared by dissolving 15 g barium hydroxide in water and diluting to 1 liter. Allow to settle, then bubble air through 15-20 ml of the solution for a period of time. The endpoint of the air titration is indicated when the solution becomes very turbid. The normal carbon dioxide content of the air requires up to 20 minutes, while bad air needs only 2 minutes or fewer. The author cites as reference: Kohn-Abrest, E. "Cours d'Hygiene de L. Bernard et Derre," Paris, Masson, t. I, p. 1218 (1929). Add. Ref.: CA **48**, 8124 (1954).

29—THE DETERMINATION OF CARBON DIOXIDE IN AIR

Brukl, A. and L. Balcarczyk. Acta Phys. Austriaca **10**, 198-205 (1956); CA **51**, 3369 (1957).

The authors attempted to find a better absorption method for the analysis of carbon dioxide in air in the range of 0.02 to 0.05%. Two methods were tested, the Pettenkofer method (Treadwell, "Analytical Chemistry Quantitative Analysis" (CA **11**, 3009)) and the Pettenkofer-Hesse method. Both of these methods use volumetric titrations of the barium hydroxide solution which is used for the absorption of carbon monoxide.

30—APPARATUS FOR THE CONTINUOUS DETERMINATION OF CARBON DIOXIDE IN AIR

Luria, L. Boll. soc. ital. biol. sper. **34** (7), 353-354 (1958); AA **6**, 4184 (1959).

An absorptiometric method using sodium bicarbonate and phenol red indicator is used.

31—LINEAR COLORIMETRIC METHOD OF DETERMINING CARBON DIOXIDE CONCENTRATIONS IN THE ATMOSPHERE

Lukina, M. T. and G. L. Borodina. Gigiena i Sanit. **24**, No. 8, 80-82 (1959); CA **53**, 21363 (1959).

An apparatus using silica gel impregnated with a colorless basic fuchsine-hydrazine hydrate is described. When a sample containing carbon dioxide is aspirated through the tube a rose color forms. The length of stain is a measure of the carbon dioxide present.

32—DETECTION OF CARBON DIOXIDE IN AIR AND GASES

Draegerwerk Heinrich und Bernhard Draeger. Ger. (Pat. No.) 1,007,525, May 2, 1957 (Cl. 42.**1**); CA **54**, 10676 (1960).

Silica gel is impregnated with a solution of 0.5% methyl violet in glycerol and this is followed by treatment with 80% hydrazine solution.

33—TWO QUICK METHODS OF ESTIMATING CARBON DIOXIDE IN THE AIR

Sengevich, A. I. and E. P. Sergeev. Gigiena i Sanit. **25** (10), 58-61 (1960).

To estimate the amount of carbon dioxide in air, aspirate the air through a phenolphthalein-colored sodium carbonate solution at 1 liter per minute until the solution is decolorized. The amount of carbon dioxide in the air is equal to the time required for complete decolorization of the carbonate solution. Another way to estimate the carbon dioxide concentration of the air is to measure the volume of the air needed to decolorize the solution. Add. Refs.: Soviet Med. **5**, Abstr. 1693 (1961); A.P.C.A. Abstr. **8**, No. 2, 4568 (1962).

34—TOXICOLOGICAL EXAMINATION OF AIR POLLUTANTS. I. SIMPLE CONTROL DEVICES

Sacchi, S., P. Giovanni, and A. R. Poggi. Chimica (Milan) **35**, 493-498 (1959); A.P.C.A. Abstr. **7**, No. 10, 4305 (1962).

The authors discuss a number of rapid methods for determination of carbon dioxide in the air. A method is described which involves measurement of the time taken for the solutions, containing phenolphthalein, to develop color when shaken with a sample of air. The solutions used were N/2500, N/1250, N/1000, and N/625 sodium carbonate and N/2500 and N/1250 potassium hydroxide. The method is extremely simple but sufficiently accurate to determine the quantity of carbon dioxide in the air.

35—RAPID METHOD FOR THE DETERMINATION OF LOW CONCENTRATIONS OF AMMONIA AND CARBON DIOXIDE IN AIR BY MEANS OF DETECTOR TUBES

Kobayashi, Yoshitaka. Kogyo Kagaku Zasshi **61**, 525-527 (1958); CA **55**, 10764 (1961).

Carbon dioxide is determined on a column of active aluminum oxide powder impregnated with thymolphthalein, which turns pink with carbon dioxide. For a carbon dioxide range of 0.05 to 0.60% the air is sampled at a rate of 100 ml in 200 seconds; for 0.02 to 0.30% the rate is 200 ml in 400 seconds. The average error of the determination is ± 5%.

36—THE PROBLEM OF REPRESENTATIVE SAMPLING IN THE FIELD OF ATMOSPHERIC POLLUTION

Avy, A. P. Pollution air et ses mefaits, Conf. soc. pathol. comparee, Paris **1956**, 87-112 (Pub. 1957); CA **51**, 13276 (1957).

37—SAMPLING AND ANALYZING AIR FOR CONTAMINANTS IN WORK PLACES

Silverman, Leslie. "Encyclopedia of Instrumentation for Industrial Hygiene" (Univ. of Michigan, Inst. of Industrial Health, Ann Arbor, Mich., 1956) pp. 7-25.

See Section One

For reference numbers 15, 29, 59, 87, 125.

Carbon Disulfide

1—TEST PAPER FOR CARBON DISULFIDE

Kuznetzov, V. I. Anilinokrasochnaya Prom. **2**, No. 3, 1-2 (1932); CA **26** 4549 (1932).

A test paper method for the detection of carbon disulfide in air is described. Strips of filter paper impregnated with a solution of copper salts in dimethylamine which, when contacted with carbon disulfide, become brown, are recommended. Other secondary amines may be substituted for the dimethylamine. The prepared reagent strips are sensitive to both carbon disulfide and hydrogen sulfide. In order to remove the hydrogen sulfide interference a cyanide solution is added to the copper dimethylamine. The reagent is sensitive to 0.001 g of carbon disulfide in 1 liter of air and to 1-2% carbon disulfide in the presence of pure hydrogen sulfide.

2—NEW MICROANALYTICAL TEST FOR CARBON DISULFIDE

Tischler, Nathaniel. Ind. Eng. Chem., Anal. Ed. **4**, 146 (1932); CA **26**, 1212 (1932).

Five drops of 0.05% copper sulfate solution and 1 cc of 1% diethylamine solution both in absolute alcohol, are added to 1 cc of the sample solution. Colorless solutions of carbon disulfide in acetone, chloroform, ether or alcohol yield a yellow color when 1 part per million of carbon disulfide is present. A precipitate is formed if an aqueous solution of carbon disulfide is used but the sensitivity remains the same.

3—DETECTION AND ESTIMATION OF METHYL MERCAPTAN AND CARBON DISULFIDE IN AIR CONTAINING HYDROGEN SULFIDE

Reith, J. F. Rec. trav. chim. **53**, 18-23 (1934) (in English); CA **28**, 1955 (1934).

In studying the gas drawn from the spinning rooms of a rayon factory, a study was made of methods for determining methyl mercaptan and carbon disulfide in air containing hydrogen sulfide. It was found necessary first to carry out a separation by means of solid lead acetate. The gas is drawn through a series of 4 wash bottles. The first 2 are Jena wash bottles with glass filter No. 83 G. 1 and contain 20 cc of 0.5 N sodium hydroxide. The next 2 are very small with gas dispersers and each contains 2 cc of sodium hydroxide in ethyl alcohol. After the absorption, unite the contents of the first 2 wash bottles, add 4 cc of 25% hydrochloric acid and connect to the apparatus for detecting mercaptan. . . . Draw air slowly through the apparatus for 30 minutes. The hydrogen sulfide is absorbed by the lead salt and the mercaptan colors the isatin reagent a grass green. Pour the contents of wash bottles 3 and 4 of the first apparatus into a beaker and rinse them out with 2.5 cc of 4 N acetic acid, then with 10 cc of copper acetate solution (0.92 mg in 250 cc of solution). After at least 2 hours filter off the cuprous xanthogenate precipitate in a 3 G 4 glass filtering crucible and wash with not over 25 cc of water. The formation of the yellow precipitate is proof of the presence of carbon disulfide.

4—THE DETECTION OF TOXIC GASES AND VAPORS IN INDUSTRY

Vallender, R. B. Chem. & Ind. (London) **58**, 330-333 (1939).

Air contaminated with carbon disulfide is bubbled through a mixture of diethylamine and copper acetate and the resulting yellow-orange to orange-brown color is compared with dilute carbon disulfide standards. The method is sensitive to 1 part in 120,000. Add. Ref.: CA **33**, 4907 (1939).

5—DETECTION OF CARBON DISULFIDE

Castiglioni, A. Z. anal. Chem. **115**, 257-259 (1939); CA **33**, 2067 (1939).

The reaction which occurs between piperazine and carbon disulfide can be utilized for the detection of carbon disulfide. If concentrated solutions in alcohol are used a pale yellow precipitate is formed. The method will detect 0.5 mg carbon disulfide at a dilution of 1:2000.

6—DETERMINATION OF CARBON DISULFIDE IN AIR BY MEANS OF COPPER AND DIETHYLAMINE IN 2-METHOXYETHANOL

Morehead, Frederick E. Ind. Eng. Chem., Anal. Ed. **12**, 373-374 (1940); CA **34**, 5375 (1940).

The stability of the color formed by carbon disulfide with diethylamine and cupric acetate is increased to 48 hours when 2-methoxyethanol is used as the solvent in place of ethyl alcohol.

7—FIELD DETERMINATIONS OF CARBON DISULFIDE IN AIR

Viles, F. J. J. Ind. Hyg. Toxicol. **22**, 188-196 (1940).

The author introduces a modification of the copper diethylamine test for carbon disulfide in air. The reagent consists of 1 ml diethylamine, 20 ml triethanolamine, and 0.05 g copper acetate in 1 liter of 85 to 100% ethyl alcohol. The reagent, which is stable indefinitely, should be kept in a rubber-stoppered glass bottle. Ten ml of solution will completely absorb and react with 1 liter of air containing 120 ppm of carbon disulfide. More than 10 ppm of hydrogen sulfide interferes by producing an orange tint; double bonded sulfur compounds also interfere. Add. Refs.: CA **34**, 4356 (1940); Jacobs, Morris B., "The Analytical Chemistry of Industrial Poisons, Hazards and Solvents," pp. 262-265, (Interscience Publishers, Inc., New York, 1941).

8—A QUANTITATIVE MICROCHEMICAL COLORIMETRIC DETERMINATION OF CARBON DISULFIDE IN AIR, WATER AND BIOLOGICAL FLUIDS

McKee, Ralph W. J. Ind. Hyg. Toxicol. **23**, 151-158 (1941).

Tischler's method (see above) was modified to use an absorbing reagent consisting of 0.5% diethylamine, 0.5% triethanolamine, and 0.001% cupric acetate in 95% ethyl alcohol. One part of carbon disulfide in 50,000,000 parts of water is detectable. Add. Ref.: CA **35**, 7434 (1941).

9—PIPERIDINE IN THE DETECTION AND DETERMINATION OF CARBON DISULFIDE

Castiglioni, Angelo. Ann. chim. applicata **31**, 218-220 (1941); CA **35**, 6538 (1941).

The addition of 2-3 drops of piperidine to the sample collected in ethyl ether, acetone or decalin produces a white precipitate if carbon disulfide is present. Hydrogen sulfide yields the same reaction but the precipitate is soluble in hot water and does not recur on cooling. This reaction can be made quantitative for carbon disulfide.

10—APPARATUS FOR CONTINUOUSLY MEASURING AND RECORDING OF HYDROGEN SULFIDE AND (OR) CARBON DISULFIDE IN THE ATMOSPHERE

Stackhouse, W. E. and Baxter Reynolds. Penn. Dept. Labor Ind., Safe Practice Bull. No. 29, 6 pp (1941); CA **36**, 2451 (1942).

A continuous recording device for measuring hydrogen sulfide and carbon disulfide is described. The apparatus consists of a sampling and absorption system, a photoelectric colorimeter and a potentiometer recorder. Changes on the order of 0.08 ppm in these gases can be recorded.

11—PHOTOELECTRIC PHOTOMETER FOR DETERMINING CARBON DISULFIDE IN THE ATMOSPHERE

Silverman, Shirleigh. Ind. Eng. Chem., Anal. Ed. **15**, 592-595 (1943): CA **37**, 6162 (1943).

The analyses covers a concentration range of 2 to 200 ppm with a precision of 1 ppm.

12—DETERMINATION OF VOLATILE SOLVENTS IN AIR, BLOOD AND ORGANS

Fabre, Rene. Ann. pharm. franc. **2**, 108-115 (1944); CA **40**, 5086 (1946).

A carbon disulfide determination, based on the photocolorimetric measurement of the yellow color of copper diethylthiosulfocarbamate produced in the presence of copper acetate by the action of carbon disulfide on an alcoholic solution of diethylamine, is described. The absorbing reagent is prepared by mixing 2 cc of each of the 2 following solutions: (A) 33% diethylamine solution 2, triethanolamine 2, 96% alcohol to 100 cc; (B) neutral copper acetate 0.10 g, acetic acid 1 drop, 96% alcohol to 100 cc. The method produces accurate results with 10-250 μg carbon disulfide. For air containing 1:30,000 carbon disulfide (0.10 mg per liter), about 250 cc of air gives a color suitable for measuring this material.

13—CHEMISTRY OF XANTHIC ACID DERIVATIVES. IV. THE INTERACTION OF SULFONYL CHLORIDES AND POTASSIUM ETHYL XANTHATE

Bulmer, Gerald and Frederick G. Mann. J. Chem. Soc. **1945**, 666-674; CA **40**, 1800 (1946).

A number of lead xanthate compounds are listed, which can be used for the rapid identification of carbon disulfide.

14—METHODS FOR THE DETECTION OF TOXIC GASES IN INDUSTRY. CARBON BISULFIDE VAPOR

Anon. Dept. of Sci. Ind. Research, London, England, Leaflet No. 6, 6 pp (1947 reprinted from 1939).

The absorbing and color reagent consists of 2 ml of a 2% diethylamine solution in benzene, and 2 ml of 0.1% copper acetate in absolute alcohol, added to 10 ml absolute alcohol in a bubbler. Air is drawn through the reagent at 125 ml per stroke and with 20 strokes the maximum sensitivity is 1 part in 120,000. Hydrogen sulfide, which interferes with the reaction, is removed by placing a lead acetate paper in the air stream ahead of the bubbler. The lead acetate paper is prepared by soaking (immersing) Whatman No. 1 filter paper in a solution consisting of 10 g lead acetate in 100 ml water and adding 5 ml of glacial acetic acid. Add. Ref.: CA **33**, 8141 (1939).

15—CARBON DISULFIDE AS TRACER IN STUDYING EARTH FORMATIONS

Bernard, George G. and Michael Savoy (to Pure Oil Co.). U. S. (Pat. No.) 2,578,500, Dec. 11, 1951; CA **46**, 2278 (1952).

The authors use the cupric acetate-diethylamine reagent to determine carbon disulfide injected into the air of wells. Sensitivity is 1 part in 400,000 in air or gas and 1 part in 2,000,000 in water or brine.

16—LIMITS OF ALLOWABLE CONCENTRATIONS OF ATMOSPHERIC POLLUTANTS. Book 1

Ryazanov, V. A., Editor, translated by B. S. Levine U. S. Dept. of Commerce, Office of Technical Services, Washington, D. C., 1952). In a discussion of carbon disulfide, the following reference is cited: "Determination of Carbon Bisulfide in Atmospheric Air" by A. Khritinina, Gigiena i Sanit. **1940**, p. 66. In the method described carbon disulfide is absorbed from an air stream by a 1.5% diethylamine solution at a rate of 0.5 liter per minute. Two ml of this solution are treated with 0.05% copper acetate solution and allowed to stand 6 to 10 minutes, then compared with standards similarly prepared. The sensitivity of the reaction is 0.0005 mg per sample aliquot.

17—CARBON DISULFIDE TESTER FOR THE MICRO-DETERMINATION IN AIR

Treiber, E. and H. Koren. Chem.-Ing.-Tech. **25**, 192-196 (1953).

Using a photoelectric instrument and a copper-diethylamine reagent, 6 μg of carbon disulfide per liter of air can be detected to within about 6%. Add. Ref.: CA **47**, 6708 (1953).

18—SIMULTANEOUS DETERMINATION OF SMALL QUANTITIES OF HYDROGEN SULFIDE AND OF CARBON DISULFIDE IN THE ATMOSPHERE

Sonnenschein, W. and K. Schaefer. Z. anal. Chem. **140**, 15-25 (1953); CA **48**, 1200 (1954).

Carbon disulfide can now be determined in the range of 0.6 mg of carbon disulfide per cubic meter of air because of improvements affected in existing analytical methods. Carbon disulfide is determined with sodium diethyldithiocarbamate which is the most sensitive method for this compound.

19—CHARACTERIZATION OF CARBON DISULFIDE-ENDANGERED ACTIVITIES

Demus, H. Faserforsch u. Textiltech. **5**, 65-67 (1954); CA **48**, 11250 (1954).

A method has been developed to determine the exposure of workers who are being studied to define the effects of carbon disulfide and hydrogen sulfide on these workers. Carbon disulfide and hydrogen sulfide are determined by a specially designed apparatus which allows a known volume of air to pass over a paper strip impregnated with a known quantity of lead acetate. The sample air is then passed through a solution, containing 0.1 g copper acetate, 1 cc diethylamine, and 20 cc of triethanolamine in 100 cc of 85% ethanol. The amount of carbon disulfide present is determined by comparison of the discolored copper solution with standard color solutions. The amount of hydrogen sulfide is determined by comparison of the degree of blackening of the paper with similar standards. Urinary carbon disulfide values are also given. Add. Ref.: IHD **18**, 1327 (1954).

20—AUTOMATIC DETERMINATION OF CARBON DISULFIDE CONCENTRATION IN THE ATMOSPHERE

Jambrich, M., A. Pikler, and G. Klokner. Chem. zvesti **10**, 468-475 (1956) (German summary); CA **51**, 6233 (1957).

A photocolorimetric method for the determination of carbon disulfide is described.

21—QUANTITATIVE DETERMINATION OF HYDROGEN SULFIDE AND CARBON DISULFIDE

Auergesellschaft Akt.-Ges. (by Hermann Heidrich). Ger. (Pat. No.) 1,031,545, June 4, 1958 (Cl. 42 **1**); C. Z. **1959**, 11024; CA **54**, 13992 (1960).

Hydrogen sulfide, and carbon disulfide can be determined simultaneously by using the reaction which occurs between lead or tin salts and formaldehyde. The air is first aspirated through silica gel impregnated with a lead salt which changes color when exposed to hydrogen sulfide. The air is then led through silica gel impregnated with an alcoholic or aqueous solution of a lead or tin salt which has been wetted with a 40% formaldehyde solution just prior to use.

22—DETECTION OF CARBON DISULFIDE IN THE AIR

Centralny Instyut Ochrony Pracy (by A. Krynska). Pol. (Pat. No.) 41,450, Nov. 28, 1958; CA **54**, 7439 (1960).

For detecting carbon disulfide in the air an indicator tube was used which was filled with silica gel prepared as follows: silica gel containing 2 to 6% alkali, calculated as sodium bicarbonate, grain size 0.4 to 0.6 mm, absorption capacity for benzene 40 to 60%, was saturated with "amino copper acetate" and dried at 100 to 130° for 30 minutes. The silica gel was then saturated with butyl alcohol containing 10 to 20% of pyridine and 10% triethanolamine. Then 3.5 ml of this solution per 5 g of silica gel was used. The fresh, moist mass was packed into tubes which were sealed immediately. Sensitivity of the test: 0.005 mg carbon disulfide per liter of air.

See Section One

For reference number 69, 81, 90, 129.

Carbon Monoxide

1—DETECTION OF CARBON MONOXIDE IN THE AIR

Gautier, Armand. J. Gas Lighting **121,** 547 (1913); CA **7,** 1460 (1913).

A method for the determination of carbon dioxide based on the reduction of iodic acid by carbon monoxide at temperatures of 60° to 80° is presented. The iodine formed is passed into a tube containing chloroform and assumes a pink coloration if carbon monoxide is present in excess of 5 ppm.

2—THE SOURCE OF CARBON MONOXIDE IN THE AIR AND ITS DETERMINATION

Meyer, Leo G. Arch. Hyg. **84,** 79-120 (1915); CA **9,** 3078 (1915).

Vogel's, Welzel's, Winkler's, and Deprex-Nicloux's methods are discussed. Palladium chloride paper, moistened with distilled water or sodium acetate, is considered superior to other methods even though it is affected by ammonia, sulfur dioxide, and carbon disulfide. It is more desirable even than the Deprex-Nicloux method (liberation of iodine from iodine pentoxide in the presence of carbon monoxide). The palladium chloride test is sensitive to from 0.05 to 0.5% carbon monoxide.

3—DETECTION OF CARBON MONOXIDE IN AIR

Desgrez, A. and A. Labat. Acad. Med. **1919;** Ann. chim. anal. chim. appl. **1,** 294-295 (1919); CA **14,** 712 (1920).

Strips of filter paper are immersed in a 10% palladium chloride solution and dried in darkness. One end of this reagent paper is moistened with water and the filter is suspended in the air to be sampled. In the presence of carbon monoxide the moist portion of the paper becomes gray, brown or black in approximately six minutes. The depth of color produced depends on the carbon monoxide concentration. One part carbon monoxide in 3000 parts of air produces a distinct gray coloration. The interference caused by hydrogen sulfide can be eliminated by aspirating the air through lead acetate before the carbon monoxide analysis is made.

4—DETECTING POISONOUS GASES IN AIR

Lamb, A. B. and C. R. Hoover U. S. (Pat. Nos.) 1,321,061 and 1,321,062, Nov. 4, 1920; CA **14,** 163 (1920).

The authors describe two methods for the preparation of "hoolamite" which can be used for the determination of carbon monoxide. The hoolamite changes from white through blue-green to violet-brown in the presence of carbon monoxide.

5—CARBON MONOXIDE DETECTOR

Gordon, C. S. and J. T. Lowe. U. S. (Pat. No.) 1,644,014, Oct. 4, 1927.

An ampule containing palladium chloride is broken inside a cotton bag. The degree of darkening on the surface of the material from the palladium liberated in the reaction is compared with a series of standards to indicate the concentration of carbon monoxide. Add. Ref.: CA **21,** 3772 (1927).

6—TESTS OF CARBON MONOXIDE DETECTOR IN MINES

Harrington, D. and B. W. Dyer. Bur. of Mines, Repts. of Investigations, Serial No. 2207 (1921); CA **15,** 779 (1921).

A simple compact apparatus has been developed for the detection of carbon monoxide in mines. The sample is drawn into a rubber bulb and forced through a glass tube filled with chemicals which change from a gray or white color to green depending on the carbon monoxide content. A color comparison scale is used for comparison and determinations of the carbon monoxide. Accurate results are obtained for concentrations of 0.1% and greater.

7—THE TANNIC ACID METHOD FOR THE QUANTITATIVE DETERMINATION OF CARBON MONOXIDE IN BLOOD

Sayers, R. R. and W. P. Yant. Bur. of Mines, Repts. of Investigations, Serial No. 2356, 7 pp. (1922); CA **16,** 3323 (1922).

A simple method for a field analysis of carbon monoxide in blood is presented. The technique can be carried out by untrained personnel.

8—DETERMINATION OF THE CARBON MONOXIDE CONTENT OF AIR

Andriska, Viktor. Z. Nahr. Genussm. **46,** 43-47 (1923); CA **18,** 539 (1924).

Welze's method (Verh. Physik-Med. Ges. Wurzburg **33,** Heft **3,** (1888)) for the determination of carbon monoxide in air is discussed. The limitations of the method are also presented.

9—THE PYROTANNIC ACID METHOD FOR THE QUANTITATIVE DETERMINATION OF CARBON MONOXIDE IN BLOOD AND AIR

Sayers, R. R., W. P. Yant, and G. W. Jones. U. S. Dept. of the Interior, Bureau of Mines, Repts. of Investigations, Serial No. 2486, 6 p. (1923).

The report describes a compact, durable, easy to use laboratory or field apparatus for the quantitative determination of carbon monoxide in blood and air. The percentage saturation of carbon dioxide in blood is determined by adding 0.04 g of a 1:1 mixture of solid pyrogallic acid and tannic acid to a 0.1 ml blood sample which has been diluted (in a diluting pipette) to 2. ml with water. After standing for 15 minutes at room temperature, the stable color formed is compared with that of known standards. The determination is accurate to within 5%. The technique is applied to the determination of carbon monoxide in air by equilibrating 0.1 ml of blood, diluted to 2. ml with water as above, with a known value of the contaminated air. The accuracy of this method is 0.005% with 0.000 to 0.05% carbon monoxide; 0.01% in the range of 0.05 to 0.08%; 0.02% in the range of 0.08 to 0.12; and 0.30% with 0.12 to 0.18% carbon monoxide. Add. Ref.: CA **17**, 2690 (1923); "Pyrotannic Acid Method for the Quantitative Determination of Carbon Monoxide in Blood and Air." U. S. Pub. Health Repts. **38**, 23-11-2320 (1923); CA **17**, 3850 (1923).

10—A NEW IMPROVED HAND APPARATUS FOR THE RAPID DETERMINATION OF CARBON MONOXIDE

Winkler, Rud. Montan. Rundschau **15**, 569-571 (1923); CA **18**, 486 (1924).

The "Palkon" apparatus consists of a glass vessel in which is suspended a strip of white filter paper moistened with an aqueous solution of a palladium salt. Coal dust and other organic materials are removed prior to analysis by aspirating the air through meerschaum moistened with silver nitrate. The time required for the palladium paper to begin to darken is noted. The percent carbon monoxide corresponding to the dark spot is read from a diagram. The method is accurate to 0.01%.

11—THE PYROTANNIC ACID METHOD FOR THE QUANTITATIVE DETERMINATION OF CARBON MONOXIDE IN BLOOD AND IN AIR

Sayers, R. R. and W. P. Yant. Dept. of Commerce, Bur. of Mines, Tech. Paper **373**, 18 pp. (1925).

The report describes a compact, durable, easy to use field apparatus for the determination of carbon monoxide in air. The technique is based on the Bureau of Mines pyrotannic acid method (see above) for the equilibration of normal, diluted blood with the air sample for 15-20 minutes. Add. Ref.: CA **20**, 60 (1926).

12—LITERATURE OF CARBON MONOXIDE POISONING

Sayers, R. R. and Davenport, Sara J. U. S. Public Health Bull. **150**, 54 pp. (1925); CA **20**, 1289 (1926).

An exhaustive review, including methods of detecting carbon monoxide in blood and in air.

13—EXPERIMENTS ON THE DETECTION OF SMALL QUANTITIES OF CARBON MONOXIDE IN GAS MIXTURES SUCH AS ILLUMINATING GAS IN AIR BY MEANS OF PALLADOUS CHLORIDE

Kunz, R. Z. oesterr. Ver. Gas-Wasserfach **66**, 193-198 (1926); CA **21**, 1071 (1927).

Palladous chloride-sodium acetate test paper, preceded by sulfuric acid and lead chloride to remove interfering substances, darkens in the presence of carbon monoxide. The stain is compared with those produced by known amounts of carbon monoxide.

14—DETECTION OF CARBON MONOXIDE

Smolczyk, E. Gasmaske **1**, 9-12 (1929); Wasser u. Abwasser **27**, 191; CA **26**, 340 (1932).

The author describes the determination of carbon monoxide by the blood method.

15—DEVICE FOR DETECTING CARBON MONOXIDE AND OTHER GAS IN THE ATMOSPHERE

Ljunggren, Gustaf. Brit. (Pat. No.) 379-304, Aug. 26, 1932; CA **27**, 3859 (1933).

16—DETECTION AND ESTIMATION OF CARBON DIOXIDE AND CARBON MONOXIDE IN AIR

Hughes, T. W. Chem. Eng. Mining Rev. **24**, 179-181 1932); CA **26**, 2394 (1932).

The author presents a review of known methods for the detection and determination of carbon dioxide and carbon monoxide in air.

17—DETECTING CARBON MONOXIDE IN THE AIR

Ljunggren, Gustaf. U. S. (Pat. No.) 1,891,429, Dec. 20, 1933; CA **27**, 1843 (1933).

18—PRACTICAL TESTS OF A NEW CARBON MONOXIDE INDICATOR (DEGEA)

Hetzel, K. W. Gasmaske **5**, 39-44 (1933); CA **27**, 2344 (1933).

The author describes the Degea carbon monoxide indicator. The analysis depends upon the reaction of carbon monoxide with iodine pentoxide which liberates free iodine. White, granular pumice is impregnated with the iodine pentoxide mixed with fuming sulfuric acid. The acid reaction of this reagent with carbon monoxide produces a greenish to brownish-black stain, the color depending on the concentration of carbon monoxide present. No color is produced with concentrations of up to 0.03 volumes per cent; concentrations of 0.03-0.05 volumes per cent produce only faint colors; concentrations above 0.06 volumes per cent yield easily recognizable colors.

19—A SIMPLE CARBON MONOXIDE-TESTING DEVICE

Dunham, A. R. Gas Age-Record **74**, 145-146 (1934); CA **28**, 7073 (1934).

Carbon monoxide detection by means of a simple apparatus is described. The reagent used is a solution of palladium salts deposited on filter paper.

20—DEPENDENCE OF THE PALLADIUM SALT TEST FOR CARBON MONOXIDE UPON THE PRESENCE OF OTHER SUBSTANCES

Daller, W. Z. anal. Chem. **103**, 83-88 (1935); CA **30**, 700 (1936).

A discussion, with equations, based on many experiments. Sodium palladous chloride solutions containing suitable quantities of sodium sulfite can be used to detect carbon monoxide in the presence of considerable hydrogen.

21—PROBLEMS OF PASSIVE DEFENSE AGAINST THE DANGER OF CHEMICAL GAS ATTACKS

Harsovescu, C. Antigaz (Bucharest) **9**, No. 9/10, 22-34 (1935); Chem. Zentr. **1936, I**, 4240; CA **31**, 7141 (1937).

The author presents a review of the properties and possible methods of recognition of carbon monoxide.

22—DETECTION OF TOXIC GASES AND VAPORS

Leroux, Lucien. Rev. hyg. et med. prevent. **57**, 81-112 (1935).

The author details several tests for carbon monoxide, including the precipitation of copper from ammoniacal cuprous carbonate or formate, and the pyrotannic acid-blood method. One part per 100,000 of carbon monoxide can liberate iodine from iodic acid at 80°C; the iodine colors chloroform rose-pink. The reaction proceeds in the cold if a mixture of iodic and fuming sulfuric acids is substituted for the iodic acid alone, on an inert carried such as pumice or, preferably, silica gel, which greatly increases the method's sensitivity. The liberated iodine forms a grayish-white color with 0.1% carbon monoxide, bluish-white with 0.3%, and blue-green with higher concentrations. Alternatively, the reagent may be sealed into ampoules, whose ends are broken just before use; the air to be tested is drawn through the reagent with a rubber bulb, after first passing through cotton and activated charcoal to remove interferences. One part of carbon monoxide in 1000 will blacken palladium chloride solution in 3 minutes. Paper impregnated with 1% palladium chloride solution turns gray after 3 minutes with 1 part per 1000 of carbon monoxide (170 ml of air); 1 part in 2000 requires 6 minutes, 1 part per 5000, 12 minutes, and 1 part per 10,000, 40 minutes. The detector paper may be stored with a hygroscopic salt to keep it moist, or, preferably, moistened just before use with neutral palladium chloride solution from a second ampoule. Hydrogen sulfide, methane, organic material, iron and other reducing metals, all interfere with both liquid and paper tests. Add Ref.: CA **29**, 3627 (1935).

23—A RAPID AND PRACTICAL METHOD FOR THE DETERMINATION OF CARBON DIOXIDE AND THE DETECTION OF CARBON MONOXIDE IN THE AIR BY MEANS OF A VERY SIMPLE APPARATUS

Mihaeloff, S. Ann. hyg. publ. sociale **1935**, 22-27; CA **29**, 7223 (1935).

The determination of carbon dioxide is carried out by bubbling air through 1 cc of 0.001 N sodium carbonate containing phenolphthalein as the indicator and noting the air volume required to decolorize the indicator. Substitution of a palladium chloride solution for the carbonate solution allows the determination of carbon monoxide with the same apparatus.

24—DETERMINATION OF SMALL QUANTITIES OF CARBON MONOXIDE IN THE AIR

Winkler, L. W. Z. anal. Chem. **102**, 99-101 (1935); CA **29**, 7222 (1935).

Two methods for the detection of carbon monoxide are presented. (1) To 100 cc of air, collected by displacement of water, add 1 cc of dilute palladium chloride solution, invert the glass-stoppered flask and look for the formation of a dark deposit of palladium. (2) Triturate 5.0 g of commercial ammonium molybdate with 100 cc of water and filter. Just before making the test, mix a little of the solution with an equal volume of normal hydrochloric acid. Take 2 flasks and fill one with 100 cc of air to be tested and the other with the same volume of air which is free from carbon monoxide. To each add 1 cc of dilute palladium chloride solution and close both flasks with Cellophane. Shake from time to time and after 24 hours add to each 5 cc of the acid molybdate solution. If the first flask contained 0.01% of carbon monoxide the liquid will be colored blue within 15 minutes; with 0.005% carbon monoxide a greenish blue develops in 2 hours. Add. Ref.: CA **29**, 3626 (1935).

25—SOME METHODS FOR THE DETECTION AND ESTIMATION OF POISONOUS GASES AND VAPORS IN THE AIR (A PRACTICAL MANUAL FOR THE INDUSTRIAL HYGIENIST)

Zhitkova, A. S., translated by J. B. Ficklen. (Service to Industry, Box 133, West Hartford, Conn., 1936), pp. 36-49.

Strips of filter paper soaked in a 1% solution of palladous chloride and dried, may be moistened with a 5% sodium acetate solution and used to detect carbon monoxide. The paper will blacken due to the formation of metallic palladium.

26—DEVICE FOR DETECTING CARBON MONOXIDE

Chaignon, E. 15me Congr. chim. ind. (Bruxelles, 1935) **1936**, 261-266; CA **30**, 5464 (1936).

The device described consists essentially of a sheet of dry paper impregnated with 2% palladium chloride solution and a sheet of plain paper of the same color held together between two plates of glass. The device is suspended in the suspected atmosphere for a definite time, and in presence of carbon monoxide the sensitized paper uniformly turns gray. Illuminating gas gives approximately the same reaction, which is advantageous rather than otherwise from a toxicological standpoint. Hydrogen sulfide produces a blackish brown coloration but only along the edges of the paper. The test can be made roughly quantitative by making the unsensitized paper into a series of panels of colors corresponding to increasing carbon monoxide contents and cutting a circle out of each panel through which the sensitized paper can be observed, so that the color produced on the sensitized paper can be compared directly with those of the various panels.

27—REAGENT FOR DETECTING CARBON MONOXIDE

Draeger, Otto H. Brit. (Pat. No.) 455,409, Oct. 20, 1936; CA **31,** 1730 (1937).

Silica gel impregnated with palladium chloride is heated to 140° in order to activate the reagent. The sample is aspirated through the tube containing the reagent. A gray color is produced upon moistening if carbon monoxide is present.

28—MODERN METHODS OF DETECTION AND DETERMINATION OF INDUSTRIAL GASES IN THE ATMOSPHERE

Leclerc, E. and R. Haux. Rev. universelle mines **12,** 293-298 (1936).

One part in one thousand of carbon monoxide turns palladium chloride detection papers brown to black in 3 minutes. The iodine pentoxide procedure also is described. Add. Ref.: CA **30,** 6672 (1936).

29—THE USE OF INDICATORS FOR THE DETECTION OF POISONOUS GASES AND VAPORS

Heering, D. Gasmaske **8,** 88-89 (1936).

The Degea carbon monoxide analyser uses a palladium-ammonium chloride paper for the analytical determination. The paper immediately turns black at 8.7 mg per liter and blue green at 1.25 mg per liter in 15 seconds. Add. Ref.: CA **30,** 7059 (1936).

30—DETECTING GASES

Chovin, Paul E. M. and Leon P. R. Gion. F. R. (Pat. No.) 799,136, June 6, 1936; CA **30,** 7396 (1936).

An apparatus is described whereby a small amount of carbon monoxide, gasoline, benzine, etc., in air is converted to carbon dioxide and this is brought into contact with an agent colored by carbon dioxide. The coloration gives a measure of the amount of carbon dioxide present.

31—SEMIAUTOMATIC DETERMINATION OF FIREDAMP OR OF CARBON MONOXIDE IN THE ATMOSPHERE

Choven, P. and L. Gion. 15me Congr. chim. ind. (Bruxelles, 1935) **1936,** 40-44; CA **30,** 5464 (1936). (C. F. Dubrisay and Gion, CA **29,** 6170 (1935)).

An apparatus which can be used to determine both methane and carbon monoxide in air is described. The sample is passed through soda lime to remove carbon dioxide, then through a furnace where methane or carbon monoxide is burned to carbon dioxide which is led through decolorized rosaniline solution. The color produced is measured in a photoelectric comparator. The instrument can be used for the analysis of most carbon containing gases. The accuracy is approximately 1%.

32—SEMIAUTOMATIC DETERMINATION OF CARBON DIOXIDE IN THE ATMOSPHERE AND IN COMBUSTION GASES

Chovin, P. and L. Gion. 15me Congr. chim. ind. Bruxelles, 1935) **1936,** 276-280; CA **30,** 5464 (1936).

The apparatus described atomizes a solution of rosaniline decolorized by hydrazine using the gas to be analyzed. If the conditions under which atomization takes place are well defined and kept constant, the color acquired by the reagent can yield an accurate measurement of the carbon dioxide content of the sample. A photoelectric comparator is used to make the color comparison. The various operations required for carrying out the determination are carried automatically by the manipulation of a single cock. By combining with a suitable combustion furnace (to burn carbon monoxide to carbon dioxide), the apparatus can be used for determining carbon monoxide. By means of special reagents for other gases, the latter can be determined or detected with the same apparatus.

33—DETECTION OF CARBON MONOXIDE

Bangert, F. Draeger-Hefte No. 190, 3492-3494 (1937); CA **31,** 6136 (1937).

The Draeger carbon monoxide detector is described in detail.

34—A METHOD OF DETECTING AND DETERMINING CARBON OXIDE AND DIOXIDE AND TOXIC VAPORS IN AIR

Demesse, J. Bull. acad. med. **118,** 771-774 (1937); CA **32,** 4831 (1938).

Two types of apparatus which contact the air with a 0.0001 or 0.001 N solution of sodium bicarbonate containing bromothymol blue, are described. The resulting color changes are caused by a pH shift and are evaluated by a table.

35—EXPERIENCE WITH THE AUER CARBON MONOXIDE TESTER IN FIGHTING MINE FIRES

Bredenbruchernst. Die Gasmaske **9,** 8-10 (1937); CA **31,** 3744 (1937).

Two uses of this detector in mines are given. It has been determined that the percentage of carbon monoxide found with this instrument checks closely with analytical determinations.

36—DETECTING THE PRESENCE OF CARBON MONOXIDE IN AIR

Ljunggren, Gustaf. Ger. (Pat. No.) 640,923, Jan. 15, 1937 (Cl. 42 1. 4.06); CA **31**, 5300 (1937).

The detection of carbon monoxide is accomplished by a color change occurring on paper impregnated with palladium chloride and a salt of a strong base and a weak acid. The use of an alkali salt of acetic acid is recommended.

37—DETERMINATION OF TRACES OF IMPURITIES IN COMMERCIAL GASES, PARTICULARLY OXYGEN

Grant, J. Ind. Gases **16**, 138-141 (1935); Chimie et industrie **37**, 655, CA **31**, 6133 (1937).

To detect carbon monoxide in commercial gases, such as oxygen, the gas is passed over a mixture of iodine pentoxide, pumice, and fuming sulfuric acid; in presence of carbon monoxide the mixture turns green and then brown, and the intensity of the coloration gives an approximate indication of the carbon monoxide content. Reduction of palladium chloride to palladium also is a sensitive test for carbon monoxide. Determination is based on absorption in an ammonium hydroxide or a hydrochloric acid solution of cuprous chloride.

38—SENSITIVENESS OF THE TEST FOR CARBON MONOXIDE USING THE DRAEGER CARBON MONOXIDE TEST APPARATUS

Hetzel, K. W. Draeger-Hefte No. **192**, 3644-3647 (1937); CA **32**, 965 (1938).

With this apparatus a concentration of 0.03 volumes per cent of carbon monoxide can be detected after some experience has ben gained and if a color comparator tube is used. Concentrations above 0.05 volumes per cent can easily be read even by inexperienced personnel without the aid of a color comparator tube.

39—THE DETECTION AND DETERMINATION OF SMALL AMOUNTS OF CARBON MONOXIDE IN AIR

Spausta, Franz, Chem. App. **25**, 137-141, 155-160, 177-181 (1938); CA **32**, 6973 (1938).

A review and bibliography are presented by the author.

40—DETECTING SMALL PROPORTIONS OF CARBON MONOXIDE IN AIR OR OTHER GASES

Schroeter, Gustav-Adolf (to Otto H. Draeger). U. S. (Pat. No.) 2,111,301, March 15, 1938; CA **32**, 3728 (1938).

The sample is drawn through a tube containing silica gel impregnated with palladious chloride which has been activated by heating in a vacuum. After the sample is collected the gel is moistened with water and if carbon monoxide is present a color change will occur.

41—SIMPLE COMBUSTION TYPE OF CARBON MONOXIDE ESTIMATOR

Ficklen, J. B. Science **88**, 411-412 (1938).

The instrument is based on the conversion of carbon monoxide to carbon dioxide which then is absorbed in a strontium hydroxide solution colored with phenolphthalein. The heater for the combustion unit is an automobile cigarette lighter. Air is drawn through the instrument with a 60 cc capacity bicycle pump and contaminants removed; carbon dioxide is absorbed by calcium oxide and silica gel, which also remove hydrocarbon vapors. The number of strokes necessary to decolorize the red solution is indirectly proportional to the carbon monoxide concentration in the air. Add. Ref.: CA **33**, 1547 (1939).

42—DETECTING CARBON MONOXIDE

Draegerwerk Heinr. u. Bernh. Draeger. Ger. (Pat. No.) 668, 512, Dec. 5, 1938 (Cl 42 1. 4.06); CA **33**, 4162 (1939).

The air sample is passed through a tube containing silica gel and sulfur trioxide followed by a section of tube containing iodine pentoxide and sulfur trioxide. In the presence of carbon monoxide the iodine pentoxide is reduced liberating iodine which yields a blue or violet coloration.

43—METHODS FOR THE DETECTION AND DETERMINATION OF CARBON MONOXIDE

Berger, L. B. and H. H. Schrenk. U. S. Dept. of the Interior, Bur. of Mines, Tech. Paper 582, 30 pp. (1938).

The author reviews several methods for the determination of carbon monoxide. 1) The pyrotannic acid method for the determination of carbon monoxide is applicable to concentrations ranging from 0.01 to 0.20 per cent. The method is based on the fact that a red suspension is formed by the addition of a mixture of pyrogallic and tannic acids to a water solution of blood that contains carbon monoxide combined with the hemoglobin of the blood. The percentage by volume of carbon monoxide in the air sample is calculated from the blood saturation. The hoolamite or activated iodine pentoxide detector provides a semi-quantitative means of estimating concentrations of carbon monoxide ranging from about 0.10 to 1.0 per cent. When hoolamite is in contact with carbon monoxide, iodine is liberated from the hoolamite (which is a mixture of iodine pentoxide and fuming sulfuric acid deposited on granular pumice stone), and the originally white granules are changed to blue green, violet, and finally black, depending upon the concentration of carbon monoxide present. 2) The ampoule-type detector is a glass tube filled with a solution of palladium chloride in a water-acetone mixture and hermetically sealed. In use the ampoule is crushed (wetting the cotton with the palladium solution) and exposed for 10 minutes to the air to be tested. The palladium chloride is reduced by carbon monoxide to a finely divided black precipitate of metallic palladium. The extent of the reaction depends on the time of exposure and temperature of the air tested. The sensitivity of this detector decreases with low air temperatures; above 50°F it indicates semiquantitatively concentrations of carbon monoxide ranging from 2 to 10 parts in 10,000 parts of air by volume. Higher concentrations are qualitatively indicated to be above 10 parts in 10,000 parts of air. 3) Carbon monoxide may be determined by the iodine pentoxide method with a precision of 0.003 per cent in samples containing less than 1.0 per cent of the gas, and concentrations of the order of 0.0005 per cent may be detected by this method, which is based on the reaction of carbon monoxide with iodine pentoxide to liberate iodine and form carbon dioxide. Several variations of the method are described. 4) The carbon monoxide recorder is an instrument that indicates and records continuously the concentration of carbon monoxide in air. Its sensitivity may be varied to suit the conditions under which it is to be used. A sensitivity of 1 part carbon monoxide in 1,000,000 parts air is attainable. 5) A portable indicator (operated on the same general principle as the carbon monoxide recorder) has been developed for determining the concentration of carbon monoxide in cockpits and cabins of airplanes, closed automobiles, city streets, and other places where its concentration in air ranges from less than 0.01 to 0.15 per cent by volume. This apparatus is made in two types. One type has a range of 0.00 to 0.15 per cent of carbon monoxide. The other type has two scales; one ranges from 0.0 to 0.01 per cent and the other from 0.00 to 0.10 per cent. A sample of the atmosphere to be tested is drawn directly into the apparatus, and the concentration of carbon monoxide is indicated by a meter. 6) A carbon monoxide alarm has been developed that samples the air continuously and sounds a warning when the concentration of carbon monoxide in the atmosphere reaches 0.02 per cent by volume. This operates on the same general principle as the recorder. 7) Carbon monoxide may be detected by its reaction with compounds of some of the noble metals. 8) Palladium chloride solution is reduced by carbon monoxide to black, scalelike particles of metallic palladium, and it is upon this principle that the ampoule-type detector is based. Add. Ref.: CA **32**, 8300 (1938) (See revision of this paper below (1955)).

44—TESTING FOR CARBON MONOXIDE

Draegerwerk Heinrich u. Bernhard Draeger. Ger. (Pat. No.) 681,471, Aug. 31, 1939 (Cl. 41 **1**. 4.06); CA **36**, 1870 (1942).

Small quantities of carbon monoxide in air can be detected with palladium chloride. Silica gel is treated with palladium chloride and heated for several hours in vacuo at 140°. The sample is aspirated through the activated gel which is then moistened with water. A gray or black stain indicates the presence of carbon monoxide.

45—IDENTIFICATION OF WAR GASES

Liberalli, Marcelo Robertson. Rev. quim. farm. (Rio de Janeiro) **4**, 49-53 (1939).

Filter paper impregnated with a solution of palladium chloride turns from white to black and has a sensitivity of 1 part per 2,000. Interference from hydrogen sulfide can be removed with lead acetate paper. Add. Ref.: CA **33**, 7921 (1939).

46—COLORIMETRIC DETERMINATION OF CARBON MONOXIDE

Chumanov, S. M. and M. B. Aksel'rod. J. Applied Chem. (USSR) **12**, 1568-1570 (1939); CA **34**, 7213 (1940).

Carbon monoxide has the ability to reduce trivalent iron salt as well as salts of palladium and gold. The amount of reduction is small without a catalyst but can be increased to almost 50 per cent in the presence of silica gel. The ferrous ion formed by the action of 0.02 mg of carbon monoxide per liter can be detected with potassium ferricyanide.

47—DETERMINATION OF CARBON MONOXIDE IN AIR

Leyton, Cesar and Jorge Villata Lena. Anales quim. farm. (Chile) **1939**, 25-30; CA **34**, 3619 (1940).

The authors discuss the hemoglobin method of Ogier and Kohn-Abrest.

48—APPARATUS (WITH A PHOTOELECTRIC CELL) FOR DETECTING THE PRESENCE OF GASES SUCH AS CARBON MONOXIDE IN AIR

Johnson, Chester W. U. S. (Pat. No.) 2,153,568, April 11, 1939; CA **33**, 5242 (1939).

A light reflective strip of cloth is used for the determinations of carbon monoxide. The cloth is impregnated with a solution of palladium chloride. When carbon monoxide reacts with the palladium the light-reflecting property is reduced. This reduction is detected by a photocell.

49—METHODS FOR THE DETECTION OF TOXIC GASES IN INDUSTRY. CARBON MONOXIDE

Anon. Dept. Sci. Ind. Research, London, Eng., Leaflet No. **7**, 9 pp (1939).

Three methods for the detection and determination of carbon monoxide are listed: (1) the reaction with the hemoglobin in blood to form carboxy-hemoglobin: accurate and sensitive, but too elaborate and delicate for routine use; (2) the reaction with iodine pentoxide to liberate iodine: apparatus too complicated and manipulation too difficult for routine use; (3) the reduction of palladium chloride to metallic palladium: method of choice. A test paper moistened with palladium chloride solution is suspended in the atmosphere for a definite time—usually 5 minutes—and the stains obtained, due to the deposit of metallic palladium, compared with standards. These may be the stain papers provided with the leaflet, or glass standards, or a photoelectric colorimeter comparator, or an optical density meter. The method may be made acceptably quantitative if the test air is drawn through a known area of the test paper at a slow and constant rate, and if interfering gases are removed by first passing the air through a tube of activated charcoal. Sampling is continued until a standard color is reached; from the time required the concentration is then obtained by referring to a chart. Sensitivity is 1 part in 500 (0.2%) in less than 2 minutes; 1 part in 2,000 (0.05%) in 6 minutes; and 1 part in 10,000 (0.01%) in half an hour. The technique is described in detail. Add. Refs.: CA **34**, 3203 (1940); same leaflet, 6 pp. revised 1951; IHD **15**, 765 (1951) J. 325.

50—THE DETECTION OF TOXIC GASES AND VAPORS IN INDUSTRY

Vallender, R. B. Chem. & Ind. (London) **58**, 330-333 (1939).

The two tests most commonly used are the reduction of palladium chloride on test paper, and the iodine pentoxide-fuming sulfuric acid reaction. The latter method produces only transient color changes and lacks the sensitivity necessary for the detection of harmful quantities of carbon monoxide. Filter paper is impregnated with the palladium chloride and air is passed slowly through the paper until a standard depth of stain is reached, the time required being used as a function to determine the air concentration. Gases which may affect the color of the paper or stain are removed by prefiltration through a tube of activated carbon. Add. Ref.: CA **33**, 4907 (1939).

51—AN INDICATOR METHOD FOR THE DETERMINATION OF CARBON MONOXIDE IN AIR

Karlson, L. E. Hig. i Sanitariya **1939**, No. 5, 50-53; Khim. Referat. Zhur. **1939**, No. 11, 58; CA **34**, 7213 (1940).

The authors describe the optimum conditions for an indicator method of determining carbon monoxide in air. Optimum conditions were found for the determination of carbon monoxide by the indicator method based on the formation of a light bluish green color appearing from the contact of carbon monoxide with a suspension of iodine pentoxide in oleum impregnated in silica gel. The optimum composition of the reagent was a 0.1% iodine pentoxide suspension in 25-30% oleum. The same silica gel should always be used dry and in a slightly acid condition. Silica gel is introduced into a tube (diam. 5-7 mm and length 7-8 cm) one side of which is drawn into a capillary. Air is first passed through a V-shaped tube, one side of which is filled with activated charcoal and the other side with calcium chloride. The color obtained on the silica gel is compared with standard colors prepared by wetting pumice with the following solutions: a weak standard saturated nickel sulfate solution 1 cc, 10% cobalt sulfate solution 0.3 cc and water 1.5 cc. It is more convenient to perform the

analysis if the amount of air which is necessary to obtain the standard color is measured. With 5 mg per liter of carbon monoxide the weak color standard is obtained by passing 12 cc of air and the intense color standard by passing 25 cc of air. With 0.5 mg per liter the weak color standard is obtained after passing 800 cc of air. The paper describes in detail the apparatus for the analysis.

52—REPORT OF THE A.P.H.A. SUBCOMMITTEE ON CHEMICAL METHODS IN AIR ANALYSIS—CARBON MONOXIDE

Goldman, F. H., Chairman, et al. Am. Publ Health Assoc. Yearbook 1940-1941, pp. 118-124.

A brief review of the methods is given.

53—A SIMPLE METHOD OF DETERMINING CARBON MONOXIDE CONTENT OF THE AIR BY PALLADIUM CHLORIDE PAPER

Komatu, Humio and Eisaku Ito. J. Oriental Med. **32**, 119-133 (German Abstr. 82-83) (1940); CA **35**, 407 (1941).

The analysis is conducted by estimating the time required for a black band to appear on the palladium chloride paper. The relationship between time and concentration is given.

54—DETECTION OF CARBON MONOXIDE WITH PALLADIUM CHLORIDE PAPER

Labat, J. A. Bull. trav. soc. pharm. Bordeaux **78**, 65-67 (1940); CA **34**, 5786 (1940).

The procedure published earlier (cf. CA **14**, 712 (1920)) is changed with respect to the test paper. Small glass bulbs which have two capillary ends and hold about 0.1 cc of 10% palladous chloride solution are prepared. Bands of filter paper 55 x 15 mm are cut. When the sample is to be analyzed the sealed ends of the bulb are broken and one of the ends is placed on a filter paper and allowed to drain. The filter paper is suspended in air for 10 minutes.

55—DETECTION OF CARBON MONOXIDE

Elverdam, Egon. Gasteknikeren **30**, 139-140, 152-159 (1941); CA **39**, 3221 (1945).

The author presents a review of methods of detection of carbon monoxide.

56—APPARATUS FOR DETERMINING (EXTRANEOUS) COMPONENTS SUCH AS CARBON MONOXIDE IN THE AIR

Draegerwerk Heinrich u. Bernhard Draeger. Ger. (Pat. No.) 730,977, Dec. 24, 1942 (Cl. 42 **1**. 4.03); CA **38**, 515 (1944).

57—GAS TESTING APPARATUS

Gross, Gustav and Gerhard Budan (to Auergesellschaft A.-G.). Ger. (Pat. No.) 731,325, Dec. 31, 1942 (Cl 42 **1**. 4.06); CA **38**, 515 (1944).

58—A COMPARISON OF METHODS FOR THE DETERMINATION OF CARBON MONOXIDE

Goldman, F. H. and A. D. Brandt. Am. J. Publ. Health **32**, 475-480 (1942).

Six methods for the determination of carbon monoxide in air, used to sample the same environment, are compared and evaluated. They are: the iodine pentoxide method, the hopcalite indicator, the Hoolamite detector, palladium chloride ampoules, the British palladium chloride method, and the pyrotannic acid method. Limitations and accuracies of the methods are discussed. Add. Ref.: CA **36**, 4057 (1942)

59—DETERMINATION OF CARBON MONOXIDE IN THE AIR OF MINES

Fekete, Laszlo. Ungar Z. Berg.-u. Huettenwes. **76**, 107-112 (1943); Chem. Zentr. **1943**, **II**, 2078-2079; CA **39**, 1116 (1945).

A review of all the various methods is presented.

60—A PROCEDURE FOR THE DETECTION OF CARBON MONOXIDE IN THE AIR AND CARBON MONOXIDE INTOXICATION

Wildhaber, Marcel A. Pharm. Acta Helv. **19**, 1-5 (1944); CA **38**, 4215 (1944).

The palladium chloride test is reviewed.

61—IMPROVEMENT IN THE USE OF PALLADOUS CHLORIDE AS REAGENT FOR CARBON MONOXIDE. NEW RAPID AND SENSITIVE METHOD FOR THE DETECTION OF THIS GAS

Voiret, E. G. and A. L. Bonaime. Ann. chim. anal. **26**, 11-12 (1944); CA **40**, 1105 (1946).

It is found possible to detect 1 part carbon monoxide in 1000 parts of air by the procedure here described. If a fairly fresh solution of cuprous chloride is added to 0.05% palladium chloride solution containing 0.5 ml concentrated hydrochloric acid in each 100 ml, there is no visible reduction of the palladium, which always occurs with more concentrated solutions, but the reagent is very sensitive to carbon monoxide. Small quantities of carbon monoxide can be determined by the black spot formed on filter paper. To prepare the cuprous chloride reagent, 1 g of copper sulfate pentahydrate plus 1 g of sodium chloride plus 10 ml of water plus some copper turnings plus 10 ml of concentrated hydrochloric acid are placed in a flask, heated to boiling, and diluted to 500 ml. Do not use the solution after it has stood a few days. The test can be made wet or dry: (1) In a 30-ml test tube add 2 ml of the palladium chloride solution and 5 drops of the cuprous chloride reagent. Introduce air sample and shake vigorously for a few seconds. If less than 1/10,000 parts of carbon monoxide is present, at least a minute is required. Compare the darkening with standards. (2) Impregnate a strip of filter paper with sodium acetate, dry, and then moisten with a large drop of the palladium chloride solution and a very little cuprous chloride reagent. Expose the treated paper to the air to be tested. The second procedure is preferred.

62—DETERMINATION OF CARBON MONOXIDE IN THE ATMOSPHERE

Renaud, R., R. Thomas, and R. Gibert. Mem. services chim. etat (Paris) **32**, 36-61 (1945); CA **42**, 2890 (1948).

The authors present a method for the determination of carbon monoxide in air. To detect carbon monoxide in the air, a spot test is recommended. Dissolve 0.5 g of palladium chloride in 5 ml of concentrated hydrochloric acid and dilute to 1 liter. One gram of copper sulfate pentahydrate and 1 g sodium chloride are dissolved in water in a 50 ml Erlemeyer flask. One gram of copper turnings and 10 ml of concentrated hydrochloric acid are added. Boil 3 minutes, dilute to 50 ml, and store in the dark. Two ml of the palladium chloride solution and 0.2 ml of the cuprous chloride solution are used for the test. With this mixture a spot test can be made on paper or air can be bubbled through the mixture at 100 ml per minute and the approximate content of carbon monoxide determined by the time required to give a distinct blackening. If hydrogen sulfide is present it must be removed or a black sulfide will form. A more precise titrimetric method, using two indicators, is described also, together with a continuous procedure based on the hopcalite method, and two methods in which an alarm rings as soon as there is a dangerous concentration of carbon monoxide.

63—DETECTION OF CARBON MONOXIDE

Russell, Eric Woodington. Brit. (Pat. No.) 578,745, July 10, 1946; CA **41**, 1578 (1947).

A reagent consisting of acidified ions of palladium, an alkali metal or ammonia, a halide, and a molybdate or tungstate admixed with partially dehydrated silica gel is presented for the detection of carbon monoxide by means of a color change. Amounts as low as 0.001% carbon monoxide are detected by this means.

64—DETECTION AND DETERMINATION OF CARBON MONOXIDE

Main-Smith, John D. and George A. Earwicker. Brit. (Pat. No.) 582,184, Nov. 7, 1946; CA **41**, 1578 (1947).

A reagent consisting of silica gel impregnated with potassium palladium sulfite is used for the colorimetric determination of carbon monoxide in gases at atmospheric temperatures. To prepare potassium palladium sulfite, 25 g of potassium metabisulfite in 100 cc of distilled water is added to 10 g of palladous chloride and well mixed. The solution is evaporated and dried at reduced pressure. The reagent consisting of 1.62 g of potassium palladium sulfite adsorbed on 500 g of silica gel turns from yellow to brown in the presence of carbon monoxide.

65—A SIMPLE TECHNIQUE FOR DETECTION OF CARBON MONOXIDE IN BLOOD

Lambrechts, A. and R. Roseman. Compt. rend. soc. biol. **140**, 801-803 (1946); CA **41**, 4823 1947).

Two cc of distilled water and 0.2 cc of the blood sample are placed in the one compartment of a Conway dish (CA **27**, 3857 (1933)). A filter paper disc wetted with 0.15 cc of 0.01 N palladium chloride is placed in the central compartment. One cc of 10% phosphoric acid is added to the diluted blood, the dish is sealed and kept at 56° for 20 minutes, then the degree of darkening of the paper disc is estimated.

66—THE DETECTION OF CARBON MONOXIDE OR TOWN GAS IN AIR

Minchin, Leslie T. Gas J. **251**, 100, 105 (1947); CA **41**, 6039 (1947).

A review of the carbon monoxide methods, with special reference to the "Mark III Carbon Monoxide Indicator Tube" in which silica gel impregnated with yellow potassium pallado-sulfate is turned brown by carbon monoxide, the size of the brown stain being proportional to the concentration of carbon monoxide in the air sample.

67—RAPID DETERMINATION OF SMALL AMOUNTS OF CARBON MONOXIDE. PRELIMINARY REPORT ON THE NBS COLORIMETRIC INDICATING GEL

Shepherd, Martin. Anal. Chem. **19**, 77-81 (1947).

This report describes the preparation and use of the NBS indicating gel for the rapid colorimetric determination of small amounts of carbon monoxide in air. The gel can detect and estimate less than 1 part carbon monoxide in 500,000,000 parts air, and will detect 0.001% by volume in less than 1 minute. The field apparatus is small, inexpensive, without maintenance problems, and the procedure is so simple that untrained personnel can obtain reliable results. Add. Ref.: CA**41**, 1952 (1947).

68—DETERMINATION OF SMALL AMOUNTS OF CARBON MONOXIDE IN AIR BY VARIOUS REFERENCE METHODS

Shepherd, Martin. J. Research Natl. Bur. Standards **38**, 351-358 (1947) (Research Paper No. 1777); CA **41**, 5054 (1947).

See previous article by this author (CA **41**, 1952 (1957)) above. Samples containing, respectively, about 0.04 and 0.01% carbon monoxide were carefully prepared by the pressure-dilution method and analyzed in various laboratories by eight different methods. The colorimetric method was found simple, easy, rapid, and inexpensive, although less accurate for larger quantities of carbon monoxide unless the original sample was first diluted with carbon monoxide-free air.

69—RAPID DETERMINATION OF LOW CONCENTRATIONS OF CARBON MONOXIDE IN AIR

Katz, Morris and John Katzman. Can. J. Research **26F**, 318-330 1948); CA **43**, 1686 (1949).

Carbon monoxide can be determined by utilizing silver permanganate deposited on zinc oxide for the oxidation of the carbon monoxide. Results accurate to 5 ppm, in the range of 100 to 200 ppm have been obtained.

70—PHOTOELECTRIC DETECTION AND ESTIMATION OF CARBON MONOXIDE WITH GRANULES COATED WITH PALLADOUS SILICOMOLYBDATE

Cole, James W., J. Melvin Salsbury, and John H. Yoe. Anal. Chim. Acta **2**, 115-126 (1948) (in English); CA **42**, 8710 (1948).

Granules of silica gel coated with palladous silicomolybdate turn from yellow to green and blue *in the presence of carbon monoxide*. The sensitivity of the photoelectric system is about 0.001% carbon monoxide with an accuracy of 10%. Flow rates of 10 to 110 ml/minute are used for continuous detection and spot test estimation, respectively.

71—MICRODETERMINATION OF CARBON MONOXIDE IN AIR. A PORTABLE INSTRUMENT

Beckman, Arnold O., James D. McCullough, and Robert A. Crane. Anal. Chem. **20**, 674-677 1948).

The instrument is based on the ability of carbon monoxide to react with red mercuric oxide to yield mercury vapor, which then reacts with selenium sulfide impregnated test paper. The length of the black stain on the paper is a function of the carbon monoxide concentration. The average error is less than 10%, and the sensitivity ranges from a few ppm to about 3% of carbon monoxide. Add. Ref.: CA **42**, 7657 (1948)).

72—FIELD TESTS FOR THE DETECTION OF CARBON MONOXIDE

Minchin, Leslie T. Chem. & Ind. (London) **(1948)**, 147-149; CA **42**, 3623 (1948).

A brief description of the carbon monoxide detecting instruments for field use currently available in England and America is provided.

73—ASPIRATING DEVICE FOR NATIONAL BUREAU OF STANDARDS CARBON MONOXIDE INDICATING TUBES

Setterlind, A. N. Ind. Hyg. Newsletter, U. S. Pub.

Health Service **8**, No. 2, 7 (1948); CA **43**, 5646 (1949).

The device described in detail is made from a 50 ml syringe.

74—APPARATUS FOR SEMIQUANTITATIVE ESTIMATION OF CARBON MONOXIDE

Beczkoy, Jozsef. Magyar Kem. Lapja **3**, 460 (1948); CA **43**, 8749 (1949).

An 0.2% solution of palladium chloride is introduced and the bulb evacuated to an absolute pressure of 20 mm Hg. In field determinations the bulb is opened and air is allowed to bubble through the liquid. An approximation of the carbon monoxide can be made on the basis of the time required to turn the liquid dark, or the time required for a precipitate to appear e.g., darkening in 30 minutes indicates 0.02% carbon monoxide, in 5 minutes 0.06%, and in 1 minute 0.20% carbon monoxide.

75—COLORIMETRIC GAS DETECTION

Shepherd, George M. U. S. (Pat. No.) 2,487,077, Nov. 8, 1949; CA **44**, 1366 (1950).

Silica gel impregnated with ammonium molybdate and palladium sulfate can be used for the determination of carbon monoxide. The color change ranges from canary yellow through emerald green to blue green, to dark blue. The indicator retains its sensitivity to $-40°$ and the reproducibility is 2 ppm in the range of 0 to 100 ppm. The entire method is described in detail.

76—DETECTION AND DETERMINATION OF SMALL AMOUNTS OF CARBON MONOXIDE

Houdek, Mirko. Paliva a vada **29**, 119-122 (1949); CA **46**, 3456 (1952).

The author reviews several known methods for the determination of carbon monoxide.

77—ESTIMATION OF CARBON MONOXIDE

Minchin, L. T. Gas. J. **260**, 719-720 (1949); CA **44**, 1851 (1950).

Carbon monoxide can be determined by aspirating a portion of the sample through a glass tube containing three columns of silica gel. The center column contains a palladium salt and the two outer columns contain untreated silica gel which act as filters and also aid in providing the proper degree of humidity before the sample reaches the sensitized column. The length of stain is a measure of the carbon monoxide concentration. Add. Ref.: IHD **14**, 509 (1950).

78—CHRONOMETRIC DETERMINATION OF CARBON MONOXIDE IN AIR WITH THE AID OF PALLADIUM CHLORIDE

Griffon, Henry and Leon Capus. Ann. med. legale, criminol., police sci., med. sociale et toxicol. **30**, 187-191 (1950); CA **44**, 8823 (1950).

The time required for the appearance of a gray spot on filter paper treated with palladium chloride is a function of the concentration of carbon monoxide present. Add. Ref.: IHD **14**, 1317 (1950).

79—STUDY OF THREE METHODS OF ESTIMATION OF CARBON MONOXIDE

Houberechts, A. Institute d'Hyg. des Mines (Hasselt, Belgium), Communication No. 74, 13 pp. (1950); IHD **15**, 766 (1951).

The hopcalite (thermal measurement) method and the potassium palladium sulfite reaction for the estimation of carbon monoxide (described in the British Leaflet No. 7, "Methods for the Detection of Toxic Gases in Industry"— see above) gave results too low under certain conditions. The silico-molybdic palladium sulfate reaction was accurate for all graduations of the scale.

80—MODIFIED IODINE PENTOXIDE METHOD FOR DETERMINATION OF CARBON MONOXIDE

Grant, G. A., M. Katz, and R. L. Haines. Canad. J. Technol. **29**, 43-51 (1951); IHD **15**, 764 (1951).

An improved iodine pentoxide method for the determination of carbon monoxide is described.

81—TUBE FOR TESTING FOR CARBON MONOXIDE, AND ITS USE IN DETECTING CARBON MONOXIDE IN MINE GASES

Schuhknecht, Wolfgang and Helmut Schinkel. Glueckauf **87**, 883-886 (1951); CA **46**, 2348 (1952).

Determinations made with the Draeger model 16 and the Shepherd NBS apparatus are compared for the following gases: methane, ethane, propane, butane, and hydrogen, either alone or mixed. The NBS method proved to be the more sensitive.

82—CONTINUOUS DETERMINATION OF CARBON MONOXIDE AND DETECTION OF DANGEROUS CONCENTRATIONS

Vallaud, A. Travail et securite (Paris) **3**, 99-104 (1951); CA **48**, 7489 (1954).

The author presents a review of chemical and physical methods for the determination of carbon monoxide.

83—DETECTION OF SMALL AMOUNTS OF CARBON MONOXIDE IN AIR

Anon. Schweiz. Ver Gas Wasserfach Monatsbull. **31**, 31-33 (1951); CA **46**, 3457 (1952).

General methods for the determination of carbon monoxide are described.

84—DETERMINATION OF CARBON MONOXIDE IN THE AIR

Revel, Paul and R. Fabre. Bull. acad. natl. med. **135**, 490-492 (1951); CA **46**, 3457 (1952).

The authors describe a modification of Wolf's procedure. (Ann. med. legale, criminol., police sci., med. sociale et toxicol. **27**, 221-22, 1947).

85—DETECTION OF CARBON MONOXIDE BY PALLADOUS SULFITE AND (OR) PALLADOSULFITES

Main-Smith, John D. and George A. Earwicker (to Minister of Supply, United Kingdom). U. S. (Pat. No.) 2,569,895, Oct. 2, 1951; CA **46**, 2966 (1952).

Silica gel impregnated with potassium palladosulfite is placed in a glass tube connected with a capillary tube and a rubber aspirator bulb. If carbon monoxide is present the yellow palladosulfite is converted to a brown color. The length of the stain is a measure of the carbon monoxide concentration. Hydrocarbons, oils, organic solvents, moisture, nitrous fumes, and dust which can affect the indicator are removed by preceding it with unimpregnated silica gel. Acetylene and hydrogen sulfide, not readily removed, also cause a similar color change. See also British Patent by same authors (1946) above.

86—CARBON MONOXIDE DETECTOR WITH THE NATIONAL BUREAU OF STANDARDS COLORIMETRIC INDICATING GEL

Klug, Charles W. U. S. (Pat. No.) 2,561,802, July 24, 1951; CA **45**, 8822 (1951).

Improvements have been made to restore the color and sensitivity of an indicating gel after it has been contaminated with carbon monoxide.

87—A RAPID METHOD FOR THE DETERMINATION OF CARBON MONOXIDE IN AIR

Gurevich, V. G., L. I. Belkina, and A. V. Nenartovich. Novosti Med. **1952**, No. 26, 62-64; CA **49**, 12197 (1955).

The authors prepare a substance with a small grainy consistency and which has a greenish-yellow color. The method of preparation and the chemical nature of the substance are withheld. The color changes are to green, bluish-green and blue depending on carbon monoxide concentration.

88—THE DETECTION AND ESTIMATION OF CARBON MONOXIDE

Grice, C. S. W. and F. J. Hartwell. Trans. Inst. Min. Engrs. **111**, 305-319 (1952); IHD **17**, 297 (1953).

The article reviews various methods for the detection and determination of carbon monoxide in mines. (1) Absorption by hemoglobin offers no special advantages. (2) Chemical absorption in liquid reagents should be reserved for laboratory procedures involving 0.25% or more of carbon monoxide. (3) The standard method of iodine pentoxide still is unequaled for concentrations between 0.0005% and 0.2%. (4) Potassium pallado-sulfite indicating tubes provide the most convenient and accurate method for detecting small quantities in the field. (5) For continual recording there is a choice between catalytic oxidation on hopcalite and infrared absorption. Birds and mice remain the only portable indicators which work continuously without human intervention.

89—CARBON MONOXIDE-DETECTING SUBSTANCES

Dore, Collis. Brit. (Pat. No.) 673,419, June 4, 1952; CA **46**, 11052 (1952).

Silica gel is impregnated with a solution containing 5% of a palladium halide and either 1% sodium alizarin-sulfonate or o-tolidine. This mixture is dried at 290° F and deposited on the adhesive side of scotch tape. If sodium alizarinsulfonate is used as the detector reagent, a pale golden-colored strip is obtained. When exposed to carbon monoxide the following color changes are seen: 0.01% CO, dark golden; 0.015% CO, light purple; 0.02%, dark purple; 0.12%, purplish black.

90—OXIDATION AGENTS AND PROCESSES

Katz, Morris (to Minister of Defence). Brit. (Pat. No.) 667,680, March 5, 1952; CA **45**, 11606 (1952).

A porous granular material is formed by mixing concentrated silver nitrate solution with an inorganic oxide such as one of the following: zinc oxide, ferric oxide, cobaltic oxide, titanium dioxide, cupric oxide, manganese dioxide, cerium dioxide, antimonic oxide, nickel oxide, stannic oxide, red lead oxide, silica dioxide, zirconium oxide, cadmium oxide, vanadium penta-oxide, or aluminum oxide. Sodium permanganate or potassium permanganate solution is added and the mixture is heated at 25-30° for 1 to 2 hours. The material is cooled, filtered, pressed and cured for from 7 to 28 days. After crushing, screening and drying the material can be used as an oxidizing agent for converting carbon monoxide to carbon dioxide at ambient temperatures. The materials may also be used in canisters of respiratory protection devices and in indicator tubes.

91—CARBON MONOXIDE—ITS DETECTION IN INDUSTRIAL ATMOSPHERES

Minchin, Leslie T. Iron and Steel (London) **26**, 425-426 (1953); CA **47**, 12713 (1953).

A method for the determination of carbon monoxide based on the length of the color stain developed in silica gel impregnated with a palladium salt.

92—ANALYTICAL PROCEDURE FOR THE DETECTION OF GASES

Guatelli, Manual A. Rev. asoc. bioquim. arg. **18**, 3-40 (1954).

Ethylene and hydrogen interfere with the reaction of carbon monoxide in the usual ammoniacal silver detection procedure. Wein's method, with ammonium palladium chloride, and Burk's method with sodium palladium chloride in 5% acetic acid are discussed. Add. Ref.: CA **48**, 8124 (1954).

93—COLORIMETRIC ESTIMATION OF CARBON MONOXIDE IN AIR

Berka, I. Pracovni Lekarstvi **6**, 27-28 (1954); CA **49**, 2944 (1955).

A new method for the determination of carbon monoxide is described. The method is based on the reduction of palladium chloride by the carbon monoxide and the subsequent determination of the excess palladium chloride by converting it to a colored complex. The complex is formed by the reaction with p-nitrosodiethylaniline.

94—A NEW METHOD FOR BLOOD CARBON MONOXIDE DETERMINATIONS

Waggoner, J. N. and M. L. Pernell. U. S. Armed Forces Med. J. **6**, 121-124 (1955).

The carbon monoxide in the blood is removed by saponin, ferrocyanide, lactic acid and caprylic acid in a stoppered flask. The air above the solution is removed and passed through an M.S.A. carbon monoxide detector tube. The color formed is compared with a standard graph for carbon monoxide-hemoglobin saturation. Add. Ref.: IHD **19**, 474 (1955).

95—DETERMINATION OF CARBON MONOXIDE IN AIR POLLUTION STUDIES

Shepherd, Martin, Shuford Schuhmann, and Marthada V. Kilday. Anal. Chem. **27**, 380-383 (1955).

A method using the NBS colorimetric indicating gel, previously developed for the detection of carbon monoxide in air (see article by Shepherd, above) was refined to determine 0.1 to 1 ppm and from 1 to 25 ppm, thus becoming suitable for air pollution studies. The gel is manufactured commercially by two licensed companies, M.S.A. and Parmelee Plastics Co. The gel was placed in specially prepared and meticulously cleaned borosilicate glass tubes of 5.1 - 5.2 mm bore and 15 cm length. Two cm of indicating gel was placed in the center and 5 cm of guard gel placed on either side, with the tube ends cork-stoppered and a layer of cotton between the cork and the guard gel. The air flow was maintained at a constant rate of 100 ml per minute. A special calibrating unit was designed so that standard tubes could be prepared. These tubes, though less convenient than those prepared commercially, are more sensitive and much more accurate. Add. Ref.: CA **49**, 8534 (1955).

96—SPECTROPHOTOMETRIC ADAPTATION OF THE DETERMINATION METHODS OF CARBON MONOXIDE BY PALLADIUM CHLORIDE

Giuliani, Vincenzo and Stanislao Zazo. Rass. med.

sper. **2**, 97-102 (1955); CA **51**, 12751 (1957).

A modification of the Morelli method (CA **48**, 9270, 10822 (1954)) for the determination of carbon monoxide in blood and air is described. The optimum concentration of potassium iodide is between 7.5 and 20%. The light absorbtion measurement is made at 510 mμ.

97—A SEMIQUANTITATIVE METHOD FOR DETERMINATION OF SMALL AMOUNTS OF CARBON MONOXIDE IN THE AIR

Kleemann, H., W. Massmann, and D. Sprecher. Zentr. Arbeitsmed. u. Arbeitsschutz **5**, 87-91 (1955); CA **49**, 15628 (1955).

A simple and rapid method for the determination of carbon monoxide is described. Air is led through a filter paper impregnated with palladium chloride. The quantity of palladium reduced by the carbon monoxide is compared with known samples. Hydrogen sulfide, carbon disulfide, nitrogen dioxide, ammonia, halogens, and hydrogen chloride have to be removed by solutions of sulfuric acid, sodium hydroxide, and potassium iodide.

98—NEW METHOD FOR THE DETERMINATION OF CARBON MONOXIDE IN AIR

Ciuhanda, Gheorghe. Acad. rep. populare Romine, Baza cercetari stiint. Timisoara, Studii cercetari stiint., Ser. I, **2**. 133-142 (1955); CA **50**, 15344 (1956).

A method for the determination of carbon monoxide based on the formation of a complex containing silver and p-sulfamoylbenzoic acid. The air sample is bubbled through 20% potassium hydroxide to remove the hydrogen sulfide interference. The sample is then aspirated through a solution prepared from 1 cc of 0.125 M silver nitrate, 1 cc of 0.1M di-sodium salt of p-sulfamoylbenzoic acid and 0.5 cc of 1 M sodium hydroxide until a yellow color is observed. The carbon monoxide concentration is determined from a reference curve, prepared from the analysis of known concentrations of carbon monoxide.

99—A NEW COLORIMETRIC METHOD FOR THE DETERMINATION OF CARBON MONOXIDE IN AIR

Ciuhandu, Gheorghe. Acad. rep. populare Romine, Studdi cercetari chim. **3**, 243-251 (1955) (French summary); CA **51**, 4877 (1957).

Sodium benzoate-p-silver sulfamide is reduced by carbon monoxide in an alkaline solution producing a brown to purple coloration. The color intensity for a given concentration of carbon monoxide is reproducible. The reagent is prepared just prior to each test from 1 part 0.1 N benzoic acid-p-sulfamide, 0, 1 part 0.1 N silver nitrate, and 0.5 Part 1.0 N sodium hydroxide. The sample is exposed for about 24 hours to 10 ml of the reagent in a 1200 ml flask. The resulting color is measured at 510 mμ.

100—DETERMINATION OF ATMOSPHERIC CARBON MONOXIDE

Stefanovic, A. Glasnik Hig. Inst. (Belgrade) **4**, No. 1-2, 77-85 (1955); Excerpta Med., Sect. XVII, **2**, 555 (1956); CA **51**, 12392 (1957).

Palladium chloride is used as the reagent for the determination of carbon monoxide. Techniques are presented for preparing test papers for the determination.

101—METHODS FOR DETECTING AND DETERMINING CARBON MONOXIDE

Beatty, R. L. U. S. Dept. of the Interior, Bureau of Mines, Bulletin 557, 34 pp. (1955); revision of Technical Paper 582 by Berger, L. B. and H. H. Schrenk (1938) (see above).

This article describes many of the existing methods which can be used for the determination of carbon monoxide. 1) The NBS colorimetric carbon monoxide indicator in a sensitive, hand-operated device for rapid detection and determination of low, concentrations of carbon monoxide in air. It is sensitive to 0.001 per cent carbon monoxide and will detect 0.01 to 0.04 per cent at ground level. The indicator is operated by squeezing a rubber bulb to aspirate the air sample through a small glass tube, which contains silica gel impregnated with palladous sulfate and ammonium molybdate. The color change of the indicating gel, from light yellow to progressively darker green, depends on the carbon monoxide concentration and the volume of air drawn through the indicator tube. By matching the test color obtained with a series of permanent color standards the carbon monoxide concentration in the sampled air may be determined. 2) The pyrotannic acid colorimetric method may be used to determine the carboxyhemoglobin saturation in samples of blood and the concentration of carbon monoxide in air by using blood reagent solutions that have been equilibrated with air samples. In analyzing air samples, the method is particularly applicable in the concentration range from 0.01 to 0.20 per cent by volume. 3) The iodine pentoxide method is the standard laboratory procedure for the sensitive, accurate, chemical determination of carbon monoxide in air and in various gaseous mixtures. The method is based upon measurement of the iodine liberated by the oxidation of carbon monoxide by heated iodine pentoxide. The reagents and procedure are discussed in detail. The analytical range of the procedure is from 0.0005 per cent up to about 1.0 per cent carbon monoxide, by volume. Low concentrations of carbon monoxide in air may be determined by the palladous chloride-phosphomolybdic acid-acetone colorimetric method. The range of the method is 0.002 per cent to 0.06 per cent carbon monoxide, and higher concentrations may be determined by measured dilution in the original air sample.
Add. Ref.: CA **50**, 3157 (1956).

102—THE COMPOSITION, METHOD, AND APPARATUS FOR DETECTING CARBON MONOXIDE

Darby, William C. U. S. (Pat. No.) 2,738,257, March 13, 1956; CA **51**. 16012 (1957).

A photoelectric device for the detection of carbon monoxide is described. The detector employs a reagent consisting of a palladium halide and sodium alizarin-sulfonate. The material consists of a regenerative gel. A regenerative or accumulative gel becomes darker depending on exposure time and the concentration of carbon monoxide. A nonaccumulative gel reaches a maximum darkness for a given concentration of carbon monoxide and depends primarily on the concentration. The method for the preparation of the gels is described.

103—A REAGENT FOR ESTABLISHING THE PRESENCE OF CARBON MONOXIDE IN THE AIR. THE SILVER COMPOUND OF p-SULFAMOYLBENZOIC ACID

Ciuhandu, Gheorghe. Acad. rep. populare Romine, Studii cercetari chim. **4**, 189-199 (1956); CA **51**, 9981 (1957).

Carbon monoxide can be determined utilizing an alkaline solution of the silver salt p-sulfamoylbenzoic acid. The reagent produces a yellow to dark-brown color which is due to the formation of stable, filterable silver sols. The presence of hydrogen, acetylene, ethylene, and sulfur dioxide do not interefere with the reaction, but hydrogen sulfide must be removed from the sample before testing. Other reducing agents cause only a gray color caused by silver suspensions instead of the intense color of the sol. The indicator solution is prepared by mixing 1 volume of 0.1 M sodium p-sulfamoylbenzoate, 1 volume of 0.1 M silver nitrate, and 0.5 volume of 1 M sodium hydroxide. Carbon monoxide concentrations for the order of 0.0001% may be determined by this method. The time required for the appearance of the yellow color is used as a relative measure of concentration.

104—SAMPLING AND ANALYZING AIR FOR CONTAMINANTS IN WORK PLACES

Silverman, Leslie. "Encyclopedia of Instrumentation for Industrial Hygiene," pp. 7-25 (Univ. of Michigan, Inst. of Industrial Health, Ann Arbor, Mich., 1956).

Impregnated granules of inert material are used for the determination of carbon monoxide, and test papers are used for detection of the gas.

105—THE DETERMINATION OF CARBON MONOXIDE IN THE AIR

Ragno, A. and C. Siniramed. Riv. combustibili **11**, 178-194 (1957); CA **51**, 11174 (1957).

A review with thirty references.

106—COMPOSITIONS FOR DETECTING CARBON MONOXIDE

Auergesellschaft Akt.-Ges. (by Walker Lemcke). Ger. (Pat. No.) 1,019,106, Nov. 7, 1957 (Cl. 42 1); CA **54**, 24135 (1960).

A reagent for use in indicator tubes for the detection of carbon monoxide is prepared by impregnating silica gel first with iodic acid then impregnating the silica gel further with a solution of free iodine added to a solution of iodine pentoxide in sulfuric acid.

107—AN INDICATOR METHOD FOR THE DETECTION OF CARBON MONOXIDE

Skala, Jiri. Protipoz. Tech. **5**, No. 9, 165 (1957); CA **54**, 25426 (1960).

A brief description is given of Czech. (Pat. No.) 79,691. Carbon dioxide is removed from air to be analyzed by passing through sodium hydroxide or soda-lime. The air is then passed through a catalyst bed, such as hopcalite, in which the carbon monoxide is oxidized to carbon dioxide, and the carbon dioxide formed is detected by indicators (e.g., phenol red or methyl red) deposited on silica gel. The apparatus is portable and permits rapid detection of 0.2 to 5% by volume of carbon monoxide or carbon dioxide in air. From Referat. Zhur., Khim. **1958**, Abstr. No. 28463.

108—M.S.A. PYROTANNIC DETECTOR

Mine Safety Appliances Co. Catalog of Industrial Safety Equipment, Catalog 7-B, Sect. 3, p. 10 (1957). A kit, based on the work of Sayers, Yant, and Jones (see above) is designed to determine carbon monoxide in blood and air.

109—M.S.A. CARBON MONOXIDE DETECTOR AMPOULE

Mine Safety Appliances Co. Catalog of Industrial Safety Equipment, Catalog 7-B, Sect. 3, p. 7 (1957). The Carbon Monoxide Detector Ampoule, based on Davenport's technique, provides a simple means of determining the presence of carbon monoxide in the air. The glass vial containing the active reagent is broken, wetting the cotton batting around the vial; the white cotton turns gray when exposed to an atmosphere contaminated with carbon monoxide. The concentration is determined by comparing the gray color on the cotton with the tints on a standard color chart card. These are labeled: Safe, Caution, Extreme Caution, and Keep Out.

110—M.S.A. COLORIMETRIC CARBON MONOXIDE TESTER

Mine Safety Appliances Co. Catalog of Industrial Safety Equipment, Catalog 7-B, Sect. 3, p. 6 (1957); Bull. No. BY-2 (1959).

The tester design is based on the original Bureau of Stand-ards method of detecting carbon monoxide. Pure anhydrous silica gel precedes the test gel to remove most interfering substances. Carbon monoxide turns the yellow test gel to green; the intensity of the green color is proportional to the concentration of carbon monoxide in the air sample. A specially adapted pump with a calibration on the barrel is sold with the instrument, and the tubes are stable for prolonged periods. The manufacturer gives the sensitivity as 0.001 to 0.10% carbon monoxide.

111—M.S.A. CARBON MONOXIDE DETECTOR

Ibid., p. 7

This is a self-contained unit sensitive to 0.1 to 1% carbon monoxide. Air is forced through silica gel, then into activated iodine pentoxide which is changed by carbon monoxide from gray-white to shades of green. The intensity of the green color is proportional to the concentration of the carbon monoxide in the air sample. The green color fades after a few minutes, so that the same tube may be used for a number of tests.

112—PHOTOMETRIC DETERMINATION OF CARBON MONOXIDE IN THE AIR

Ciuhandu, Gheorghe. Z. anal. Chem. **155**, 321-327 (1957); CA **51**, 14485 (1957).

The determination of 0.001 to 0.5% carbon monoxide in the air can be done by the previously described method (see above).

113—DETERMINATION OF CARBON MONOXIDE IN AIR BY MEANS OF INDICATOR TUBES

Mokhov, L. A. and A. V. Demidov. Lab. Delo. **3**, (1) 48-50 (1957); AA **4**, 3143 (1957).

A method for the preparation of indicator tubes for the determination of carbon monoxide is presented. Palladium sulfate stabilized with ammonium sulfate, and ammonium molybdate is applied to silica gel. Air is aspirated through the tube at a rate of 50 ml in 30 seconds. The color produced is compared with a series of standards to determine the concentration. The range of detection is 0.005 to 1 mg carbon monoxide per liter. Add. Ref.: CA **52**, 6057 (1958).

114—FIELD TYPE COLORIMETRIC TESTERS FOR GASES AND PARTICULATE MATTER

McConnaughey, Paul W. Presented before the annual meeting of the Am. Ind. Hyg. Assoc., Atlantic City, N. J. (1958).

The carbon monoxide detector tube developed by the Bureau of Standards uses impregnated silica gel, with palladium molybdate the active reagent which turns from yellow to green to blue. The tubes are incorporated into a new field kit for the determination of alveolar air carbon monoxide concentration. The kit also may be used for the determination of carbon monoxide hemoglobin saturation.

115—DETERMINATION OF CARBON MONOXIDE IN AIR

Del Vecchio, V. Minerva med. **1958**, 1028-1048; CA **52**, 12286 (1958).

The author presents a thorough description of the Draeger detector along with instructions for its use under a variety of conditions. Several other techniques used for the determination of carbon monoxide in air are also discussed.

116—CARBON MONOXIDE DETERMINATION IN EXPIRED AIR AS A PRACTICAL METHOD OF DIAGNOSIS OF ACUTE CARBON MONOXIDE INTOXICATION

Parmeggiani, L., S. Cambruzzi, and G. Colombo. Med. lavoro (Milan) **49**, 428-441 (1958); APCA Abstracts **V**, No. 7, 2803 (1959).

Several methods for the determination of carbon monoxide in expired air were investigated. The containers found to be most suitable for the collection and storage of expired air samples were found to be rubber footballs covered with plastic. The simplest and most reliable sampling technique consisted in collecting the last fractions of expired air, without effort, through a filter. Iodine pentoxide indicator ampoules gave a false positive carbon monoxide reaction in a range of 0.5% in the presence of ethanol vapors, 0.2% with acetone vapors, and 0.1% with benzol vapors. Metabolic products from ethanol excreted through the lungs within 2 hours from time of ingestion can interfere more markedly with the colorimetric reaction.

117—REPORT ON THE DRAEGER GAS DETECTOR. CARBON MONOXIDE

Transactions of the Twenty-First Annual Meeting of the Am. Conf. of Gov. Ind. Hyg., pp. 125-127 (1959).

Two types of Draeger carbon monoxide tubes are available. One tube is used for the 10-3000 ppm range the other for 5000 to 100,000 ppm.Data indicates that the tubes show higher than true values for concentrations below 100 ppm and less than the true value for concentrations above 200 ppm.

118—NOTES ON INTERFERENCES BY OXIDES OF NITROGEN WITH ESTIMATIONS OF CARBON MONOXIDE IN AIR BY THE NBS INDICATING TUBES

Ayer, Howard E. and Bernard E. Saltzman. Am. Ind. Hyg. Assoc. J. **20**, 337-339 (1959).

The interference of nitrogen dioxide and nitric oxide with determinations of carbon monoxide by the NBS indicating tube was investigated. Both compounds were found to interfere, the nitrogen dioxide interference being the most serious. The use of a U tube containing solid potassium permanganate in the upstream leg and Ascarite in the downstream leg will eliminate the nitrogen dioxide interference and greatly reduce the nitric oxide interference. The U tube is flushed with sample air and connected to the front of the indicator tube and carbon monoxide deter-

mined in the usual manner. No interference may be expected from concentrations of nitrogen oxides up to 15% of that of carbon monoxide. Add. Ref.: IHD **23**, 1059 (1959).

119—BLEACHING EFFECT OF NITROGEN DIOXIDE ON CARBON MONOXIDE INDICATOR TUBES

Horn, Wm. A. and E. L. Geiger. Reynolds Electrical and Engineering Co., Inc. Research Report (Nov. 1, 1959).

The Draeger and the M. S. A. carbon monoxide detectors were compared to determine the effect of nitrogen dioxide on the carbon monoxide determination. The Draeger indicating gels were not significantly affected by nitrogen dioxide; the M. S. A. tubes showed a bleaching approximately equal to the nitrogen dioxide concentration. At 0.1 mg nitrogen dioxide per liter this represented a 60% bleaching effect. The carbon monoxide concentrations studied ranged from 100 to 1000 ppm; the nitrogen oxides varied from 0.01 to 0.5 mg per liter.

120—COMPARISON OF CARBON MONOXIDE DETECTORS HAVING DIFFERENT COLORIMETRIC PRINCIPLES UNDER UNDERGROUND CONDITIONS

Greig, J. P. J. Mine Ventilation Soc. S. Africa, Apr. **1957**, 77-85; CA **54**, 20358 (1960).

The author tested the effectiveness of 3 different types of chemical carbon monoxide detectors under a varying range of temperature, pressure, and humidity. All 3 were effective unless interfering gases were present. More than 0.003% of nitrous fumes seriously affected indicator gels depending on the yellow silicomolybdate complex; the gels depending on iodine pentoxide and palladosulfite were less affected by the fumes. Add. Ref.: Fuel Abstr. **22**, Abstr. No. 6031 (1957).

121—NOTES ON INTERFERENCES BY OXIDES OF NITROGEN WITH ESTIMATIONS OF CARBON MONOXIDE IN AIR BY THE NBS INDICATING TUBES

Ayer, Howard E. and Saltzman, Bernard E. Am. Ind. Hyg. Assoc. J. **20**, 337-339 (1959).

The authors, investigating interferences by nitrogen dioxide and nitric oxide in carbon monoxide estimations by the NBS indicating tube, found that both oxides interfere seriously, the nitrogen dioxide to a greater extent. They describe a modification to eliminate or reduce the interferences. Add. Ref.: IHD **23**, 1059 (1959).

122—SENSITIVE METHOD FOR DETECTION AND EVALUATION OF CARBON MONOXIDE IN AN ATMOSPHERE

Paulin, Pierre. Bull. soc. chim. France (Paris) **1959**, 1845-1849.

Dissolve in a little water 2 g of monobasic potassium phosphate, 0.1 g of dibasic sodium phosphate, and 0.1 g of arsenous oxide. Boil the solution for 5 minutes, cool, and diluted to 100 ml. This solution does not keep. Immerse a strip of O. S. I. filter paper in this freshly-prepared solution and dry in the air. (The impregnated filter paper keeps less than a month). Prepare a 2% acid (pH 1.0) solution of auric chloride. (This keeps well in a glass-stoppered bottle; do not use a rubber or plastic stopper). Just before use, add to the impregnated dry paper a small drop of the gold chloride, which will make a pale yellow stain with a narrow, colorless border. Detect carbon monoxide by measuring the time needed to form a black circle on the paper. In the absence of carbon monoxide, a gray, slowly blackening, ring eventually appears; carbon monoxide quickly causes a deep black ring. The size and blackness of the ring are proportional to the quantity of carbon monoxide, while the time for the appearance of the black ring on the paper is inversely proportional to the cube root of the carbon monoxide concentration. The reaction rate is a linear function of the temperature. The method, though unsuited to quantitative determination, is sensitive to 1 part carbon monoxide in 10,000 parts of air. Hydrogen sulfide, arsine, acetylene, aniline, and mercury vapor interfere by staining the reagent paper, sulfur dioxide by turning the entire test spot gray, and acetone and acid vapors by delaying or preventing the stain. Interference from these more slowly diffusible gases may be minimized by placing the test paper between two sheets of glass, or by passing the air sample through activated charcoal. Add. Refs.: CA **54**, 25425 (1960); A.P.C.A. Abstracts **8**, No. 5, 4743 (1962).

123—REACTIVE MASS FOR CARBON MONOXIDE-DETECTING TUBES

Leers, Rainer. Ger. (East) (Pat. No.) 16,885, May 11, 1959 (Cl. 42.**1**); CA **54**, 17991 (1960).

A homogeneous mixture is prepared from silica gel, sulfur trioxide, and iodine pentoxide. In an example, an amount of iodic acid corresponding to 15 g of iodine pentoxide was dissolved in 1500 ml of distilled water, and 1 kg. dry, active silica gel of grain size 0.5 to 0.75 mm soaked with this solution. By subsequent drying of the mass for several hours, iodic acid was transformed to iodine pentoxide. Then 800 g of oleum containing 60 to 65 g of free sulfur trioxide was added, and the mass was mixed thoroughly. Tubes filled with this product indicated by a distinct green color the presence of carbon monoxide, when 100 ml of air containing 0.001% carbon monoxide was sucked through.

124—CARBON MONOXIDE INDICATOR

Bangsgaard, Asger Holm. Ger. (Pat. No.) 1,113,596 (Cl. 42.**1**), appl. Sept. 4, 1959; Dan. Sept. 4, 1958; CA **56**, 3778 (1962).

A carbon monoxide indicator is prepared by treating silica gel with a 1% aqueous palladium chloride solution and, after drying, with a 0.5% cupric chloride or ammonium nitrate solution. The yellow products is pasted on yellow cardboard; air with 0.01% carbon monoxide turns it black during 15 minutes. The original color can be regenerated by exposing the card to atmospheric oxygen.

125—REAGENT AND INDICATOR IN TEST TUBES FOR DETECTION AND DETERMINATION OF CARBON MONOXIDE IN AIR AND IN OTHER GASES

Auergesellschaft G.m.b.H. (by Herman Heidrich). Ger. (Pat. No.) 1,120,768 (Cl. 42.**1**), Dec. 28, 1961, Appl. July 22, 1960; CA **56**, 10921 (1962).

Estimate carbon monoxide in air, 0.0005 to 0.3% by volume or more, by passing the sample through a small tube filled with a mixture of 2 silica gels. Both contain iodine pentoxide and oleum, but one gel was shaken with dry iodine pentoxide and the other with aqueous iodine pentoxide and dried; both then were mixed with 65% oleum containing iodine pentoxide. Carbon monoxide forms a well-defined dark green zone.

126—NEW SIMPLE CARBON MONOXIDE DETECTOR

Bangsgaard, A. and J. B. Dalgaard. Acta. Pathol. Microbiol. Scand. (Copenhagen) Suppl. **154**, 357-358 (1962).

A device for the detection of carbon monoxide is based on the reduction of palladium chloride to black metallic palladium by the gas, the black residue acting as a visual indicator. The detector base is a 5 x 5 cm yellow plastic plate with a disk-like depression filled with a palladium chloride-impregnated hydrophilic gel the same color as the plate. 0.01% of carbon monoxide will turn the insert gray to black in 15 minutes, 0.02% almost immediately. The plate regenerates itself after several hours and may be reused several times, but hydrogen sulfide will blacken it irreversibly. Ammonia, hydrogen chloride, and nitrous gases interfere somewhat in high concentrations, but gasoline and sulfur dioxide fumes do not interfere. In a modification a detachable button contains the reagent, and the whole unit comes in a sealed plastic bag, so that the reagent life, about 4 weeks outside the bag, is about 1 year in the sealed container.

127—POTASSIUM PALLADO SULFITE METHOD FOR CARBON MONOXIDE DETECTION

Silverman, L., G. R. Gardner, AIHAJ. 26(2) 97-105 (1965).

An improved palladium type method for carbon monoxide analysis is described by the authors. The reagent consists of silica gel impregnated with potassium pallado sulfite.
See Section One
For References 6, 25, 29, 35, 46, 69, 71, 81, 104, 119, 125.

Chlorinated Hydrocarbons

1—TESTING FOR HYDROGEN CHLORIDE, ACID CHLORIDES AND CHLORINE-CONTAINING ORGANIC COMPOUNDS IN AIR.

Anger, Vincenz. Ger. (Pat. No.) 733,761, March 4, 1943 (Cl. 421.4.06); CA **38**, 934 (1944).

The air sample is aspirated through a chromium trioxide sulfuric acid mixture maintained at 160-170°C. The resulting vapor is tested for chromyl chloride. This is accomplished by aspirating the gas through a water-alcohol solution of diphenylcarbazide or diphenylcarbazone or over a filter paper saturated with one of these solutions.

2—AN APPARATUS FOR THE DETECTION AND ESTIMATION OF CHLORINATED HYDROCARBON VAPORS IN AIR

Timmis, L. B. J. Soc. Chem. Ind. **63**, 380-382 (1944); CA **39**, 1786 (1945).

A test paper is attached to the front of a glass tube containing a centrally located filament which can be heated. The sample is passed over the heated filament to decompose the chlorinated hydrocarbon into products which yield a color on the test paper.

Chlorine

1—SIMPLE METHODS FOR THE DETERMINATION OF GASEOUS IMPURITIES IN THE AIR OF FACTORIES

Hahn, Martin. Gesundh. Ing. **31**, 693-697 (1910); CA **4**, 1074 (1910).

The author describes the determination of free chlorine which depends on noting the quantity of air required to decolorize a 0.25000 N iodine solution colored with starch.

2—NEW REAGENT FOR FREE AND COMBINED CHLORINE AND BROMINE

Deniges, G. and L. Chelle. Compt. rend. **155**, 1010-1012 (1913); CA **7**, 746 (1913).

A reagent for the detection of free and combined chlorine and bromine is described. The reagent is prepared by mixing 10 cc of a 1:1000 basic fuchsin solution with 100 cc of a 1:20 sulfuric acid solution. In order to carry out the determination 25 cc of the reagent plus 25 cc of acetic acid and 1 cc of sulfuric acid. One drop to several cc of sample is added. In the presence of chlorine a yellow color is produced while bromine produces a red-violet color. The limit of detection is 0.05 mg chlorine and 0.0005 mg bromine.

3—o-TOLIDINE AS A REAGENT FOR THE COLORIMETRIC ESTIMATION OF SMALL QUANTITIES OF FREE CHLORINE

Ellms, J. W. and Hauser, S. J. J. Ind. Eng. Chem. **5**, 915-917 (1914).

The o-tolidine reagent is not satisfactory for the determination of small quantities of free chlorine because of the influence of the normal alkalinity of the water. The alkalinity makes the colors produced unstable. The use of a 0.1% solution of o-tolidine in 10% hydrochloric acid solves this problem and colors are sufficiently stable for matching with color standards. The color standards should be prepared from copper sulfate and potassium dichromate. The limit of detection is 0.005 ppm free chlorine.

4—FREE CHLORINE IN AIR. A COLORIMERIC METHOD FOR ITS ESTIMATION

Porter, Lyman E. Ind. Eng. Chem. **18**, 730-731 (1926).

A rapid method for estimating free chlorine in air uses a reagent of 1 g of o-tolidine dissolved in 100 cc of concentrated hydrochloric acid and diluted to 1 liter. Pass a measured volume of the air to be tested through 10 cc of the reagent in an absorption tube. Transfer quantitatively to a Nessler tube, dilute to mark, let stand 2 minutes, then compare the color with those in a set of permanent standards made from copper sulfate and potassium dichromate solutions. Add. Ref.: CA **20**, 2800 (1926).

5—NEW INDICATOR FOR CHLORINE

Alfthan, Knut and Alec C. Jarvis. J. Am. Water Works Assoc. **20**, 407-411 (1928); CA **22**, 4681 (1928).

The authors after considering known methods for the determination of chlorine, describe, what is in their opinion, a better method. The dimethyl-p-phenylenediamine hydrochloride method described yields a bright red color with chlorine. The sensitivity of the method is 0.01 mg in 100 cc of water. There are, however, certain disadvantages: 1 The reagent is sensitive to iron in concentrations greater than 0.1 mg per liter and 2 the pH must be kept between 2.6 and 3.4. The technique has the advantage of being rapid and sensitive.

6—DETERMINATION AND COLLECTION OF GASES

Kolobaev, N. Khim. Oborona **10**, No. 11, 12-13 (1934); Chem. Zentr. **1935 I**, 2631; CA **30**, 5463 (1936).

Various types of apparatus for the detection of war gases are described. The Prokofjew apparatus can be used for the detection of chlorine and phosgene when both are present in the sample. The air is passed first over fluorescein paper, then through chemical chlorine absorbents and activated carbon, and finally over filter paper previously treated with gaseous dimethylaminobenzaldehyde and diphenylamine for the detection of phosgene. A Boguzkij gas collecting apparatus is recommended and a description of the apparatus is presented. A larger portable combined apparatus for gas determinations on the field contains reagents for the detection of chlorine, carbon monoxide, hydrogen cyanide, phosgene, yperite and arsine. This apparatus can be used for the detection of the above gases in both soil and water.

7—DETECTION OF CHLORINE AND BROMINE IN AIR, GAS MIXTURES AND SOLUTIONS BY THE FORMATION OF IRIS BLUE

Eichler, Hermann. Z. anal. Chem. **99**, 272-275 (1934); CA **29**, 1359 (1935).

Resorufin produces an intense yellow-red fluorescence in the presence of alkali carbonates and reacts with bromine to produce tetrabromoresorufin. The disappearance of the fluorescence of the resorufin can be used for the determination of chlorine or bromine.

8—THE DETECTION OF TOXIC GASES AND VAPORS

Leroux, Lucien. Rev. hyg. et med. prevent. **57**, 81-112 (1935).

Three papers, described for the detection of chlorine, are applicable also to bromine. Nitrous fumes interfere with all three. (1) Starch-iodide paper: filter paper impregnated with starch paste and a solution of zinc chloride and potassium is first dried, then moistened with ammonium thiocyanate. In the presence of chlorine the paper turns blue, with a sensitivity of 1 part per 450,000. The test paper should be stored in a closed container protected from light. (2) Fluorescein paper: filter papers are impregnated with a solution containing 0.2 g fluorescein, 30 g potassium bromide, 2 g potassium hydroxide, and 2 g potassium carbonate in 100 ml of water. Chlorine turns the filter paper rose-color, with a sensitivity of 1 part per 100,000. (3) Ortho-tolidine paper: on a water bath dissolve 0.10 g o-tolidine in a mixture of 10 ml hydrochloric acid and 40 ml of water. Dilute to 100 ml with water. Chlorine colors this test paper yellow. The sensitivity is 1 part per 500,000. Add. Ref.: CA **29**, 3627 (1935).

9—SIMPLE METHODS FOR THE DETECTION AND DETERMINATION OF POISONOUS GASES, VAPORS, SMOKES, AND DUSTS IN FACTORY AIR

Weber, Hans H. Zentr. Gewerbehyg. Unfallverhuet. **23**, 177-180 (1936).

Starch iodide paper is used to test for chlorine according to the technique of Smolczyk and Cobler (Gasmaske **2**, 27 (1930)). The paper turns blue immediately with 0.143 mg chlorine per liter; in from 3 to 5 seconds with 1/10 that amount; and light blue in 10 seconds with 1/100 as much. The latter concentration (0.00143 mg per liter) is no longer detectable by odor. W. Deckert (Z. Hyg. **109**, 485 (1928/1929)) exposes filter paper strips moistened with a 5% to 10% solution of dimethylaniline in benzol to the suspected atmosphere; chlorine turns the paper reddish yellow to orange-brown (bromine gives orange-brown to red-orange and nitrogen gases give sea green to olive green). Add. Ref.: CA **32**, 1609 (1938).

10—THE USE OF INDICATORS FOR THE DETECTION OF POISONOUS GASES AND VAPORS

Heering, D. Gasmaske **8**, 88-89 (1936).

Starch-iodide paper turns blue in 3 to 5 seconds in air containing 0.0143 mg per liter of chlorine, and light blue in 10 to 30 seconds in concentrations of chlorine as low as 0.00143 mg per liter. Add. Ref.: CA **30**, 7059 (1936).

11—MODERN METHODS OF DETECTION AND DETERMINATION OF INDUSTRIAL GASES IN THE ATMOSPHERE

Leclerc, E. and R. Haux. Rev. universelle mines **12**, 293-298 (1936).

Starch iodide paper turns blue with chlorine, and is sensitive to 1 part per 150,000 by volume. Chlorine colors fluorescein test paper rose; the paper is sensitive to 1 part per 100,000. The author refers to Leroux' previous article in Revue d'hygiene et de med prevent. **57**, 81-112 (1935) (see above). Add. Ref.: CA **30**, 6672 (1936).

12—SOME METHODS FOR THE DETECTION AND ESTIMATION OF POISONOUS GASES AND VAPORS IN THE AIR. (A PRACTICAL MANUAL FOR THE INDUSTRIAL HYGIENIST)

Zhitkova, A. S., translated by J. B. Ficklen. (Service to Industry, Box 133, West Hartford, Conn., 1936) pp. 75-81.

Filter paper strips are moistened with a mixture (2 g potassium carbonate in 50 ml water; 0.5 g fluorescein and 30 g potassium bromide in 50 ml water; mix; add 20 ml glycerin) and dried. The yellow, dried strips turn red in the presence of chlorine. Chlorine turns starch-iodide paper blue, but the reaction is not specific for chlorine.

13—SHORT SCHEME OF ANALYSIS FOR THE DETECTION OF POISON GASES

Studinger, J. (With Notes on Their Odour and Irritant Action by R. Mueller). Chem. & Ind. (London) **15**, 225-231 (1937). Translated by F. G. Crosse from the original article in Mitteilungen aus dem Gebiete der Lebensmitteluntersuchung und Hygiene **27**, 8-23 (1936) (see CA **31**, 6367 (1937)).

Chlorine is detected in the presence of nitric oxide with the following reagents: soluble starch (1 g) dissolved in 100 cc of water, and containing cadmium iodide 5 g, and sodium acetate 5 g. Filter-paper is moistened with this mixed solution and held in the suspected atmosphere. A blue coloration is due to separated iodine. Nitric oxide reacts only after addition of a drop of strong acid to the paper. Chlorine also may be detected with o-tolidine. Dissolve 0.1 g o-tolidine in 100 ml of 10% hydrochloric acid. In the presence of chlorine, filter paper moistened with this solution turns yellow. Add. Ref.: CA **31**, 3588 (1937).

14—NEW REAGENT FOR CHLORINE AND OXIDIZING AGENTS

Noriega del Aguila, M. Prim. congr. peruano quim. (Actas y trab). **1938**. 999-1000; Chim. & ind. (Paris) **43**, 469 (1940); CA **34**, 4355 (1940).

The detection of chlorine, bromine, or oxides of nitrogen in air can be accomplished by aspiration through a solution of pyramidone acidified with acetic acid. Another technique which can be used for the determination of these gases is to impregnate filter paper with the same reagent. In the presence of these gases a violet-red coloration occurs. This method is less sensitive than the starch-iodide technique.

15—CHEMICAL DETECTORS FOR POISON GASES

Noriega del Aguila, M. Prim. congr. peruano quim. Actas y trab.) **1938**, 1001-1005; Chim. & ind. (Paris) **43**, 470 (1940); CA **34**, 4179 (1940).

Poison gases can be classified into groups according to whether they contain chlorine, chlorine and sulfur, chlorine and nitrogen, chlorine and arsenic or a metal. This is done by utilizing tests for halogen, nitrogen, sulfur and Pringsheim's test.

16—A METHOD FOR THE RAPID AND ACCURATE DETERMINATION OF SMALL CONCENTRATIONS OF CHLORINE IN AIR

Mal'chevskii, A. N. Hig. i Sanitariya 1938, No. 11-12, 37-43, Khim. Referat. Zhur. **2**, No. 4, 74-75 (1939); CA **34**, 1273 (1940).

The author presents a method for the determination of chlorine in air. The sample is aspirated through a solution containing potassium iodide, starch, and a standardized solution of arsenic trioxide or sodium thiosulfate. The amount of chlorine is determined from the volume of air which it is necessary to pass through the absorber to give a blue color to the starch.

17—COLOR TESTS FOR CHLORINE, OZONE AND HYPOCHLORITES WITH METHANE BASE

Masterman, A. T. Analyst **64**, 492-499 (1939); CA **33**, 6750 (1939).

Methylene base i.e., 4,4'-tetramethyldiaminodiphenylmethane can be used for the determination of chlorine etc. It dissolves readily in ethyl alcohol, carbon tetrachloride or methyl acetate. The addition of chlorine gives the colors, blue, grass-green, olive-green, orange, yellow and finally complete bleaching.

18—TESTS AVAILABLE FOR THE IDENTIFICATION OF SMALL QUANTITIES OF THE WAR GASES

Cox, H. E. Analyst **64**, 807-813 (1939).

The two reagents which the author mentions for chlorine testing are o-tolidine and aniline acetate. Paper impregnated with the latter turns blue in the presence of chlorine. Add. Ref.: CA **34**, 541 (1940).

19—METHODS FOR THE DETECTION OF TOXIC GASES IN INDUSTRY. CHLORINE

Anon. Dept. of Sci. and Ind. Research, London, Engl. Leaflet No. 10, 6 pp. (1939, reprinted 1947).

Contaminated air is drawn with a hand pump of definite capacity through a bubbler into a reagent consisting of 1 g specially purified o-tolidine dissolved in 100 ml concentrated hydrochloric acid and diluted to 1 liter with distilled water. The reagent is stable for 6 months. Sampling is continued until a definite color is established. The sample color then is compared with those of standard solutions prepared with accurate dilutions of potassium dichromate in tubes of exactly the same bore as that of the bubbler. A maximum sensitivity of 1 ppm is possible with 25 strokes, or when 3.15 liters of air passes through 10 ml of the reagent. Add. Refs.: J 298; IHD **20**, 1062 (1956); CA **34**, 1934 (1940).

20—USE OF SPOT TESTS FOR THE EXAMINATION OF PHARMACEUTICALS. IX. DETECTION OF FREE CHLORINE AND SUBSTANCES CONTAINING CHLORINE

Frehden, O. and Chen-Hua Huang. Mikrochemie **26**, 41-43 (1939); CA **33**, 3526 (1939).

A test paper is prepared by moistening filter paper with a solution of 0.1 g fluorescein and 0.5 to 0.8 g potassium bromide in 100 ml of dilute potassium hydroxide. When the resulting pale yellow paper is held over the air to be tested, a violet-red coloration is produced if free chlorine is present. The limit of sensitivity is 4 μg chlorine. Hydrogen peroxide and per salts give a slight coloration after some time. Chlorides treated with manganese dioxide and sulfuric acid will give the test.

21—IDENTIFICATION OF WAR GASES

Liberalli, Marcelo Robertson. Rev. quim. farm. (Rio de Janeiro) **4**, 49-53 (1939).

Chlorine turns starch-iodide paper blue. Other oxidizing vapors interfere, such as ozone, oxides of nitrogen, etc. Paper impregnated with a reagent (100 parts saturated aqueous solution of aniline, 20 parts saturated aqueous solution of aniline, 20 parts saturated aqueous solution of o-tolidine, and 30 parts glacial acetic acid) turns from blue to violet to green in the presence of chlorine. Add. Ref.: CA **33**, 7921 (1939).

22—THE DETECTION OF TOXIC GASES AND VAPORS IN INDUSTRY

Vallender, R. B. Chem. & Ind. (London) **58**, 330-333 (1939).

Air contaminated with chlorine is bubbled through an acid solution of o-tolidine, which turns yellow at any concentration above 1 part per 1 million (using 25 strokes of the pump). Add. Ref.: CA **33**, 4907 (1939).

23—DETECTION OF WAR GASES

Fenton, Paul F. J. Chem. Education **21**, 488-489 (1944).

To a small portion of the silica gel (see Ibid., Section One) add a drop of potassium bromide-fluorescein reagent (0.2 g fluorescein, 30 g potassium bromide, 2 g potassium hydroxide, and 2 g sodium carbonate in 100 ml water). A red color indicates chlorine. Add. Ref.: CA **39**, 135 (1945).

24—IDENTIFICATION OF GAS WARFARE AGENTS

Zais, Arnold M. J. Chem. Education **21**, 489-490 (1944).

A systematic procedure is presented for detecting various war gases. Chlorine, determined by exposing a freshly prepared aniline hydrochloride paper to the suspected atmosphere, forms transitive colors to blue and finally to black. Add. Ref.: CA **39**, 135 (1945).

25—SAMPLING AND DETERMINATION OF CHLORINE IN AIR

Wallach, Abraham and William A. McQuary. Am. Ind. Hyg. Assoc. Quart. **9**, 63-65 (1948).

Chlorine gas can be collected in a fritted bubbler containing 100 ml of 0.0125 to 0.1 N sodium hydroxide. The standard o-tolidine method used in water analysis can be slightly modified for use in determining chlorine in air. The method is 99.9% efficient for concentrations up to 150 ppm at a sampling rate up to 3 liters per minute. Add. Ref.: CA **43**, 7373 (1949).

26—PHOTOCHEMICAL TRANSFORMATION OF CHLOROPICRIN TO PHOSGENE. I. NEW REAGENTS SENSITIVE AND SPECIFIC FOR THESE TWO SUBSTANCES

Moureu, Henri, Paul Chovin, and Louis Truffert. Arch. maladies profess. med. travail et securite sociale **11**, 445-452 (1950); CA **45**, 6495 (1951).

Paper impregnated with o-phenetidine gives an intense red to black color with chlorine and may be used to detect 60 to 70 mg chlorine per cubic meter of air.

27—COLOR TESTS FOR CHLORIDES, BROMIDES, AND IODIDES

Kuznetsov, V. I. Doklady Akad. Nauk. U.S.S.R. **77**, 281-284 (1951); CA **45**, 6967 (1951).

The author describes several tests and results that can be obtained with color tests using organic reagents: 1) 4-(8-hydroxy-5-quinolylazo)benzenesulfonic acid, silver complex at pH 6.5 to 7.0, pink originally, yellow after addition of halide . . . ; 2) mercurous complex in acetic acid solution, red, yellow, (usable to) 1 μg chlorine . . . ; 3) mercuric complex in acetic acid solution, red, yellow, under 0.5 μg chlorine; 4) 2-(8-hydroxy-5-quinolylazo)-5-nitrobenzenesulfonic acid, mercurous complex, orange-red, yellow, -; 5) mercuric complex, same colors, 0.2 μg chlorine . . . ; 6) 5-(8-hydroxy-5-quinolylimino) 8(5H) quinolone, mercuric complex, in acetic acid solution, blue, brown-pink, 0.3 μg chlorine; 7) 3-(8-hydroxy-5-quinolylimino)-6-oxo-1,4-cyclohexadiene-1-carboxylic acid, silver complex in neutral solution, violet, red-orange,-; 8) mercurous complex in acetic acid, red-violet, orange-pink,-; 9) mercuric complex in acetic acid, same colors. The reagents also give color tests with cyanide and thiocyanate ions, as well as with sulfides, thiosulfates, nitrilotriacetates, and some other complex-forming ions. Cations of elements that bind the 8-quinolinol more effectively than silver or mercury also give colors. The colors can be compared with standards and used for estimation of the halides. Mercuric nitrate solution appears to be most satisfactory for conversion of the sodium salts of the reagents into the complexes.

28—APPARATUS FOR DETECTING CHLORINE GAS LEAKS FROM CONTAINERS

Sundstrom, Carl. U. S. (Pat. No.) 2,606,101, Aug. 5, 1952; CA **47**, 8 (1953).

An apparatus is detailed which uses the chlorine-sensitive test strip described below.

29—TEST STRIPS FOR DETECTING LOW-CHLORINE CONCENTRATIONS IN THE AIR

Cook, Daniel A. U. S. (Pat. No.) 2,606,102, Aug. 5, 1952; CA **47**, 8 (1953).

To a solution consisting of 1 to 10 g o-tolidine in 800 to 900 g alcohol add 1 g o-phosphoric acid and 100 to 200 g glycerol. Soak paper strips in this solution and dry in an air stream away from direct light. Coat one-half of each strip with paraffin. When exposed to chlorine gas the sensitized part of the paper strip turns bluish-green in contrast with the almost white, paraffin-coated part.

30—DETERMINATION OF CHLORINE IN THE ATMOSPHERE

Krivoruchko, F. D. Gigiena i Sanit. **1953**, No. 3, 53-54; CA **47**, 9856, (1953).

The determination of chlorine is carried out by aspirating the sample through 2 ml of a 0.000055 N solution of methyl orange containing 0.1 ml of 0.05 N sulfuric acid. The color is compared with a standard scale prepared from known quantities of chlorine.

31—ANALYTICAL PROCEDURES FOR THE DETECTION OF GASES

Guatelli, Manuel A. Rev. asoc. bioquim. arg. **18**, 3-40 (1954).

Chlorine, bubbled through potassium iodide and identified by starch, may be isolated by a chloroform-carbon disulfide extraction. Ortho-tolidine papers, prepared by dipping filter paper strips into a solution of 1 g o-tolidine dissolved in 100 ml hydrochloric acid and diluted to 1 liter with water, turn yellow in the presence of chlorine, with a sensitivity of 1 part per 500,000. Papers impregnated with ammonium iodide and starch paste turn blue with chlorine; the sensitivity is 1 part in 150,000. Other reference papers are prepared by dipping the same type of paper into a di-chromate-copper sulfate solution. Chlorine also can be identified by the Deniges reaction, which utilizes an aniline solution, and by fluorescein-impregnated test papers, which turn rose-color with chlorine and are sensitive to 1 part in 100,000. Add. Ref.: CA **48**, 7124 (1954).

32—CHLORINE-GAS CONCENTRATION IN SOME PLANTS MANUFACTURING ELECTROLYTIC SODIUM HYDROXIDE

Kitagawa, Tetsuzo and Yoshitaka Kobayashi. Japan Analyst **3**, 42-43 (1954); CA **48**, 7460 (1954).

A detector tube consisting of silica gel impregnated with o-tolidine hydrochloride in ethyl alcohol is described for the determination of chlorine.

33—RAPID DETERMINATION OF ACTIVE CHLORINE IN THE PRESENCE OF HYDROGEN CHLORIDE IN THE AT-MOSPHERE OF INDUSTRIAL ESTABLISHMENTS

Litvinova, N. S. and N. Ya Khlopin. Gigiena i Sanit. **1953**, No. 4, 45-46; CA **47**, 11074 (1953).

Rosaniline hydrochloride which is deep red in aqueous solution, undergoes a change from red to yellow to color-less when chlorine is reacted with this reagent. This method is suitable for corolimetric determination by visual compari-son with known samples. With 0.0003 to 0.0005 per cent solutions of the dye, about 2 ml of 0.01 N hydrochloric acid is needed per 100 ml to establish a stable color; fur-ther addition of hydrochloric acid (such as by absorption from air) has no effect on the color.

34—LIMITS OF ALLOWABLE CONCENTRATIONS OF AT-MOSPHERIC POLLUTANTS

Ryazanov, V. A., Editor, translated by B. S. Levine. U. S. Dept. of Commerce, Office of Technical Serv-ices, Washington, D. C., 1955). Book 2, chapter heading, "Determination of Chlorine," reference cited, Krivoruchko, F. D., Gigiena i Sanit. **1953**, No. 3, p. 53 (see above).

Chlorine is absorbed in a standardized methyl orange so-lution. The pink color formed deepens as the chlorine con-tent increases. The absorbing solution is a 1 to 20 dilution of a methyl orange stock solution (0.1 g methyl orange in 80 to 100 ml distilled water; 0.5 g potassium bromide dis-solved in 20 ml alcohol; mix; dilute to 1 liter.) A color com-parator is used with synthetic standards in the range of 0.2 to 3 μg per sample. Micro-bubblers are used for sam-pling.

35—DETERMINATION OF ACTIVE CHLORINE IN AIR

Polezhaev, N. G. Gigiena i Sanit. **1955**, No. 11, 46-47; CA **50**, 6715 (1956).

The sample is absorbed in 1% potassium iodine in 1%

sodium acetate. One drop of 0.03% of aqueous dimethyl-p-phenylenediamine hydrochloride is added to the solu-tion. The color that develops is compared with a standard scale prepared from known solutions of iodine.

36—ESTIMATION OF TOXIC GASES IN AIR. VII. CHLOR-INE DETERMINATION

Fukuyama, Tomitaro, Tokuro Sato, and Aiko Wata-nabe. Bull. Inst. Public Health (Tokyo) **4**, 10-13 (1955); AA **4**, 3470 (1957).

The authors describe a simplified method for the deter-mination of chlorine in air using o-tolidine as the reagent. One ml of 0.1% o-tolidine in 1.75 N hydrochloric acid is mixed with 20 ml of water. The air is bubbled through this solution at a rate of 200 to 500 ml per minute. This mix-ture is incubated at 25° for 5 minutes. The analysis is com-pleted by determining the extinction at 405 mμ or by com-paring the color density with a postassium chromate or di-chromate solution in a phosphate buffer at pH 6.45. This method is applicable for up to 20 ppm of chlorine. From add. ref. CA **50**, 8392 (1956).

37—DETERMINATION OF TOXIC GAS COMPONENTS IN AIR BY THE REICH STOP-METHOD

Kraus, F. Chem. Tech. (Berlin) **7**, 552-555 (1955); CA **50**, 12750 (1956).

The determination of traces of hydrogen sulfide, sulfur di-oxide, chlorine, ammonia, and hydrogen chloride based on the Reich method for the estimation of sulfur dioxide in roast gases is described. The determination involves the ab-sorption of the gases containing sulfur dioxide in an iodine starch solution until decolorization occurs. At this point the gas flow is stopped. Chlorine is determined by a solution containing sodium thiosulfate and potassium iodide, hydro-gen chloride and ammonia by using mixed indicators con-taining methyl red and methylene blue. Ozone is deter-mined by absorption in a 0.01 N solution of arsenous oxide containing dilute potassium iodide and starch.

38—SAMPLING AND ANALYZING AIR FOR CONTAMI-NANTS

Silverman, Leslie. Air Conditioning, Heating, and Ventilating, 88-100 (Aug. 1955).

S. S. No. 598 filter paper, treated with 5% potassium iodide, 0.5% starch solution, glycerin, and sulfurous acid, turns brown to black in the presence of 0.25 to 12. ppm of chlorine. All other halogens interfere.

39—METHODS OF DETERMINING ATMOSPHERIC POL-LUTION

Martin, Maurice. Pollution air et ses mefaits, Conf. soc. pathol. comparee, Paris (1956). 113-121 (Pub. 1957); CA **51**, 13277 (1957).

The determination of chlorine involves bubbling the gas into an o-tolidine solution and comparing the resulting material with standards made from copper sulfate and bichromate.

40—FIELD TYPE COLORIMETRIC TESTERS FOR GASES AND PARTICULATE MATTER

McConnaughey, Paul W. Presented at the annual meeting of the Am. Ind. Hyg. Assoc., Atlantic City, N. J. (1958).

In a detector tube the reaction between chlorine in air and tetraphenylbenzidine impregnated on silica gel, gives a blue stain.

41—RAPID METHOD FOR THE DETERMINATION OF CHLORINE IN THE ATMOSPHERE

Russkikh, A. A. Trudy Khim. i Khim. Tekhnol. **1**, No. 1, 157-161 (1958); CA **54**, 12440 (1960).

The author proposes a rapid method for the determination of chlorine in the atmosphere of industrial plants based on its aspiration through filter papers treated either with fluorescein or benzidine. The fluorescein papers are prepared by soaking filter paper circles approximately 13 mm in diameter in the fluorescein reagent prepared according to Koreman (Indiktsiya Boevykh Otravlyayuschchikh Veshchestv, Gorki, **1942**, p. 7) diluted in 5 parts water. The benzidine filter paper circles are soaked in a saturated solution of benzidine in 30% acetic acid and glycerol is added to the reagents. The porosity of the paper is not affected by this treatment. The fluorescein papers keep well for several weeks in a closed flask; the benzidine papers for several days. The air is aspirated through a circle of reagent paper placed in a special funnel of "organic glass" with a 5 mm opening. The eosin reaction on the fluorescein paper and the benzidine blue on the benzidine paper is produced on an area of only 0.2 sq. cm., which yields a high degree of sensitivity. Between 50 and 400ml is used at the rate of 70 ml per minute; higher rates of aspiration gives losses. Standards are prepared at the same time from air containing a known concentration. Concentrations of standards and sensitivities are given.

42—M.S.A. CHLORINE-IN-AIR DETECTOR

Mine Safety Appliances Co., 201 N. Braddock Avenue, Pittsburgh, Pa. Bull. 0805-2 (1959).

The unit consists of a rubber bulb aspirator, a detector tube holder, and a barrel with calibration curves. Impregnated silica gel in the detector tube turns blue in the presence of chlorine, and is sensitive to 0.5 to 20 ppm. The length of the stain on the impregnated silica gel is a function of the concentration of the chlorine. A total of either 3 or 10 aspirations is used.

43—DETERMINATION OF GASEOUS CHLORINE IN AN INDUSTRIAL ATMOSPHERE

Popa, I. and L. Armasescu. Farmacia (Bucharest) **7**, 499-502 (1959); CA **54**, 14517 (1960).

Chlorine is estimated by utilizing it to oxidize a solution of arsenic trioxide, potassium iodide and starch. The end point of the reaction is recognized by a blue color. Formulae and calculations are given.

44—"WATCHDOG" SYSTEM DETECTS CHLORINE LEAKS AT SEATTLE

Allen, E. J. and Norman R. Angvik. Water Works Engineering **114**, 614-615 (1961).

A continuous sampling apparatus, to detect chlorine leaks in unmanned storage reservoirs in the vicinity of large populations, uses a sensitized paper strip, which darkens if chlorine is present. The lack of reflectance from the paper, caused by the chlorine, sets off an alarm when the chlorine concentration reaches 3 ppm. Add. Ref.: CA **55**, 22677 (1961).

See Section One

For references 6, 15, 25, 29, 33, 35, 41, 52, 54, 48, 64, 81, 88, 95, 96, 109, 119, 125.

Chlorine Dioxide

1—A RAPID METHOD FOR THE DETERMINATION OF CHLORINE DIOXIDE IN LOW CONCENTRATION IN AIR WITH THE AID OF DETECTOR TUBES

Kitagawa, Tetsuzo and Yoshitaka Kobayashi. J. Chem. Soc. Japan, Ind. Chem. Sect. **58**, 177-179 (1955); AA **3**, 404 (1956).

Small quantities of chlorine dioxide in air can be determined by the use of a detector containing o-tolidine. Pure silica gel is digested with an ethanolic solution of o-tolidine containing a small amount of hydrochloric acid, then dried and packed in a glass tube. The sample (100 ml) is passed through this tube and the length of the yellowish zone is measured. The logarithm of the length in millimeters is proportional to the logarithm of the concentration of chlorine dioxide up to 300 ppm. The presence of oxidizing agents such as chlorine, nitrogen dioxide, ozone, bromine, and hydrogen peroxide interferes with the estimation. Add. Refs.: IHD **20**, 135 (1956); CA **49**, 13833 (1955).

Chloroacetone

1—IDENTIFICATION OF WAR GASES

Liberalli, Marcelo Robertson. Rev. quim. farm. (Rio de Janeiro) **4**, 49-53 (1939).

Chloroacetone may be identified with the sodium nitroprusside reaction, in which colored derivatives are formed. Add. Ref.: CA **33**, 7921 (1939).

Chloroacetophenone

1—PROBLEMS OF PASSIVE DEFENSE AGAINST THE DANGER OF CHEMICAL GAS ATTACKS

Harsovescu, C. Antigaz (Bucharest) **9**, No. 9/10, 22-34 (1935); Chem. Zentr. **1936**, I, 4240; CA **31**, 7141 (1937).

The author presents a review of the properties of chloroacetophenone. Methods for prevention of contact of war gases with drink are also discussed.

2—TESTS AVAILABLE FOR THE IDENTIFICATION OF SMALL QUANTITIES OF THE WAR GASES

Cox, H. E. Analyst **64**, 807-813 (1939).

Warm alkaline solutions hydrolize chloroacetophenone, freeing chloride. Air is passed into alcoholic ammonia and if chloroacetophenone is present an indole is formed. The indole can be oxidized to indigo by adding perhydrol or it can be recognized by the red color produced when p-dimethylaminobenzaldehyde is added to the acidified liquid. Add. Ref.: CA **34**, 541 (1940).

See Section One

For references 33, 52, 54, 64, 66.

Chloropicrin

1—THE DETECTION OF TOXIC GASES AND VAPORS

Leroux, Lucien. Rev. hyg. et. med. prevent. **57**, 81-112 (1935).

Chloropicrin vapor is passed through a hot quartz tube containing sodium sulfate. The liberated chlorine colors starch-iodide reagent paper blue. Add. Ref.: CA **29**, 3627 (1935).

2—THE USE OF INDICATORS FOR THE DETECTION OF POISONOUS GASES AND VAPORS

Heering, D. Gasmaske **8**, 88-89 (1936).

Filter papers immersed in a benzene solution of dimethylaniline turn from yellow to brown when exposed to chloropicrin. Add. Ref.: CA **30**, 7059 (1936).

3—CHEMICAL REACTIONS OF WAR GASES

Hennig, H. Gasschutz u. Luftschutz **7**, (1937); CA **31**, 2311 (1937).

Chloropicrin is determined qualitatively by means of test papers saturated with a 5 to 10% solution of dimethylaniline in benzene. Expose the paper to the contaminated atmosphere. The paper changes from white to yellow and finally to maroon in the presence of chloropicrin. Add. Ref.: J 602.

4—COLORIMETRIC PROCEDURE FOR DETERMINING SMALL QUANTITIES OF CHLOROPICRIN IN AIR, WATER AND FOODSTUFFS

Deckert, W. and Butra Prathithavanija. Z. anal. Chem. **113**, 182-189 (1938); CA **32**, 7858 (1938).

The method is based on the colorimetric reaction of chloropicrin with dimethylaniline in the presence of oxygen.

5—DETECTION METHODS OF WAR MATERIALS PROPOSED IN LITERATURE

Dultz, George. Wien. Pharm. Wochschr. **72**, 548-522 (1939); CA **34**, 542 (1940).

The author presents a review dealing with chloropicrin.

6—IDENTIFICATION OF WAR GASES

Liberalli, Marcelo Robertson. Rev. quim. farm. (Rio de Janeiro) **4**, 49-53 (1939).

A paper impregnated with a benzene solution of dimethylaniline turns light yellow to brown with chloropicrin, the intensity of the color depending on the concentration of the gas. Add. Ref.: CA **33**, 7921 (1939).

7—TESTS AVAILABLE FOR THE IDENTIFICATION OF SMALL QUANTITIES OF THE WAR GASES

Cox, H. E. Analyst **64**, 807-813 (1939).

There are several procedures for identifying chloropicrin: 1) By passing the gas through filter paper impregnated with a petroleum spirit solution of Sudan red; the paper turns blood red. 2) By passing the gas into an alcoholic solution of potassium iodide to form potassium nitrite; the nitrite is confirmed with the Griess-Ilosvay reaction. 3) By heating to decompose into chlorine, which gives the Beilstein halogen test. 4) By applying the Guillemard and Labat test with resorcinol. Add. Ref.: Guillemard and Labat, Ann. chim. anal., **2**, II, 120 (1920); CA **34**, 541 (1940).

8—DETECTION OF GASES USED IN WARFARE

Gigon, A. and M. Noverraz. Schweiz. med. Wochschr. **69**, 859-860 (1939); CA **34**, 1589 (1939).

A method is presented for the determination of gases used in chemical warfare. The air is bubbled through a tube containing 2 cc of an alcohol-water solution to which bromophenol blue has been added. The acid reaction of the war gas changes the color of the indicator. The method is a modification of Kling's technique (cf. CA **32**, 8034 (1937)). With chloropicrin as an example, it was found that a concentration which produced a change in color in 1½ minutes would be harmless even after prolonged inspiration of the gas, whereas a concentration which produced a color change in 1 to 2 seconds would be lethal after 10 minutes of respiration.

9—VAPOR DETECTOR TUBES AND DETECTOR KIT FOR SOME CHEMICAL AGENTS USED IN GAS WARFARE

Fenton, Paul F. J. Chem. Education **20**, 564-565 (1943).

After air contaminated with chloropicrin was adsorbed on a 1-2 cm long column of silica gel in a type A tube (2 mm internal diameter) a drop of dimethylaniline turned the silica gel a deep orange. Sodium alcoholate was added to another tube containing chloropicrin on silica gel and the tube heated over a match. Addition of sulfanilamide reagent produced a bright purple color. A special detector tube was constructed, containing silica gel, sulfanilamide powder, and solid N-(1-naphthyl)-ethylenediamine dihydrochloride, separated by small cotton plugs. After addition of a drop or two of sodium alcoholate the contaminated silica gel was heated over a burning match. Several drops of concentrated hydrochloric acid, added so as to flow through the entire tube to the sulfonamide and the substituted diamine, produced a bright purple color in the presence of chloropicrin. Add. Ref.: CA **38**, 898 (1944).

10—DETECTION OF WAR GASES. HYDROCYANIC ACID AND CHLOROPICRIN

Fenton, Paul F. J. Chem. Education **21**, 92 (1944).
Chloropicrin forms a bright yellow-orange color on silica gel impregnated with dimethylaniline in special detector tubes. The tubes usually are stable for a month; if they turn green on standing they must not be used for the test. Add. Ref.: CA **38**, 1811 (1944).

11—DETECTION OF WAR GASES

Fenton, Paul F. J. Chem. Education **21**, 488-489 (1944).
The reagents used in the two tests mentioned are dimethylaniline and sulfanilamide. Chloropicrin is present if a tiny drop of dimethylaniline produces an orange color on a small portion of contaminated silica gel (see ibid., Section One). Five drops of sodium alcoholate are added to another small portion of the silica gel, and ignited with a match. The burning of the alcohol will produce sufficient heat to decompose the chloropicrin and form sodium nitrite. If the nitrite ion is present it will give a purple color with sulfanilamide reagent (0.2 gm sulfanilamide and 0.2 gm N-(1-naphthyl)-ethylene diamine dihydrochloride dissolved in 20 ml of concentrated hydrochloric acid). Add. Ref.: CA **39**, 135 (1945).

12—PHOTOCHEMICAL TRANSFORMATION OF CHLOR-OPICRIN TO PHOSGENE. I. NEW REAGENTS SENSITIVE AND SPECIFIC FOR THESE TWO SUBSTANCES

Moureu, Henri, Paul Chovin, and Louis Truffert.

Arch. maladies profess. med. travail et securite sociale **11**, 445-452 (1950); CA **45**, 6495 (1951).

To test for chloropicrin use filter paper impregnated with a mixture of 10 ml pyridine-methyl alcohol solution containing 33.5 mg per ml cyanide ion as sodium cyanide and 1 ml methyl alcohol containing 20 mg per ml of a phenol. Phloroglucinol, which gives a red-violet color with as little as 50 mg chloropicrin per cubic meter, and m-diethylaminophenol, which gives a blue color, are suitable. Chlorine interferes with this reaction.

13—COLORIMETRIC MICRO - DETERMINATION OF CHLOROPICRIN IN AIR

Fournier, R. M. and M. Person. Chim. Anal. **39**, 263-266 (1957): AA **5**, 275 (1958).

The authors describe two procedures based on the reaction between chloropicrin and either dimedone phloroglucinol in the presence of pyridine and potassium cyanide, followed by the determination of the extinction of the colored product. If dimedone is used, a rose coloration is obtained on heating the solution at 100° for 5 minutes; the sensitivity is 0.4 μg of chloropicrin per ml and one determination can be made in approximately 7 minutes. If phloroglucinol is used, the sensitivity is 2 μg per ml. The color develops immediately and a quantitative result can be obtained in approximately 3 minutes.

14—CONCERNING A NEW DETECTOR FOR CHLORO-PICRIN

Daecke, H. and R. Kraul. Z. anal. Chem. **178**, 412-414 (1961).

Three reagents are used in the test: potassium bromide-potassium cyanide mixture (dissolve 10 g potassium bromide in 40 ml of distilled water, then add 60 ml absolute alcohol; dissolve 10 g potassium bromide in another 40 ml of water, and add 60 ml absolute alcohol; for use mix equal parts of the 2 solutions); pyridine; and 10% aqueous aniline hydrochloride solution. According to the method of detection chosen, these 3 reagents may be mixed in the ratio of 2:1:1, or they may be used consecutively in the same proportions. Air contaminated with chloropicrin is drawn through the reagents in a washbottle. In a few seconds even minute traces of chloropicrin will change the colorless reagents from yellow to deep orange to red. Alternatively, chloropicrin in the air may be detected with filter paper impregnated with drops of the reagent mixture. Tiny traces of chloropicrin will turn the drops yellow to orange, the color deepening as the reagent solvent evaporates. The reagent in this simple technique will detect 0.3 to 0.4 μg of chloropicrin per ml of air. Add. Ref.: CA **55**, 11176 (1961).

See Section One
For references 25, 33, 35, 36, 37, 41, 42, 52, 54, 64, 66.

Chromium

1—STABLE COLORIMETRIC REAGENT FOR CHROMIUM

Ege, J. F., Jr. and Leslie Silverman. Anal. Chem. **19**, 693-694 (1947).

A new reagent for the estimation of the concentration of chromic acid mists in air by a direct field method is prepared by adding 4. g powdered phthalic anhydride to 0.25 g s-diphenylcarbazide in 100 ml of 95% ethyl alcohol. Airborne mists are drawn through dry filter papers previously impregnated with this reagent and a humectant, glycerol. The intensity of the stain color that develops is proportional to the quantity of hexavalent chromium in the air, and is compared with a set of artificial color standards. Add. Ref.: CA **41**, 6835 (1947).

2—A RAPID METHOD FOR THE DETERMINATION OF CHROMIC ACID MIST IN AIR

Silverman, Leslie and John F. Ege, Jr. J. Ind. Hyg. Toxicol. **29**, 136-139 (1947).

A measured volume of air containing chromic acid mist is drawn through a filter paper impregnated with 0.25 s-diphenylcarbazide and 4% phthalic anyhdride in 95% ethyl alcohol. Twenty ml of glycerol are added to 100 ml of this solution as a humestant. Permanent standards may be prepared by impregnating filter paper with a mixture of equal parts of methyl violet 2-B and basic fuchsin. Add. Ref.: CA **41**, 3015 (1947).

3—CHROMIUM COMPOUNDS IN GASEOUS ATMOSPHERES

Silverman, Leslie and John F. Ege, Jr. U. S. (Pat. No.) 2,483,108, Sept. 27, 1949; CA **44**, 490 (1950).

Hexavalent chromium is determined in gases by passing the gas through an absorbent paper which has been previously impregnated with a reagent consisting of 4 g of phthalic anhydride and 0.25 g of s-diphenylcarbazide in 100 ml of 95% ethyl alcohol, plus 20 ml of glycerol. The color that develops is compared with a series of permanent standards that are prepared with methyl violet 2-B and basic fuchsin. Shelf life of the test paper is at least 6 months if properly stored. The color produced is stable for at least 4 hours. The method is particularly adapted to the determination of chromic oxide mists in air.

4—PRESERVATION OF COLOR CHARTS FOR DETERMINATION OF CHROMATES

Odell, Louis E. (to Dearborn Chem. Co.). U. S. (Pat. No.) 2,605,164, July 29, 1952; CA **48**, 506 (1954).

Color charts for the determination of chromate concentrations are prepared by impregnating blotting paper with a solution of benzidine dihydrochloride 1, citric acid 20, corn starch 0.5 and water 250 ml. To prevent the deterioration that interferes with sharp color changes, the charts must be stored in a dry atmosphere, as by sealing in containers with silica gel or by wrapping in wax paper in the presence of a desiccant.

5—M.S.A. SAMPLAIR

Mine Safety Appliances Co. Catalog of Industrial Safety Equipment, Cat. 7-B, Sect. 3, p. 38 (1957). (201 N. Braddock Ave., Pittsburgh, Pa.)

6—A SPOT TEST ANALYSIS OF THE GROUP III CATIONS

Marion, Stephen P. and Isaac Zlochower. J. Chem. Education **36**, 379-380 (1959).

Add a drop or two of 6 M sodium hydroxide to make the test solution alkaline. Cautiously add sodium or hydrogen peroxide, then warm until chromate is formed. Acidify the solution, checking for acidity with litmus paper. Add a drop of 1% diphneylcarbazide in ethanol. A violet color indicates chromium *This test might be used in a field detector.* Add. Ref.: CA **54**, 2093 (1960).

7—M.S.A. CHROMIC ACID MIST DETECTOR

Mine Safety Appliances Co. Bull. 0811-8 (1959).

The M.S.A. Sampler is a lightweight, hand-operated instrument for estimating quickly chromic acid mist concentrations in working atmospheres. Essentially the Samplair is a specially constructed positive displacement hand pump with a filter holder, drawing 500 ml air per stroke. When chromic acid mists in the test atmosphere are drawn through s-diphenylcarbazide - impregnated filter paper, the paper turns a lilac color, which then is compared with the two color standards (1 and 2 mg per 10 cubic meters) attached to the instrument. The shelf life of the paper is approximately 6 months from the date of manufacture.

See Section One

For references 5, 81, 98.

Cobalt Carbonyl

1—NEW TEST FOR DETECTING COBALT CARBONYL TAKES ONLY ABOUT 10 MINUTES

Anon. Oil and Gas J. **60**, No. 24, 109 (1962).

The test method consists of passing air samples through a resin-loaded filter paper. After treatment with an indicator solution and other chemicals, the color of the paper is compared with a standard color.

2—A RAPID FIELD TEST FOR COBALT CARBONYL

Fanney, J. H., Jr. Presented at the American Industrial Health Conference, Washington, D. C. (May 15, 1962).

The method measures the collected cobalt carbonyl compounds at the ppm level. Draw 10 liters of air sample through a resin-impregnated filter (Amberlite ion exchange resin-loaded paper, grade WA-2, 2.5 cm diameter) at a rate of 2.5 liters per minute. Remove the exposed filter disc from its holder and place on a fresh filter backer, exposed side up. Place 2 drops of buffer solution No. 1 in the center of the filter disc, allowing the filter to become saturated and placing another drop on the outer edge of the filter if necessary. Place 2 drops of chelating indicator Solution No. 2 in the center of the filter and allow the color to develop for at least 1 minute, then add 2 or 3 drops of acid Solution No. 3 so as to saturate the filter with the acid. Within 5 minutes compare visually the pink color on the filter disc with that of the permanent standard. If the disc is lighter than the standard, report the concentration of cobalt carbonyl and/or its decomposition products as "less than 0.1 ppm per sample;" if the disc color equals or is darker than that of the standard, report the concentration as "greater than 0.1 ppm." Do not try to interpret the results more quantitatively. Prepare field test Solution No. 1 by dissolving 68.0 g of monobasic potassium phosphate and 16.0 g of sodium hydroxide in distilled water and diluting to 1 liter with water, to make a pH 7.4 phosphate buffer solution. To 100 ml of the buffer add 1.0 g of sucrose, being sure to dissolve the sugar completely. For Solution No. 2 dissolve 253 mg of 2-nitroso-1-naphthol-4-sulfonic acid in 1 liter of distilled water. Store in a dark bottle and replace the solution every 6 months. Solution No. 3 is 2 N nitric acid (12.6 ml of concentrated acid diluted to 100 ml with water). Add. Ref.: Am. Ind. Hyg. Assoc. J. **24**, 245-252 (1963).

Coal Dust

1—THE PHOTOELECTRIC MEASUREMENT OF COAL DUST STAINS ON FILTER PAPER

Davies, C. N. and Mary Aylward. Brit. J. Appl. Phys. **2**, Suppl. 1, 352-359 (1951).

Nine kinds of filter paper for the collection of coal dust stains or deposits from air-borne clouds were studied for their light-screening power. The porosity of the paper was found more important than the fibre diameter, with optical homogeneity of the paper also an essential.

2—TRIALS WITH AN EXPERIMENTAL LONG-PERIOD SAMPLER FOR AIR-BORNE DUST

Dawes, J. G., S. R. Howarth, and A Slack. Ministry Fuel and Power (Brit.) Safety in Mines Research Estab. Research Rept. No. **87**, 19 pp. (1954); CA **48**, 9648 (1954).

The requirements for a portable sampler that can be used in mine work are described. A satisfactory instrument for control of airborne dust concentrations in coal mines should be 1) portable, 2) self contained for use anywhere in a mine, 3) be capable of operation by relatively unskilled personnel, with the sample continuously unattended for a whole shift, 4) simple in design and construction for easy maintenance, 6) have small possibility of failure in operation, 6) designed to detect failure to operate satisfactorily during sampling period, 7) nonelectric, and evaluation of the sample should be easy, rapid, and not require a high degree of training or complex equipment. Such a sampling system is described. Dust of respirable size is collected on filter paper by using a water aspirator, and the sample is evaluated by using either a densitometer or an air- resistance method.

3—HANDPUMP SAMPLING IN COAL-DUST CLOUDS: OPTICAL DENSITY METHOD

Dawes, J. G. Ministry Fuel and Power (Brit.) Safety in Mines Research Estab. Research Rept. No. **83**, 3-24 (1954); IHD **19**, 1275 (1955).

Whatman No. 1 filter paper was replaced by an esparto filter paper for obtaining coal dust stains by the handpump method. Density calculations are given, and the performance of the handpump for determining the concentration of air-borne coal dust is examined. Add. Ref.: CA **48**, 8514 (1954).

4—THE PENETRATION OF FILTER PAPER BY COAL-DUST PARTICLES IN THE RESPIRABLE SIZE RANGE

Stanley, N. Ann. Accup. Hyg. **4**, 295-299 (1962).

A simple method for measuring the concentration of air-borne dust is to measure the reduction in the amount of light transmitted through filter paper on which the dust particles deposit. The author studied the extent to which the penetration of the filter paper by the respirable size fraction would affect the validity of such measurements. At the low air flow rates used, coal dust particles more than 5μ in diameter did not penetrate either of the 2 types of filter paper tested. Some particles smaller than 5μ did penetrate, but they were too few to lower significantly the dust concentration estimated densitometrically.

Copper

1—o-HYDROXYPHENYLFLUORONE AS SPECIFIC REAGENT FOR MOLYBDENUM AND COPPER

Gillis, J. A., Claeys, and J. Hoste. Mededel. Koninkl. Vlaam. Acad. Wetenschap., Belg., Klasse Wetenschap. **9**, No. 11, 13 pp. (1947); CA **42**, 3279 (1948).

To test for copper, place 1 drop of the neutral sample solution on a drop plate, add 1 drop of potassium fluoride solution (5 g of potassium fluoride, 5 ml of water, 0.4 ml of 6 N hydrochloric acid), 1 drop of hydrogen peroxide-potassium tartrate solution (5 g of potassium tartrate in 20 ml of 10% hydrogen peroxide) and 1 drop of reagent (0.1% o-hydroxyphenylfluorone in 94% ethyl alcohol slightly acidified with hydrochloric acid). Only copper gives an intensely pruple precipitate which gradually turns violet. The sensitivity of this specific reaction is 1:3.10⁴. Gold and ruthenium interfere.

2—A NEW ANALYTICAL TEST FOR COPPER WITH BENZIDINE

Sierra, F. and J. Sierra. Anales fis. y. quim. (Madrid) **43**, 1169-1178 (1947); Pubs. inst. quim. "Alonso Barba" (Madrid) **1**, 339-348 (1947); CA **42**, 3279 (1948).

Dissolve 38 g of potassium thiocyanate in 100 ml of water, add 62 g of mercuric thiocyanate, filter, and dilute to 400 ml. To 0.5 ml of sample containing cupric ion add 1 drop of the 25% potassium mercuric thiocyanate and 1 drop of benzidine acetate solution (prepare by adding 0.4 g of benzidine to 4 ml of glacial acetic acid, heating until completely dissolver, adding 95 ml of boiling water, and filtering). The cupric ion forms an intense blue color. The limit of dilution is 1:2,000,000. *This might be applied to a field detector.*

3—HIGHLY SELECTIVE SPOT TEST FOR COPPER BASED ON FORMATION OF COPPER (1) ACETYLIDE

Whitehead, T. H., G. Katcher, Chemist-Analyst 52(4) 109 (1963) CA **61** 11310 (1964).

The authors find that the formation of Cu(1) acetylide is a very selective and sensitive method of detection. The sample is made alkaline with NH₃. Three drops are placed on a spot plate and the following materials added: 1 drop concentrated NH₃, 2 drops hydroxylamine, 1 drop acetylene solution. If 45-50 µg Cu/ml are present an intense red color is observed.

See Section One
For references 5, 6, 94, 98.

Copper Tartrate

1—POROUS SOLID FILTERS FOR SAMPLING INDUSTRIAL DUSTS

Briscoe, H. V. A., Janet Matthews, P. F. Holt, and Phyllis M. Sanderson. Institution of Mining and Metallurgy (London) Transactions **46**, 145-153 (1938).

An air-elutriated copper tartrate dust is prepared to produce a particle size of 0.1 to 0.2 microns in diameter. Any material which passes the filter is collected on a filter paper and analyzed by the rubeanic acid test for copper. The method involves moistening the paper with 1 to 1 hydrochloric acid and the same amount of water. The acid is neutralized by holding the paper over concentrated ammonia and subsequently treating the paper with a 1% solution of rubeanic acid. Copper yields a greenish-black stain the intensity of which permits the determination of as little as 0.01 micrograms of copper. (1.0 µg = one millionth of a gram).

2—FINAL PROGRESS REPORT, AEC CONTRACT NO. AT-30-1-GEN-238

Silverman, Leslie, Melvin W. First, G. S. Reichenbach, Jr., and Philip Drinker. Harvard Univ., School of Public Health, Dept. of Ind. Hyg., p. 35 (Feb. 1, 1950).

A modification of Sanderson's technique for filtering airborne cupric tartrate dust and quantitating the copper directly on the filter paper uses the confined area Yagoda spot test paper, sampling at a rate of 3 liters per minute. After collection of the sample, add 1 or 2 drops of 1:1 hydrochloric acid to the spot, dry partially, then add 1 or 2 drops of distilled water, and neutralize the solution by exposure to ammonia vapor. When the paper is almost dry add 1 drop of 0.1 per cent solution of rubeanic acid in methyl alcohol, allow the paper to dry, then compare the resulting green to black stain with standard copper stains. The sensitivity is 0.1 µg copper with an upper limit of approximately 5 µg copper. If preserved under glass the standard stains are stable indefinitely. Add. Refs.: NYO 1527; NSA **4**, 5834 (1950).

Cyanide

1—DETECTION AND DETERMINATION OF CYANIDES AND CYANOGEN HALIDES

Falkof, Melvin M., Benjamin Witten, and Bernard Gehauf (to the U.S.A., as represented by the Secy. of War). U. S. (Pat. No.) 2,678,260, May 11, 1954; CA **48**, 9279 (1954).

A sensitive colorimetric method for the qualitative and

quantitative analysis of cyanides and cyanogen halides is described. Filter paper or silica gel is impregnated with a reagent containing pyridine and 1-phenyl-3-methyl-5-pyrazolone. If a cyanogen halide is present the reagent assumes a magenta color which changes to deep blue. In order to determine hydrogen cyanides or alkali cyanides they must first be converted to cyanogen halides. The test for cyanide in solution involves the addition of a sodium bicarbonate buffer and a drop of chloramine T followed by a drop of the pyridine-pyrazolone solution. The hydrogen cyanide in air determination involves passing the air through some type absorbing solution followed by the analysis as outlined above.

2—DETECTION OF CYANIDES

McConnaughey, Paul W. (to Mine Safety Appliances Co.). U. S. (Pat. No.) 2,728,639, Dec. 27, 1955; CA **50**, 5470 (1956).

The author describes a simple reliable method for the detection of hydrogen cyanide or acrylonitrile in air. A reagent is prepared consisting of silica gel impregnated with 0.02 g o-tolidine, 0.02 g anhydrous copper sulfate, and 2.5 g glycerol. Cyanides in contact with this reagent produce a blue or blue green color. The limit of detection is 0.54 micrograms per liter of air. The method can also be used for the quantitative analysis of cyanides. The gas is aspirated through a tube containing the above reagent and the length of stain is a direct measure of the cyanide concentration.

3—DETECTION OF CYANIDE ION

Yankov, S. Zhur. Anal. Khim. **12**, 759 (1957); CA **52**, 8846 (1958).

One part of benzidine is mixed with 20 parts of finely divided aluminum oxide and placed in a glass tube. A solution of 100 ml of 1% copper acetate and 5 ml of 5% acetic acid. 0.05 ml of this reagent is transferred to the column and 0.05 ml of the suspected cyanide ion solution is added. The presence of cyanide is indicated by the presence of a blue band. The sensitivity is about 0.15 micrograms. Chlorine, bromine, iodine, and thiocyanate interfere by reacting with the benzidine. The halide interference is removed sufficiently to permit detection of 1 microgram cyanide by adding a 95% standard solution to the column.

4—CRAYON MARK'S COLOR CHANGE IS POISON GAS WARNING

Anon. Chem. Processing, April, 1957; personal communication, July 1957.

Hydrogen cyanide detector crayon pairs, available commercially from Aromil Chem. Co., Baltimore 7, Md., are sensitive to hydrogen cyanide when one is applied over the other. Ten ppm of hydrogen cyanide in the atmosphere turns the mixed crayon mark a reddish-pink after 5 minutes; on standing, the pink color darkens to purple or blue. Crayon B alone can be used to detect cyanogen halides; its mark turns reddish-pink in 1 minute when exposed to 4 ppm of cyanogen chloride or cyanogen bromide. The crayons consist essentially of commonly known, sensitive detector chemicals mixed with fillers and binders, and incorporated into crayon form. The original research was done by the Army Chemical Corps.

5—THE CHEMICAL ANALYSIS OF AIR POLLUTANTS

Jacobs, Morris B. Interscience Publishers, New York, 1960, 246-247.

Cyanide in air is detected on a test paper. Dissolve 5 g of hydrated ferrous sulfate in 50 ml of water and filter. Immerse a single sheet of Whatman No. 50, smooth-glazed, acid-and alkali-treated filter paper in the ferrous sulfate solution and air dry. Dip the ferrous sulfate impregnated paper into a 20% solution of sodium hydroxide and again dry in the air. Cut circular pieces of the paper with the same diameter as the ground glass flanges of the glass test-paper holder. The papers are stable for several weeks if stored in a dark, cool place. Pass the air sample through the test-paper in the holder by aspiration or by suction. Remove the test-paper from the holder and place it in a dilute solution of hydrochloric acid (1:4), wash with water, and dry. A blue stain indicates the presence of cyanide.

Cyanogen

Although most of the detectors described for cyanide are sensitive also to cyanogen and cyanogen halides, their exact sensitivities are unknown; therefore, the detectors should be selected with a full understanding of the system being used.

1—THE DETECTION AND DETERMINATION OF CYANOGEN AND HYDROGEN CYANIDE

Rhodes, F. H. J. Ind. Chem. **4**, 652-655 (1913); CA **7**, 1468 (1913).

Hydrogen cyanide can be easily absorbed in a silver nitrate solution slightly acidified with nitric acid forming silver cyanide. Cyanogen is not absorbed by this method. Small quantities of cyanogen can be detected by removing the hydrogen cyanide and then absorbing the cyanogen in 0.05 N potassium hydroxide solution. To this solution is added 5 cc of ferrous sulfate and a drop of ferric chloride followed by acidification with sulfuric acid.

This is not directly applicable to air analysis; however, the technique of removing the hydrogen cyanide before detection of the cyanogen is a means of handling a mixed atmosphere.

2—PROBLEMS OF PASSIVE DEFENSE AGAINST THE DANGER OF CHEMICAL GAS ATTACKS

Harsovescu, C. Antigaz (Bucharest) **9**, No. 9/10, 22-34 (1935); Chem. Zentr. **1936, I,** 4240; CA **31,** 7141 (1937).

The authors present a review of the properties and methods of recognition of cyanogen chloride. Methods for the prevention of contact of foods and drink are also discussed.

3—DETECTION AND DETERMINATION OF CYANIDES AND CYANOGEN HALIDES

Falkof, Melvin M., Benjamin Witten, and Bernard Gehauf (to the U.S.A., as represented by the Secy. of War). U. S. (Pat. No.) 2,678,260, May 11, 1954; CA **48,** 9279 (1954).

A sensitive colorimetric method for the qualitative and quantitative analysis of cyanides and cyanogen halides is described. Filter paper or silica gel is impregnated with a reagent containing pyridine and 1-phenyl-3-methyl-5-pyrazolone. If a cyanogen halide is present the reagent assumes a magenta color which changes to deep blue. In order to determine hydrogen cyanides or alkali cyanides they must first be converted to cyanogen halides. The test for cyanide in solution involves the addition of a sodium carbonate buffer and a drop of chloramine T followed by a drop of the pyridine-pyrazolone solution. The hydrogen cyanide in air determination involves passing the air through some type absorbing solution followed by the analysis as outlined above.

4—SENSITIVE DETECTOR CRAYONS FOR PHOSGENE, HYDROGEN CYANIDE, CYANOGEN CHLORIDE, AND LEWISITE

Witten, Benjamin and Arnold Prostak. Anal. Chem. **29,** 885-887 (1957).

Cyanogen chloride is detected by a modification of the reaction reported by Rudner et al (q.v.). Ten per cent of 4-benzylpyridine, 4 per cent of barbituric acid, and 86 per cent of blanc fixe, neutral, amorphous, dry, are compressed into a crayon in a ⅝" diameter cylinder under approximately 6000 psi. The white mark made by the crayon on a surface to be tested first turns red and then blue in the presence of cyanogen halide. The concentration-time equivalent of 1 mg minute per cubic meter is equivalent to 0.4 ppm (1 mg per cubic meter) of cyanogen chloride in 1 minute. The crayons are stable for at least 3 years when stored at room temperature. Add. Refs.: CA **51,** 11915 (1957); IHD **21,** 904 (1957).

See Section One

For references 52, 86.

Cyanogen Chloride

1—GAMMA BENZYLPYRIDINE-BARBITURIC ACID REAGENT. A NEW DETECTOR FOR CYANOGEN CHLORIDE

Rudner, Bernard, Bernard Gehauf, Benjamin Witten, and Melvin M. Falkof. T. D. M. R: 1059, Project A 10.5 (1945).

The most sensitive, stable, and convenient detector for cyanogen chloride was a mixture of barbituric acid and gamma benzylpyridine, which changed from colorless to red. Detector papers, silica gel tubes, and detector crayons were impregnated with a solution consisting of 10 parts acetone, 1 part gamma benzylpyridine, and 5 parts saturated aqueous solution of barbituric acid. Detector papers also were prepared by impregnating filter paper with a saturated aqueous solution of barbituric acid, drying, and spotting with gamma benzylpyridine. The sensitivity of freshly prepared detector paper or crayon to cyanogen chloride is 1 to 3 mg minutes per cubic meter, with the detector tube the most sensitive of the three. High concentrations of phosgene, bromobenzyl cyanide and chloropicrin interfere. Hydrogen cyanide can be detected by adding either an aqueous solution of chloramine T or an organic solution of an impregnite to the detector immediately before or after sampling.

Cyclohexane

1—DETERMINATION OF SOLVENT VAPORS IN AIR. I. CYCLOHEXANE

Kobayashi, Yoshitaka. J. Soc. Org. Synthet. Chem., Japan **12,** 63-66 (1954); CA **51,** 952 (1957).

The detector consists of orange silica gel impregnated with chromic acid and sulfuric acid. Thirty ml of the air sample is passed through the detector in 150 seconds. The cyclohexane concentration is determined by the length of the greenish-black stain produced. Cyclohexane can be determined in the range of 0.01 to 100 mg per liter. The error is less than plus or minus 5 per cent.

1,4-Diketones

1—A SEMI-MICRO QUALITATIVE TEST FOR 1,4-DIKETONES

Leach, W. G. Analyst **67,** 53 (1942).

Mix a few drops of the test solution with a slight excess of solid ammonium acetate and 2 drops of glacial acetic acid, boil for half a minute, and allow to cool. Add an excess of dilute sulfuric acid, then at once place a piece of filter paper moistened with dilute hydrochloric acid over the mouth of the tube. Cover the filter paper with a light watch glass, and boil the solution gently. A pink stain on the paper indicates the presence of a 1,4-diketone. 0.0001 g of acetonyl acetone in an aqueous solution containing 0.002 g per ml may be detected. Add. Ref.: CA **36**, 5444 (1942).

Dimethylaniline

1—DETERMINATION OF SMALL QUANTITIES OF DIMETHYLANILINE IN AIR

Fomicheva, N. I. and P. A. Mel'nikova. Gigiena i Sanit. **1952**, No. 5, 49-52; CA **46**, 9019 (1952).

The air sample is aspirated through 2 absorbers containing 1 ml of 1% hydrochloric acid and 0.2 ml 10% sodium nitrite until a yellow color is observed in the first absorber. The color is compared with standards. The color produced is due to the p-nitroso derivative formed. The method can be used for determinations in the range of 0.0005 to 0.008 mg but requires 10 to 20 minutes for completion.

See Section One
For reference 60.

Dimethyl Ether

1—A RAPID METHOD FOR THE DETERMINATION OF DIMETHYL ETHER IN METHYL CHLORIDE BY DETECTOR TUBES

Kobayashi, Yoshitaka. J. Soc. Org. Synthet. Chem., Japan **13**, 417-421 (1955); CA **51**, 1776 (1957).

A 30 cc sample of the test gas is aspirated through a detector tube in 60 minutes. The detector tube contains silica gel impregnated with chromic and sulfuric acid. The concentration of dimethyl ether in methyl chloride is determined by the length of the green-black stain produced. The range of the determination is 0.01 to 10%.

Dioxane

1—DETERMINATION OF SMALL QUANTITIES OF DIOXANE IN THE ATMOSPHERE OF INDUSTRIAL ESTABLISHMENTS

Chemodanova, L. S. Gigiena i Sanit. **13**, No. 11, 31 (1948); CA **43**, 8976 (1949).

Dioxane is aspirated through a potassium dichromate solution at the rate of 10 to 15 liters per hour until a color change occurs. The dioxane is oxidized to carbon monoxide by this treatment.

Diphenylamine

1—COLORIMETRIC DETERMINATION OF SMALL QUANTITIES OF DIPHENYLAMINE IN AIR

Ponomarenko, B. V. Zavodskaya Lab. **13**, 937 (1947); CA **44**, 3410 (1950).

Diphenylamine is collected in a 50% sulfuric acid solution. The sample is reacted with diazosulfanilic acid in an acid solution producing a violet-red reaction product. Add. Ref.: IHD **15**, 628 (1951).

See Section One
For reference 60.

Diphenylaminecyanarsine
Diphenylchloroarsine
Diphenylcyanoarsine

1—TESTS AVAILABLE FOR THE IDENTIFICATION OF SMALL QUANTITIES OF THE WAR GASES

Cox, H. E. Analyst **64**, 807-813 (1939).

Both absorb iodine quantitatively from alcoholic iodine solution. The cyanide produced on hydrolysis is recognizable by acidifying the alkaline solution and warming it while a piece of filter paper, previously soaked in a mixture of benzidine and copper acetates, is held in the tube. The method of making a sensitive benzidine copper acetate paper is described in the pamphlet, "Methods for the Detection of Toxic Gases in Industry. Hydrogen Cyanide Vapour." (Dept. of Sci. Ind. Research, London, England, Leaflet No. 2, 9 pp. (1938, reprinted 1947)). (cf. Analyst **63**, 659 (1938)).

See Section One
For reference 52.

Diphosgene (Surpalite)

1—TESTS AVAILABLE FOR THE IDENTIFICATION OF SMALL QUANTITIES OF THE WAR GASES
Cox, H. E. Analyst **64**, 807-813 (1939).
Diphosgene is decomposed completely into phosgene by passing it through a tube heated to 300-350° C., after which tests for phosgene may be applied. Add. Ref.: CA **34**, 541 (1940).
See Section One
For references 35, 41, 42, 52, 54, 64.

Dust

1—QUANTITATIVE ESTIMATION OF THE SOOT IN AIR
Orsi, G. Arch Hyg. **68**, 11-21 (1910); CA **4**, 289 (1910).
A modification of the Rubner technique is used for the determination of soot. The sample is filtered and the resulting spot is compared with spots produced by known amounts of petroleum soot. Good results were also obtained by using a photometer to compare the sample spot with spots produced by various known amounts of petroleum soot on a white surface.

2—DUST FALL SAMPLING METHODS
Mabuce, E. M. Proc. Smoke Prevent. Assoc. Am., 99-101, 1947.
This method is based on a density determination of dust collected on a cellophane tape and measured photoelectrically.

3—DETERMINATION OF HAZE AND SMOKE CONCENTRATIONS BY FILTER PAPER SAMPLERS
Hemeon, W. C. L., G. F. Haines, Jr., and H. M. Ide. Air Repair **3**, 22-28 (1953).
The authors' method for the assessment of smoke concentrations by collection on a white filter paper measures light transmission, converts to optical density, and finally describes the smoke concentration in "Coh units" per linear foot of air. A Coh unit is the quantity of light-scattering solids producing an optical density of 0.01. When the optical density is below 0.30 (50 per cent transmission) the relation between optical density and smoke concentration is almost linear. A method for stack gas, by dilution with air, is described and illustrated. Add. Ref.: IHD **17**, 1095 (1953).

4—AIR SAMPLING WITH MEMBRANE FILTERS
First, M. W. and Leslie Silverman. Arch. Ind. Hyg. Occ. Med. **7**, 1-11 (1953).
The membrane filters and midget impingers described by the authors give comparative dust counts with savings in time, labor, and equipment. They are nearly 100% efficient for collecting acid mists and metal fumes as well. Add. Ref.: IHD **17**, 302 (1953). (Many methods of sampling atmospheric pollution, including special dusts, incorporate visual, reflectance, absorptiometric, or fluorescent techniques for final estimation of the amount of the dust retained on a special medium. Some of the methods use the Hemeon continuous sampler (see above), or simple modifications of the filter head. The blackening on filter paper may be compared with gray color scales, which may be calibrated for specific uses. Complete review of all these methods is beyond the scope of this bibliography.)

Epoxy Resins

1—NEW SPOT TEST FOR EPOXY RESINS
Swann, Melvin H. Offic. Dig., Federation Paint and Varnish Production Clubs **30**, 1277-1279 (1958); CA **53**, 23047 (1959).
A new spot test, which is specific for the bisphenol epoxy resins, is described. When a drop of the resin in sulfuric acid solution is placed on filter paper a bright purple color is produced. The cellulose of the filter paper acts as the reagent. *Glass filters impregnated with methyl cellulose in a 70% sulfuric acid solution, air dried at 15% humidity, then placed in a filter holder with another glass filter for a backup, were stained violet by epoxy resin fumes evolved when the resin was heated on a hot plate. Statistical data have not been accumulated. Silica gel, treated similarly in a silica gel tube of 3 mm bore, was colored violet only on the first fraction of a millimeter. Glass filters, 1⅛" diameter, dipped into a 70% sulfuric acid solution containing a dissolved filter paper (Whatman No. 41), gave a brilliant red-violet stain when air containing evaporated epoxy resin was pulled through the paper by suction. The stain faded rapidly, leaving a gray to black residue.*

Ethyl Acetate

1—DETERMINATION OF SOLVENT VAPORS IN AIR. IV. ETHYL ACETATE
Kobayashi, Yoshitaka. J. Soc. Org. Synthet. Chem.,

Japan **12**, 358-360 (1954); CA **51**, 952 (1957).
The reagent and apparatus used to determine cyclohexane were used. The effective range is 0.005 to 5.0 volume per cent.

2—SPOT TEST FOR ACETATE IN FORMIC ACID AND FORMATES

Feigl, F. and C. Stark. Chemist-Analyst **45**, 46-47 (1956); CA **50**, 10611 (1956).

One drop of the sample is placed in a micro test tube. Calcium carbonate is added and the mixture is dried. A filter paper wetted with a nitroprusside-morpholine solution is placed over the mouth of the tube. The sample is heated and a blue color indicates the presence of formate.

Ethyl Alcohol

1—A CORRECT ALCOHOLOMETER READING

Kreipe, H. Z. Spiritusind. **59**, 185-186 (1936); CA **31**, 4539 (1937).

Sources of error associated with the use of the alcoholometer are discussed, with special reference to its use with liquids of low ethanol. Methods for minimizing such errors, are described, the necessity for cleanliness of the instrument and of the liquid surface being stressed. *(Most of the alcohol breath-meters commercially available will, after calibration, determine ethyl alcohol in air. The use of permanganate, dichromate, and iodine pentoxide in these instruments is well known.)*

2—COLOR STANDARD FOR DRUNKOMETER

Harger, R. N. Am. J. Police Sci. (in J. Criminal Law Criminol.) **40**, 813 (1950); CA **44**, 7370 (1950).

The authors describe two end-point color standards for the Harger Drunkometer. One of these, having a limited shelf life, consists of 6 ml 0.1% solution of DuPont Tartrazine and 4 ml 0.1% solution of DuPont crocein scarlet N extra in 1 liter of distilled water. The second standard, having an adequate shelf life, is prepared by combining 27 ml 5% cobaltous sulfate containing 0.6 ml 50 volumes per cent sulfuric acid per 100 ml with 1 ml 1 per cent potassium dichromate and with 89 ml distilled water. Stock solutions of both standards are stable. *These standards could be adapted for ethanol in air analyses.*

3—GAS ANALYSIS BY MEANS OF DETECTOR TUBES. VIII. RAPID METHOD FOR THE DETERMINATION OF ETHYL ALCOHOL AND METHANOL IN AIR

Kobayashi, Yoshitaka. J. Chem. Soc. Japan, Ind. Chem. Sect. **56**, 526-527 (1953); CA **48**, 11978 (1954).

The detector is composed of silica gel impregnated with a solution of potassium dichromate acidified with sulfuric acid. Charts and graphs showing the relationships between ethanol concentration and stain length are presented. The accuracy is claimed to be ± 5%.

A large number of detector techniques involving the reduction of chromic acid are reported in the literature. These, however, are non-specific and usually involve further laboratory analysis for confirmation. The tube described above is available commercially.

4—A NEW PROCEDURE FOR THE DEMONSTRATION OF ETHYL ALCOHOL IN THE EXPIRED AIR

Scheibe, Ernst and Horst Frey. Klin. Wochschr. **31**, 817 (1953); CA **47**, 12482 (1953).

The expired air sample is passed through a tube containing potassium dichromate in some inert adsorbent. Sufficient potassium dichromate is used so that a green color will result when the blood alcohol content exceeds 20 mg per cent. *This method could be applied to the detection of ethanol in air.*

5—DETERMINATION OF ALCOHOL IN THE BREATH AS AN ANALYTICAL PROBLEM

Grosskopf, K. Angew. Chem. **66**, 295-297 (1954); CA **48**, 9870 (1954).

A critical evaluation of the determination of alcohol by the chromometric testing tube was made. A standard curve relating length of stain and blood alcohol content is shown. The author feels that the method could be used for the determination of ethanol in air.

6—DETECTION OF ALCOHOL IN ALVEOLAR AIR BY A DETECTION TUBE

Nishiyama, Seijiro and Nobuo Motohashi. Science and Crime Detection **7**, 281-285 (1954); CA **49**, 6785 (1955).

Two methods for the determination of ethanol in expired air are described. In one method the breath sample is passed through potassium permanganate in a concentrated sulfuric acid-water solution. The optical density of the resulting colored solution is evaluated with a photoelectric colorimeter. The second method involves aspirating the sample through a tube containing silica gel impregnated with potassium dichromate. In the presence of ethanol a greenish-yellow to greenish-blue color is observed.

7—A SIMPLE METHOD OF DETERMINING ALCOHOL ON THE BREATH

Kitagawa, Tetsuzo and Yoshitaka Kobayashi. Japan Analyst **4**, 444-445 (1955); CA **50**, 16563 (1956).

A detector tube consisting of silica gel soaked with potassium dichromate acidified with sulfuric acid is used to detect ethanol in breath. In the presence of ethanol the original orange yellow color changes to blue.

8—RAPID DETERMINATION OF ALCOHOL VAPOR IN EXPIRED AIR

Mokhov, L. A. and I. P. Shinkarenko. Sovet. Med. **19**, No. 11, 67-70 (1955); CA **50**, 7010 (1956).

Ethyl alcohol in expired air can be determined utilizing a detector tube. Silica gel impregnated with chromium trioxide in sulfuric acid is the reagent used. The sample is analyzed by blowing into the detector tube for 20 to 25 seconds. A color change from orange to green indicates ethyl alcohol, ethyl ether, acetone, aldehydes, methanol, and large quantities of hydrogen sulfide; no reaction is caused by chloroform, carbon tetrachloride, ethylidene chloride, phenol, or acetic acid. The authors feel that this method could be adapted to the determination of ethanol in air.

9—SPOT TEST FOR TRACE ETHANOL

Feigl, F. and C. Stark. Chemist-Analyst **45**, 39-40 (1956); CA **50**, 10611 (1956).

Spot tests for the detection of trace amounts of ethanol are described. A blue color is obtained when acetic acid contacts a nitroprusside solution containing morpholine or piperidine. This reaction takes place only in the presence of secondary amines and has been recommended as a test for them. The authors feel that this test might be modified to determine whether the permissable limit for ethanol has been exceeded.

10—METHOD FOR DETECTING ETHANOL

Draegerwerk Heinrich und Bernhard Draeger. Ger. (Pat. No.) 1,037, 726, Aug. 28, 1958; CA **55**, 1300 (1961).

11—REPORT ON DRAEGER GAS DETECTOR. ALCOHOL

Transactions of the Twenty-First Annual Meeting of the Am. Conf. of Gov. Ind. Hyg., p. 127 (1959).

The efficiency of an ethyl alcohol detection tube is described. The range of the tube is 200 to 1500 ppm. Results for alcohol concentrations below 1000 ppm showed considerable variations and usually read less than the true value. It was found to be difficult to note the color change in the tube at the threshold limit value.

See Section One

For reference 97.

Ethyl Bromoacetate
Ethyl Iodoacetate

1—TESTS AVAILABLE FOR THE IDENTIFICATION OF SMALL QUANTITIES OF THE WAR GASES

Cox, H. E. Analyst **64**, 807-813 (1939).

These products are slowly decomposed by water, forming bromo- and iodo-acetic acids. They are quickly absorbed by alcoholic potassium hydroxide solution, forming potassium bromide and iodide and glycollic acid. Glycollic acid is characterized by adding to the alkaline solution a small particle of guaiacol and then a few drops of sulfuric acid. When this solution is warmed a red-violet color is formed. Add. Ref.: CA **34**, 541 (1940).

Ethyldichloroarsine (Dick)

1—TEST AVAILABLE FOR THE IDENTIFICATION OF SMALL QUANTITIES OF THE WAR GASES

Cox, H. E. Analyst **64**, 807-813 (1939).

Ethyldichloroarsine is determined by aspirating the sample into 1 ml of acidified (nitric acid) mercurous nitrate solution. If the ethyl compound is present a white precipitate which changes slowly to gray, is produced. Add. Ref.: CA **34**, 541 (1940).

2—ORGANIC REAGENTS FOR THE IDENTIFICATION OF CERTAIN VESICANTS

Yoe, John H. and Everett C. Cogbill. Mikrochemie ver. Mikrochim. Acta **38**, 492-497 (1951); CA **46**, 2443 (1952).

The authors list fifteen organic reagents that give color reactions with lewisite and ethyldichloroarsine. A test paper impregnated with one of these reagents can be used to identify arsenical vesicants. Ten of the papers give colors with ethyldichloroarsine which distinguish it from lewisite or from the mustard vesicants, and 5 of the 10 also will differentiate lewisite from the other toxics. Two papers can identify lewisite alone. Three give identical tests with the two arsenicals but do not react with vesicants of the mustard type.

3—SENSITIVE DETECTOR CRAYONS FOR PHOSGENE, HYDROGEN CYANIDE, CYANOGEN CHLORIDE, AND LEWISITE

Witten, Benjamin and Arnold Prostak. Anal. Chem. **29**, 885-887 (1957).

A benzene-chloroform solution of 4,4'-bis(dimethylamino)-thiobenzophenone was completely absorbed by the blanc fixe (neutral, amorphous, dry, 86%). The solvent is removed by overnight evaporation followed by 12 hours under vacuum. The mixture is powdered and pressed into crayons. The light tan marks produced by these crayons become greenish-blue in the presence of ethyldichloroarsine. Add. Refs.: CA **51**, 11915 (1957); IHD **21**, 904 (1957).

See Section One

For references 52, 86.

Ethylene

1—RAPID ESTIMATION OF SMALL AMOUNTS OF ETHYLENE IN AIR. PORTABLE INSTRUMENT

Stitt, Fred, A. H. Tjensvold, and Yoshio Tomimatsu. Anal. Chem. **23**, 1138-1141 (1951).

A portable instrument provides a simple, reliable, field method for estimating 5 to 200 ppm of ethylene in air. A fixed volume of gaseous sample is passed first over granular red mercuric oxide at 285° C, then over a strip of sensitized seleno-cyanate paper at 125°C. A black coloration forms, the length of which is directly proportional to the ethylene content of the sample, with an error of less than 10 per cent. (S. and S No. 610 filter papers impregnated with 0.010 and 0.1 molar seleno-cyanate solution, show a 50 mm length of blackening for samples containing 20 and 200 ppm of ethylene, respectively.) Interfering substances are removed by pumice saturated with 95% sulfuric acid in a glass tube inserted between the pump and the reaction tube. Add. Ref.: CA **46**, 63 (1952).

2—REMOVAL AND RECOVERY OF TRACES OF ETHYLENE IN AIR BY SILICA GEL

Stitt, Fred and Yoshio Tomimatsu. Anal. Chem. **25**, 181-183 (1953).

Different temperatures caused differences in the absorption of ethylene on silica gel when the ethylene was measured by the method described above. Add. Ref.: CA **47**, 3184 (1953).

3—DETERMINATION OF ETHYLENE IN GASES

Stitt, Fred, Yoshio Tomimatsu, and Arnt H. Tjensvold (to the U. S. A., as represented by the Secy of Agr.) U. S. (Pat. No.) 2,648,598, Aug. 11, 1953; CA **48**, (1954).

A sensitized filter paper strip is used for the determination of ethylene. The filter strip is prepared by impregnating it with an aqueous solution of potassium selenocyanate. The treated paper is exposed to hydrogen chloride fumes to separate out the selenium. The sample is passed over hot mercuric oxide at a temperature of 285°. The gaseous reaction products are passed over the sensitized filter strip at 125°. The amount of ethylene present is determined by comparing the blackened sample strip with standard strips.

4—GAS ANALYSIS BY MEANS OF DETECTOR TUBES. III. RAPID DETERMINATION OF LOW CONCENTRATIONS OF ETHYLENE AND ACETYLENE

Kitagawa, Tetsuzo and Yoshitaka Kobayashi. J. Chem. Soc. Japan, Ind. Chem. Sect. **56**, 56-58 (1953); CA **48**, 8128 (1954).

The detecting reagent is prepared by placing a mixture of ammonium molybdate and palladium sulfate on silica gel. In the presence of ethylene the yellow color changes to deep blue. Data of a semiquantitative nature is presented.

5—GAS ANALYSIS BY MEANS OF DETECTOR TUBES. VII. RAPID METHOD FOR THE DETERMINATION OF ETHYLENE

Kitagawa, Tetsuzo and Yoshitaka Kobayashi. J. Chem. Soc. Japan, Ind. Chem. Sect. **56**, 448-449 (1953); CA **48**, 11028 (1954).

Silica gel granules impregnated with ammonium molybdate and cadmium sulfate and dried are used for the determination of ethylene. The light-yellow column changes to deep blue when 10 (or 100) cc of air containing more than 0.002 volumes per cent of ethylene is drawn through it within 40 (or 400) seconds. The concentration of ethylene can be determined by measuring the length of blue-colored portions and using the correction curves provided. An error of $\pm$ 5 per cent is claimed.

6—RAPID METHOD FOR THE DETERMINATION OF LOW CONCENTRATIONS OF ETHYLENE BY MEANS OF A DETECTING TUBE

Kobayashi, Yoshitaka. Yûki Gôsei Kagaku Kyôkai Shi **14**, 137-141 (1957); CA **51**, 7240 (1957).

A mixed solution of ammonium molybdate and palladium sulfate absorbed on silica gel is used as a detector for ethylene oxide in air. When the air sample is aspirated through the tube at a constant rate in the presence of ethylene the light-yellow color of the reagent changes to dark blue. The concentration of ethylene in air is determined by measuring the length of this dark-blue layer. Volume of test gas, introducing speed, measurable range of ethylene in air are as follows: 10 cc to 15 cc per minute, 0.05-1.2%; 100 cc, 15 cc per minute, 0.002-0.12%; 100 cc, 100 cc per minute, 0.5 ppm; 1000 cc, 100 cc per minute, 0.05 ppm; 3000 cc, 100 cc per minute, 0.01 ppm. The effect of the diameter of this tube, of temperature, and of other gases is also described. At the temperature range of 10-30°, no correction is necessary.

Ethylene Oxide

1—THE DETECTION OF ETHYLENE OXIDE (T-GAS) IN AIR AFTER FUMIGATION

Deckert, Walter. Z. angew. Chem. **45**, 559-562 (1932); CA **26**, 5877 (1932).

The author presents a qualitative test for the detection of ethylene oxide. Concentrated sodium chloride and ethylene react to produce chlorohydrin and sodium hydroxide. A two hundred cc air sample is drawn through 5 cc of 22% sodium chloride containing phenolphthalein or bromothymol blue in a test tube, which is then heated to 100° for 1 minute. If there is no color change the concentration of ethylene oxide is under 0.5 mg per liter (phenolphthalein) or 0.1 mg per liter (bromothymol blue) and the air is safe. A mixture of both indicators is used for the determination of higher concentrations of ethylene.

2—THE DETECTION OF ETHYLENE IN AIR AFTER FUMIGATION

Deckert, Walter. Angew. Chem. **45**, 758 (1932); CA **27**, 685 (1933).

The author describes a modification of a previously reported method. One drop of 1:1000 phenolphthalein solution is added to 1 to 2 cc of a 40% solution of potassium thiocyanate in a test tube. A 50 cc air sample is aspirated through the reagents. The test tube is warmed and if no red color appears after 2 minutes the room can be considered free from ethylene oxide.

3—DETECTION OF TOXIC GASES AND VAPORS

Leroux, Lucien. Rev. hyg. et med. prevent. **57**, 81-112 (1935).

Using a 22% solution of sodium chloride and 200 cc of air, a negative reaction indicates, with phenolphthalein, less than 0.5 mg per liter, or with bromothymol blue, less than 0.1 mg per liter. Add. Ref.: CA **29**, 3627 (1935).

4—THE USE OF INDICATORS FOR THE DETECTION OF POISONOUS GASES AND VAPORS

Heering, D. Gasmaske **8**, 88-89 (1936).

Bromothymol blue in 22% sodium chloride solution in a special apparatus turns light blue with 0.8 mg per liter of ethylene oxide. Add. Ref.: CA **30**, 7059 (1936).

5—DETERMINATION OF ETHYLENE OXIDE AND METHODS OF ITS RECOVERY FROM FUMIGATED SUBSTANCES

El Khishen, Shafik Ali. J. Sci. Food Agr. **1**, 71-77 (1950); CA **44**, 7187 (1950).

The author describes a method for the detection of small quantities of ethylene oxide in air by (A) bubbling the oxide-air mixture through a freshly prepared saturated solution of potassium iodide containing phenolphthalein. A pink color results in 2 minutes. (B) The oxide-air mixture is bubbled through a saturated solution of sodium thiosulfate containing phenolphthalein. A pink color appears rapidly. Method (B) is more sensitive than (A). Both are sensitive as an indicator for ethylene oxide in air when filter paper is moistened with either solution and exposed to the atmosphere.

6—RAPID METHOD FOR THE DETERMINATION OF ETHYLENE OXIDE VAPOR BY MEANS OF DETECTOR TUBES

Kobayashi, Yoshitaka. J. Soc. Org. Synthet. Chem., Japan **13**, 596-600 (1955); CA **51**, 1776 (1957).

Silica gel impregnated with potassium dichromate acidified with sulfuric acid is used as an indicator.

7—RAPID METHOD FOR THE DETERMINATION OF ETHYLENE OXIDE VAPOR BY MEANS OF A DETECTOR TUBE

Kitagawa, Tetsuzo and Yoshitaka Kobayashi. J. Chem. Soc. Japan, Ind. Chem. Sect. **58**, 514-517 (1955); CA **49**, 15634 (1955).

The authors describe a detector tube for the analysis of ethylene oxide. The detector tube consists of a glass tube (2 mm in diameter) filled with 0.2 g of silica-gel granules on which potassium dichromate acidified by sulfuric acid has been adsorbed and dried. The working curves to interpolate the ethylene oxide concentration from measuring (a) color changed length of detecting column (from orange-yellow to dark yellow-green) after 100 cc of gas iş allowed to flow at a rate of 1 cc per second, or (b) volume of gas needed to change the color up to a certain length of the detecting column. At the procedure (a), the calibration for temperature is carried out by a given diagram. The range of concentration of ethylene oxide to be analyzed with an accuracy of ± 5% is: (a) 0 to 4.0%; (b) 0.003 to 0.5%. Interfering materials include alcohols, aldehydes, diethyl ether, sulfur dioxide, hydrogen sulfide, acetone, benzene, aniline, petroleum, carbon disulfide, nitrous oxide, and hydrochloric acid.

8—FERRIC THIOCYANATE PAPER AS AN ANALYTICAL REAGENT IN THE ANALYSIS OF AIR

Deckert, Walter. Z. anal. Chem. **150**, 421-425 (1956).

The test paper, S and S No. 2043bM chromatographic paper, is impregnated with 96 ml of 40% potassium thiocyanate and 4 ml of 10% ferric ammonium sulfate, leaving the upper edge unimpregnated. The paper is dried at not more than 20°C in the absence of ammonia. If ammonia is present in the air, it will bleach the paper. The test paper can be used for detecting and determining basic gases in the atmosphere, such as ammonia, amines, and ethylene oxide. Although the technique is primarily chromatographic, it has other possible uses because acid gases in the air can be detected by the reclorizing of the bleached paper. Add. Ref.: CA **50**, 10608 (1956).

Ethyl Ether

1—GAS ANALYSIS BY MEANS OF DETECTOR TUBES. IX. RAPID METHOD FOR THE DETERMINATION OF ETHER VAPOR

Kobayashi, Yoshitaka and Tetsuzo Kitagawa. J. Chem. Soc. Japan, Ind. Chem. Sect. **56**, 526-527 (1953); CA **48**, 11978 (1954).

A detector tube, similar to the one previously reported, was constructed for the determination of ether. The method depends upon the color change produced in a silica gel column into which a chromium trioxide-sulfuric acid solution was soaked and dried. The graphs expressing the relations between length of color change and concentration as well as temperature correction (10-30°) are given.

2—DETERMINATION OF SOLVENT VAPORS IN AIR. II. ETHER

Kobayashi, Yoshitaka. J. Soc. Org. Synthet. Chem., Japan **12**, 112-115 (1954); CA **51**, 952 (1957).

The reagent and apparatus used for the detection of cyclohexane are applied to the determination of ether in air. One hundred ml of air is passed through the tube in 200 seconds. The effective range is 0.005 to 2.0 volume per cent. The error is less than $\pm$ 3%.

Ferrocyanides

1—PRECIPITATION CHROMOTOGRAPHY. SEPARATION OF METALS AS FERROCYANIDES ON FILTER PAPER

Liimatta, Adele M., J. D. Spain. Anal. Chem. **35** (12) 1898-1900 (1963) CA **60** 1089 (1963).

Several metallic elements are determined by means of filter paper treated with 0.1 MK_4 Fe(CN)$_6$. This paper is dried and then immersed in 0.2 M Mn (NO$_3$)$_2$ solution. Test solutions are applied as nitrates.

Ion	Color formed	Limit of Detection
Ag$^+$	white	45g
Ca^{++}	wine-red	0.045 g
Fe^{+++}	deep blue	0.045 g
Hg^{++}	bluish green	0.27 g
Co^{++}	mint green	0.20 g
Ni^{++}	pale greenish white	cannot be detected alone
Zn^{++}	white	cannot be detected alone
Bi^{+++}	light yellow green	0.5 g
Sn^{++++}	greenish white	0.5
UO$_2$$^{++}$	light orange red	0.15

This method could be adapted for a rapid field detection method.

Fluorine
Fluoride

1—SENSITIVE SPOT REACTION FOR FLUORIDE

Pavelka, F. Mikrochemie **6**, 149-151 (1928).

Moisten filter papers with a solution of basic zirconium chloride to which has been added an excess of alcoholic solution of alizarin. Then moisten the dried papers with a drop of 50% acetic acid and a drop of the suspected solution; the red paper will turn yellow if the solution contains 0.01 mg or more of fluorine. Sulfates, oxalates, and phosphates interfere. *Although designed for fluorine in solution, the test possibly might be applied to air samples containing fluorine.* Add. Ref.: CA **23**, 3871 (1929).

2—DETECTION OF FLUORIDES USING THE ZIRCONIUM LAKE OF ALIZARIN

Stone, Irwin. J. Chem. Educ. **8**, 347-349 (1931).

The color reaction between fluorides and the red zirconium lake of alizarin is used to test for fluorine. Immerse Whatman No. 50 filter paper in a solution of 2. g of zirconium chloride dissolved in 100 ml of alcohol, dry, then immerse in a solution of 0.1 g alizarin in 100 ml of alcohol, and dry again. Cut off and discard the edges of the dried paper, and cut the remainder into strips 5 mm wide. Acidify the neutral or slightly acid solution to be tested with an equal volume of hydrochloric acid, then immerse the test paper in it for from 5 to 10 seconds; if fluorides are present, the reddish paper turns yellow (in about 10 seconds with 0.3 mg fluorine per ml, more rapidly with higher concentrations). High concentrations of sulfate and phosphate interfere unless the red color is read within 20 seconds. *Although this test is designed for fluorides in solution, it might be applicable also to air samples containing fluorides.* Add. Ref.: CA **25**, 1181 (1931).

3—ANALYTIC ASPECTS OF THE CHEMICAL BEHAVIOUR OF 8-HYDROXYQUINOLINE (OXINE)

Feigl, F. and G. B. Heisig. Anal. Chim. Acta **3**, 561-566 (1949).

Expose qualitative filter paper to vapor suspected of containing hydrogen fluoride, then spot the paper with a chloroform solution of aluminum oxinate (oxine), and examine under ultraviolet light. Hydrogen fluoride will quench the fluorescence of the oxine. The test is sensitive to 0.05 μg of fluorine. Add. Ref.: CA **44**, 6332 (1950).

4—DEVICE AND TECHNIQUE FOR RAPID DETERMINATION OF EFFLUENT FLUORIDES

Harrold, Gordon C. and Ralph V. Hurlburt. Anal. Chem. **21**, 1504-1506 (1949).

Impregnate Whatman No. 41-H filter paper with brown-colored zirconium azoarsenate (from the reaction in the paper between p-dimethylaminoazobenzenearsonic acid and zirconium oxychloride). The chemicals must be deposited uniformly on the paper, and the excess p-dimethyl-aminoazobenzenearsonic acid must be washed out completely. Just before use wet the paper with 2 N hydrochloric acid. Draw air through the filter paper with a hand operated 50 ml pump. The depth of the pink color produced by fluoride ion is proportional to the fluorine content of the air being drawn through the paper. The method is semi-quantitative; 6 to 10 ppm can be determined within ± 1 ppm. Add. Ref.: CA **44**, 1362 (1950).

5—FLUORINE CHEMISTRY. II. THE DETECTION OF TRACES OF SAFETY REFRIGERANTS

Mueller, Richard and H. Fischer. Chem. Tech. (Berlin) **5**, 298-301 (1953); CA **48**, 13537 (1954).

The authors describe the colorimetric reaction of pyridine in sodium hydroxide for the detection of small quantities of refrigerants. The limits of sensitivity of this test for Eskimon 22, 12, 11, and 113 are described and shown to be of possible technical value for the detection of Eskimon 22 and 12. For the detection of monochlorodifluoromethane (Eskimon 22) a strip of filter paper (3 x 25 cm) is rolled up, placed into a glass tube, moistened with 0.7 cc purest pyridine. The air-monochlorodifluoromethane mixture to be tested is passed through the tube containing the paper plug, and the paper treated with 0.4 cc 20% aqueous carbonate-free sodium hydroxide. The pyridine to be used in this test must be stable against alkali solutions. Pyridine, which develops a color with alkali, is refluxed 0.5 hour with about 5% of its weight of potassium carbonate and finally distilled at 114-115°. Ammonium hydroxide and sodium carbonate do not develop a color under similar conditions. The volume per cent monochlorodifluoromethane in air, the content of monochlorodifluoromethane (in micrograms) in 92.0 cc air used for the test, the shade of the red color developed with liquid pyridine and with pyridine on filter paper, and the time (in minutes) necessary for the development of the color after the addition of the sodium hydroxide in a series of tests are tabulated. The same type of tabulation is made for a series of tests with dichlorodifluoromethane. The sensitivity of the test for dichlorodifluoromethane is only about 1/7 that for monochlorodifluoromethane and requires, therefore, the passage of the air to be tested through liquid pyridine in a fritted gas washer to concentrate the contaminant. Air was passed at room temperature through trichloromonofluoromethane, b. 23.7°, and the mixture washed with α-dibutylphthalate to remove any contaminating carbon tetrachloride, the trichlorofluoromethane condensed again and rectified, and only the cut boiling at 23.7° taken. The concentration of trichlorofluoromethane in the air-trichlorofluoromethane vapors was determined by drying the vapor mixture with

concentrated sulfuric acid and passing through two washers containing methyl silicone oil with a viscosity of 43.0 centipoises at 20°; to each washer was attached a tube with silica gel in order to avoid weight losses. Air (88.07 cc) containing 0.2403 g of trichlorofluoromethane passed during 1 minute at room temperature through the pyridine-sodium hydroxide reagent developed a slight red color, which depened considerably within 5 minutes, even without heating. In a similar run, the temperature of the washer was maintained at 0° and the reagent then heated to develop the red color reaction somewhat faster; with 0.02403 g trichlorofluoromethane the red color formation was considerably less intense; with 0.002403 g trichlorofluoromethane no color developed. Carbon tetrachloride showed, under similar conditions, a stronger color reaction although the maximum color formation was reached with 0.1, 0.01, 0.001, and 0.00001 g carbon tetrachloride in 86.7 cc of air only after 15, 30, 60, and 120 minutes respectively. An air-stream was passed at a rate of 20 cc per minute at 22° through a fritted glass bubbler containing trichlorotrifluoroethane (Eskimon 113) and through the pyridine-sodium hydroxide reagent. After 3 minutes a slight orange, and after 6 minutes, a strong red color developed in the pyridine-sodium hydroxide reagent; the amount of trichlorotrifluoroethane passed through the reagent in 3 minutes was 1.2 g. By addition of acetone to the reagent trichlorotrifluoroethane gave a yellow color reaction." Add. Ref.: CA **47**, 4523 (1953).

6—MICRO-DETERMINATION OF ELEMENTAL FLUORINE

Peregud, E. A. and B. S. Boikina. Zhur. Anal. Khim. **12**, 513-515 (1957); J. Anal. Chem. U.S.S.R. **12**, 531-533 (1957) (English translation).

Sieve coarse silica gel so that the 260 to 300 micron size is retained, wash with 6-N hydrochloric acid by boiling, then wash with water, calcine at 750° C, and treat with the desired active agent. Impregnate one batch of silica gel with potassium bromide and another with fluorescein; the fluorine then liberates bromine, which reacts with the fluorescein to form eosin. The depth of the red color developed is a measure of the concentration of the fluorine. The lower limit of detection is 0.35 μg per liter. Methyl red is used in a less sensitive, liquid absorption method; the amount of decolorization of the methyl red is measured colorimetrically. The sensitivity of this method is 0.35 μg fluorine in 2 ml. The authors investigated 10 other reagents also. Add. Ref.: AA **5**, 1201 (1958); CA **52**, 1852; 18073 (1958).

7—COMPOSITION FOR DETERMINING HYDROFLUORIC ACID AND FLUORIDES

Auergesellschaft Akt.-Ges. (by Hermann Heidrich). Ger. (Pat. No.) 1,000,170, Jan. 3, 1957 (Cl. 42 **1**); CA **54**, 2096 (1960).

The detector tube for the determination of hydrofluoric

acid vapors and fluorides, consists of silica gel soaked with ferric thiocyanate containing a small quantity of hydrochloric acid. The reagent was prepared by mixing 10 g of silica gel and 10 cc of a 0.5% ethereal ferric thiocyanate with 3 drops of concentrated hydrochloric acid. The mixture was stirred until a slightly yellowish-red color was observed. The ferric thiocyanate solution was prepared by dissolving 0.95 g ferric chloride hexahydrate and 0.8 g ammonium thiocyanate in 100 cc water. The 2 solutions were combined, and the ferric thiocyanate was extracted with ether.

8—FLUORIDE-ION INDICATOR

Mavrodineanu, Radu (to Boyce Thompson Institute for Plant Research, Inc.) U. S. (Pat. No.) 2,823,984, Feb. 18, 1958; CA **52**, 7790 (1958).

The author describes an indicator for the determination of atmospheric fluoride. Filter paper is dipped in an aqueous solution of 1.75 g per liter of zirconium nitrate for 5 minutes and inan aqueous solution of 1 g per liter of sodium alizarinsulfonate for 10 minutes. The indicator paper is exposed for about 10 hours and then placed in 0.01N hydrochloric acid for 15 minutes. The lake formed on the exposed paper loses color proportional to the amount of fluoride present.

9—A NEW SPOT TEST FOR THE DETECTION OF FLUORIDE ION

Belcher, R., M. A. Leonard, and T. S. West. Talanta **2**, 92-93 (1959); CA **53**, 12951 (1959).

Fluoride ion produces a colored complex with the cerium-III chelate of alizarin complexon (1,2-dihydroxy-3-anthraquinonylmethylamine-N,N-diacetic acid). If an acetate buffer is used, the red color of the cerium-II-alizarin complexon changes to the lilac-blue color of the double complex. The reaction forms a suitable basis for a sensitive spot test for the detection of fluoride ion. This method or some modification of it might find an application in the field detection of fluoride ion.

10—AUTOMATIC ATMOSPHERIC FLUORIDE POLLUTANT ANALYZER

Adams, Donald F. and Robert K. Koppe. Anal. Chem. 31, No. 7, 1249-1254 (1959).

A zirconium-Eriochrome Cyanine R reagent is used in a field instrument for the determination of fluorine. Color changes are detected by photometric procedures. Sampling of atmospheres of hydrogen fluoride in the concentration range of 0.4 to 35. μg per cubic meter showed no statistically significant differences between the results from the automatic analyzer and those of standard laboratory methods. Continuous concentrations of sulfur dioxide at 0.5 ppm and a phosphorus pentoxide to fluorine ratio of 7 to 1 were tolerated by the fluoride reagent. Add. Ref.: Anal. Chem., Anal. Reviews **33**, No. 5, 3R-13R (1961).

11—METHODS OF DETECTING THE VOLATILE PRODUCTS OF THE THERMAL DECOMPOSITION OF ORGANIC FLUOROPOLYMERS

Peregud, E. A. and B. S. Boikina. Gigiena i Sanit. **27**, No. 4, 53-55 (1962); CA **57**, 3745 (1962).

Carbonyl fluoride is a major, volatile, and toxic product of the thermal decomposition of fluoride containing plastics. The carbonyl fluoride analysis consists of aspirating the sample through a tube containing silica gel, potassium bromide, potassium bromate, and fluorescein. The hydrogen fluoride present is formed by hydrolysis and liberates bromine. The stain length is a measure of the fluoride concentration.

12—FLUORIDE MEASURING KIT

Engineering Spcialties Co. P. O. Box 102, Saxonville, Mass.

A new gaseous fluoride ion measuring kit can be applied to the accurate measurement of hydrogen fluoride and other easily dissociated fluorides. The operating principle is that of fluorescence quenching. When a fluorescent indicator, impregnated on filter paper, is exposed to fluorides, the fluorescence is destroyed. The analysis is made with completely dry indicator papers; the change is light output under ultraviolet irradiation indicates directly the concentration of fluoride in contact with the indicator. The reaction is almost completely specific, is unaffected by halogen acids and other similar materials, and the papers are stable indefinitely. The kit can detect 0.02 μg fluoride with an accuracy of plus or minus 10%.

See Section One

For references 15, 81, 116.

Fluorine Monoxide

1—MICROMETHOD FOR DETERMINATION OF FLUORINE MONOXIDE

Peregud, E. A. and B. S. Boikina. Zhur. Anal. Khim. **14**, 141-142 (1959); CA **53**, 9889 (1959).

One liter of air to be analyzed is drawn for 20 minutes through a glass tube packed with silica gel which is saturated with a solution of fluorescein containing potassium bromide and potassium carbonate. The length of the red bromofluorescein zone indicates the amount of fluorine monoxide present (1 mm corresponds to 0.334 μg fluorine monoxide).

Formaldehyde

1—PHOTOMECHANICAL FORMATION OF FORMALDEHYDE IN GREEN PLANTS

Schryver, S. B. Proc. Roy. Soc. London (B) **82**, 226-232; CA **4**, 1313 (1910).

A slightly modified Rimini reaction for the determination of formaldehyde is described. The limit of detection is approximately 1 ppm.

2—ANALYSIS OF ETHYLENE FOR ANESTHETIC USE

Busi, M. and C. Collina. Atti soc. ital. progresso sci. **19**, 195-199 (1931); CA **26**, 1707 (1932).

The authors present methods for the determination of formaldehyde in ethylene.

3—DETECTION OF TOXIC GASES AND VAPORS

Leroux, Lucien. Rev. hyg. et med. prevent. **57**, 81-112 (1935).

A neutral rosaniline hydrochloride paper turns blue in the presence of formaldehyde and acid aldehyde. A reagent consisting of fuchsin and dried serum also is described. Add. Ref.: CA **29**, 3627 (1935).

4—THE USE OF SPOT TESTS FOR THE EXAMINATION OF DRUGS. I. ALDEHYDE AND AMINE REACTIONS FOR THE RECOGNITION OF ETHEREAL OILS

Wasicky, R. and O. Frehden. Mikrochim. Acta **1**, 55-63 (1937).

Adlehydes react with o-dianisidine to form colored Schiff bases. The very sensitive reaction can detect, in a spot test, as little as 40 μg of formaldehyde, the pale yellow color produced with the formaldehyde differing from that obtained with 33 other aldehydes. Prepare the reagent by saturating acetic acid with o-dianisidine; clarify the solution of necessary by filtration after warming it with activated charcoal. Add. Ref.: CA **31**, 5944 (1937).

5—REACTIONS AND REAGENTS FOR THE DETECTION OF ORGANIC COMPOUNDS

Eegriwe, Edwin. Z. anal. Chem. **110**, 22-25 (1937); CA **31**, 8442 (1937).

Formaldehyde can be determined by the sensitive chromotropic acid method. An approximately 72% solution of sulfuric acid with a small quantity of chromotropic acid is added to 1 drop of the aldehyde sample in solution; if formaldehyde is present a violet coloration will appear.

6—DETECTION AND DETERMINATION OF FORMALDEHYDE

Duchesnoy, R. Rev. gen. mat. plastiques **15**, 198-200 (1939); CA **33**, 9198 (1939).

A number of tests for the detection of formaldehyde are presented.

7—THE DETERMINATION OF SMALL AMOUNTS OF FORMALDEHYDE IN AIR

Kersey, R. W., J. R. Maddocks, and T. E. Johnson. Analyst **65**, 203-206 (1940.)

The article details an application of Schryver's method (see above). Prepare a 1% phenylhydrazine hydrochloride solution by suspending 1 g of phenylhydrazine in about 5 ml of water, adding 2 ml of concentrated hydrochloric acid (sp. gr. 1.16) and diluting to about 80 ml. Filter and dilute the filtrate to 100 ml with water. An intense magenta color is formed when dilute solutions of formaldehyde phenylhydrazone are treated with potassium ferricyanide in presence of an excess of hydrochloric acid, the depth of color (between certain limts) being proportional to the concentration of formaldehyde present. The working range of the test is approximately 1 to 5 parts of formaldehyde per million of solution, although 0.5 ppm is detectable. Add. Ref.: CA **34**, 4016 (1940).

8—A NEW COLOUR REACTION FOR SULPHUROUS ACID, THE THIOL GROUP, AND FORMALDEHYDE

Steigmann, A. J. Soc. Cem. Ind. **61**, 18-19 (1942).

The author's decolorized fuchsin-sulfuric acid solution, with thioglycollic acid instead of sulfurous acid might be modified for use as a detection method for formaldehyde. Mix 2 ml of basic fuchsin (BDH stain solution), 30 ml of dilute sulfuric acid (38. ml water plus 2. ml concentrated sulfuric acid), and 100 ml water; when the solution is nearly colorless, add 3 ml of 1:100 thioglycollic acid. After 2 days filter off the slight precipitate that forms. Formaldehyde reacts immediately with this reagent to give a blue color; most other aldehydes do not react at all, acetaldehyde only after 8 to 12 hours. The test is sensitive to 1.5 μg of formaldehyde. Add. Ref.: CA **36**, 3454 (1942).

9—A SIMPLE AND RELIABLE METHOD FOR THE DETERMINATION OF METHYL ALCOHOL AND FORMALDEHYDE IN THE AIR

Ackerbauer, C. F. and R. J. Lebowich. J. Lab. Clin. Med. **28**, 372-377 (1942).

Air is drawn through a series of four bubblers, containing (1) 75 ml of 1% phosphoric acid and 75 ml of 2% barium chloride, mixed; (2) 200 ml of an alkaline solution of 5% potassium permanganate; (3) 225 ml of modified Schiff's reagent of Wright; and (4) 200 ml of 2 N sodium bisulfite. The laboratory procedure which is described is applicable also to field analysis, absorber 4 being eliminated in the field. Formaldehyde gives a violet color which is compared with a set of standards, either visually, or, preferably, in a Hellige colorimeter. Add. Ref.: CA **37**, 6592 (1943).

10—RAPID AND SIMPLE DETECTION OF FORMALDEHYDE WITH ORTHO CONDENSED PYRROLES

Fuerst, K. Mikrochemie ver. Mikrochim. Acta **33**, 348-351 (1948) (in German); CA **42**, 6272 (1948).

An aqueous solution of formaldehyde in methyl or ethyl alcohol can be detected by means of a 0.5% solution of carbazole in sulfuric acid with a lower limit of detection of 10 micrograms of formaldehyde. The determination can be carried out in a test tube or a spot plate and a blue to green color results if formaldehyde is present. Many aldehydes will produce the same type of reaction with indole in ethyl alcohol in the presence of sulfuric acid. Formaldehyde, for example, produces a red-violet coloration.

11—MICROCHEMICAL TESTS FOR SULFITE, THIOSULFATE, SULFIDE, HYDROGEN PEROXIDE, AND FORMALDEHYDE

Hovorka, V. and Z. Holzbecher. Collection Czechoslov. Chem. Communs. **15**, 117-118 (1950); CA **45**, 1914 (1951).

Moisten pieces of filter paper 1 x 1 cm with 0.002 N potassium permanganate for 30 minutes and dry. Place a micro drop (0.003 ml) of solution suspected of containing formaldehyde on the paper, then dip the paper for a few seconds into a 0.5% solution of benzidine in 10% acetic acid. Green spots on the paper indicate formaldehyde. Although designed for solutions containing formaldehyde, the test might be modified for use with air samples.

12—USE OF DIMEDONE FOR THE DROP DETECTION OF ALDEHYDES

Kul'berg, L. M. and I. S. Mustafin. Zhur. Anal. Khim. **8**, 122-126 (1953) CA **47**, 10409 (1953).

A modification of this method could be used for the detection of formaldehyde in air; it is based on the production of an intense red-brown color when the reaction product of dimedone and formaldehyde is brought into contact with an equilibrium solution of silver chromate in either ammonium hydroxide or ethylenediamine. The method is sensitive to 1 μg of formaldehyde; the sensitivity is increased when an ethylenediamine solution of silver chromate is used as the reagent.

13—FORMALDEHYDE IN AIR—A SPECIFIC FIELD TEST

MacDonald, William E., Jr. Am. Ind. Hyg. Assoc. Quart. **15**, 217-219 (1954).

The article describes the reagents and field equipment for the determination of formaldehyde with 1% chromotropic acid. The purple color produced is compared visually with freshly prepared standards ranging from 1. μg to 20. μg of formaldehyde per ml. Although the visual field method is specific, rapid, and sensitive, the samples nevertheless are returned to the laboratory for analysis. Add. Refs.: CA **48**, 13535 (1954); IHD **18**, 1164 (1954).

14—A NEW SPOT TEST FOR FORMALDEHYDE

West, Philip W. and Buddhadev Sen. Anal. Chem. **27**, 1460-1461 (1955).

Suspend 0.5 g nickel dimethylglyoxime in 100 ml water;

add 0.4 g potassium cyanide. Shake the suspension, allow to stand for at least 24 hours, then filter, and store the filtrate in a borosilicate glass bottle in the dark. Dip 11 cm diameter Whatman No. 1 filter paper circles in the reagent, dry quickly under an infrared lamp, and store in a stoppered bottle. Place a drop of the test solution on the paper, and dry quickly. A red color indicates formaldehyde. A water blank should be used if there is less than 2. μg of formaldehyde; 0.5 μg is the lower limit of detection. Add. Ref.: CA **50**, 6255 (1956).

15—ESTIMATION OF TOXIC GASES IN AIR. IX. FORMALDEHYDE

Fukuyama, Tomitaro, Tokuro Sato, Aiko Watanabe, and Hideko Kimura. Bull. Inst. Public Health, Tokyo, **5**, (3), 1-6 (1956); AA **4**, 3470 (1957).

The Schryver hydrazone method for the determination of formaldehyde is modified to obtain a better analysis. The modification involves substituting 15 N sulfuric acid for the hydrochloric acid previously used.

16—RAPID ANALYTICAL METHOD FOR THE ESTIMATION OF FORMALDEHYDE IN AIR

Fedotov, V. Gigiena i Sanit. **21**, No. 9, 87-89 (1956); Referat. Zhur., Khim. **1957**, 310-311, Abstract No. 15916.

The method is based on the formation of a bright red color from the oxidation of formaldehyde on silica gel saturated with phenylhydrazine hydrochloride. Prepare the indicator tubes by saturating 0.5 g of silica gel granules (0.25 to 0.6 mm diameter) with a freshly prepared 0.3% alcoholic solution of phenylhydrazine hydrochloride, mix well, and dry completely. Pour a 2cm column of the resulting mixture into a glass tube (diameter 5 mm, length 6 cm) and hold in place between 2 cotton plugs. The tubes are stable for 8 to 10 hours. Prepare the oxidizing solution by dissolving 0.04 g of potassium ferricyanide in 10 ml of hydrochloric acid (sp. gr. 1.12); the solution is stable for 3 to 4 days. Draw air through the indicator tube at a rate of 1 liter in 2.5 minutes, then draw 0.25 ml of the oxidizing solution into the tube and hold in a vertical position to allow the solution to drain through the silica gel. Within 1 or 2 minutes compare the color of the resulting stain with a set of standard water color stains on a chart, corresponding to a range of from 0.0002, 0.0005, and 0.001 to 0.20 mg per liter of formaldehyde. Vapors of acetaldehyde, acrolein, furfural, acetone, phenol, hydrogen sulfide, and sulfur dioxide in concentrations less than 0.1 mg per liter do not interfere. Data obtained by the suggested method agreed with the results obtained by methods accepted by the Department of Labor (HOST 5607-50). Add. Refs.: AA **4**, 3767 (1957); CA **51**, 3892 (1957); IHD **21**, 667 (1957).

17—DETERMINATION OF FORMALDEHYDE IN AIR. BI-SULFITE METHOD

Committee on Recommended Analytical Methods, A.C.G.I.H. "Manual of Analytical Methods Recommended for Sampling and Analysis of Atmospheric Contaminants." American Conference of Governmental Industrial Hygienists, 1014 Broadway, Cincinnati 2, Ohio (1957).

The standard procedure in the Manual is adaptable to field use.

18—QUANTITATIVE DETERMINATION OF FORMALDE-HYDE IN AIR OR GAS

Grosskopf, Karl (to Otto H. Draeger). U. S. (Pat. No.) 2,908,555, Oct. 13, 1959; CA **54**, 2096 (1960).

An ampule mounted above the reaction layer is filled with 70% by volume sulfuric acid. The reaction layer consists of purified silica gel (100 g) mixed with 0.4 g dry, purified 2-naphtholsulfonic acid. Glass powder sintered with inorganic color pigments to a lemon-yellow color is placed below the reaction layer for color comparison. The analysis is carried out by breaking the ampule which allows the sulfuric acid to flow into the reaction layer thereby dissolving the 2-naphtholsulfonic acid. Air is drawn in through the tube until the reaction layer turns the same color as the comparison layer. From the number of strokes required to draw the gas through the tube, the concentration of forfaldehyde in air is determined by comparison with a calibrated color chart.

19—VAPOR-FORMING REAGENTS IN THE SMALL TEST TUBE TECHNIQUE FOR THE DETERMINATION OF ORGANIC VAPORS AND GASES

Grosskopf, Karl. Z. anal. Chem. **170**, 271-277 (1959); CA **54**, 2836 (1960).

In the author's apparatus, the test air is passed over a volatile reagent, then both the air and the reagent pass to a second reagent; all 3 react to form a color. The length of the colored layer is proportional to the amount of test substance present in the air. Formaldehyde (5 to 100 ppm) is determined with sulfuric acid + xylene.

20—MICRODETERMINATION OF FORMALDEHYDE IN AIR

Rayner, A. C. and C. M. Jephcott. Anal. Chem. **33**, 627-630 (1961).

Collect a formaldehyde-containing air sample at 1 cubic foot per minute through an impinger containing 0.005 N hydrochloric acid. (The collecting efficiency of this solution is 72% with a standard deviation of 5%.) Add Schiff's reagent to the formaldehyde solution to produce a magenta color; increase the depth and stability of the color with acetone. The method is sensitive to 0.1 μg of formaldehyde per ml of collecting solution; 5 ppb can be determined with a sampling period of 1 hour. For quantitation

the absorbance can be measured spectrophotometrically at 560 mμ, against similarly prepared standards. High concentrations of acrolein interfere but the acrolein color fades on standing overnight. Other aldehydes, and the acids and alcohols which the authors tested do not interfere. Oxides of nitrogen cause high, and sulfur dioxide low, results, but sulfur dioxide interference can be eliminated by treatment with iodine. Add. Ref.: CA **55**, 14770 (1961).

See Section One
For reference 81.

Furfural

1—FURFURAL AS AN INDUSTRIAL POISON AND ITS DETERMINATION IN AIR

Korenman, I. M. and J. B. Resnik. Arch. Hyg. **104**, 344-356 (1930); CA **25**, 2783 (1931).

Small quantities of furfural in air may be detected by the red coloration produced on filter strips treated with a reagent consisting of a mixture of equal volumes of aniline and 80% acetic acid. A quantitative estimation may be made by passing the air sample through water containing the reagent and comparing the resulting color with that produced by a known concentration of furfural.

2—THE USE OF SPOT TESTS FOR THE EXAMINATION OF DRUGS. I. ALDEHYDE AND AMINE REACTIONS FOR THE RECOGNITION OF ETHEREAL OILS

Wasicky, R. and O. Frehden. Mikrochim. Acta **1**, 55-63 (1937).

Aldehydes react with o-anisidine to form colored Schiff bases. The very sensitive reaction can detect, in a spot test, as little as 0.02 μg of furfural, the deep red-violet color produced with furfural differing from that obtained with 33 other aldehydes. Prepare the reagent by saturating acetic acid with o-anisidine; if necessary, clarify the solution by filtration after warming it with activated charcoal. An analogous reaction between furfural and anthronilic acid also can be used as a spot test. *The reactions might be applied to field detectors.* Add. Ref.: CA **31**, 5944 (1937).

3—USE OF DIMEDONE FOR THE DROP DETECTION OF ALDEHYDES

Kul'berg, L. M. and I. S. Mustafin. Zhur. Anal. Khim. **8**, 122-126 (1953) CA **47**, 10409 (1953).

This method possibly might be applied to the detection of furfural in air; it is based on the production of color when the reaction product of dimedone and furfural is brought into contact with an equilibrium solution of silver chro-

mate in either ammonium hydroxide or ethylenediamine. The method is sensitive to 2. mg of furfural; the sensitivity is increased when an ethylenediamine solution of silver chromate is used as the reagent.

4—A NEW REACTION OF FURFURAL AND SUGARS

Malowan, L. S. Ciencia (Mex.) **14**, 18 (1954); CA **49**, 4462 (1955).

The author describes a reagent which produces an intensely colored material with furfural and sugars. The reagent consists of isoamyl, propyl, or butyl alcohol mixed with an equal volume of concentrated sulfuric acid.

5—CYCLIC KETONES SUCH AS CYCLOPENTANONE AND CYCLOHEXANONE AS REAGENTS FOR FURFURAL AND a-FORMYLTHIOPHENE

Pallaud, R. Chim. anal. **38**, 155-156 (1956); CA **50**, 12753 (1956).

The reaction of furfural and a-formylthiophene with cyclopentanone and cyclohexanone in the presence of sodium hydroxide, is described. The reaction products are soluble in mixtures of ethyl alcohol and ethyl acetate.

See Section One
For reference 6.

Gasoline

1—APPARATUS FOR INDICATING OR RECORDING THE PRESENCE OF GASES, APPLICABLE TO THE DETECTION OF GASOLINE FUMES IN SHIPS

Ringrose, Henry T. Brit. (Pat. No.) 412,761, July 5, 1934; CA **29**, 391 (1935).

The abstract does not describe the apparatus.

2— DETECTING GASES

Chovin, Paul E. M. and Leon P. R. Gion. Fr. (Pat. No.) 799,136, June 6, 1936; CA **30**, 7395 (1936).

An apparatus which converts carbon monoxide, gasoline, benzine etc. in air to carbon dioxide is described. The carbon dioxide is reacted with some reagent capable of producing a color with carbon dioxide. The coloration produced gives a measure of the concentration of carbon monoxide present.

3—DETECTING FOREIGN SUBSTANCES IN THE ATMOSPHERE

Etablissements Luchaire. Fr. (Pat. No.) 816,128, July 30, 1937; CA **32**, 1984 (1938).

An apparatus for detecting poisonous gases by bubbling them through reagents, indicates the presence of gasoline vapor.

4—RAPID DETERMINATION OF GASOLINE VAPOR

Kobayashi, Yoshitaka. Bunseki Kagaku **5**, 409-410 (1956) CA **51**, 14245 (1957).

Silica gel impregnated with a mixture of sulfuric acid and chromic oxide is placed in a glass detector tube and utilized for the determination of gasoline in air. The original orange-yellow color changes to a dark brown stain in the presence of gasoline. The length of the colored stain is proportional to the gasoline concentration.

See Section One
For references 88, 96.

Germanium

1—PHENYLFLUORONE, A SPECIFIC REAGENT FOR GERMANIUM

Gillis, J., J. Hoste, and A. Claeys. Mededel. Koninkl. Vlaam. Acad. Wetenschap., Belg., Klasse Wetenschap. **9**, No. 5, 16 pp. (1947); CA **42**, 3278 (1948).

Impregnate SS No. 589g drop paper with 0.05% phenylfluorone in ethyl alcohol and acidify with a few drops of 6 N hydrochloric acid. A solution containing germanium turns the paper an intense rose color not disappearing when treated with 6 N nitric acid. The color intensity increases with time, and the sensitivity of the reaction is $1:3.10^5$. The treated paper keeps only for a short time, and strongly oxidizing ions may decompose the reagent.

2—o-HYDROXYPHENYLFLUORONE AS SPECIFIC REAGENT FOR MOLYBDENUM AND COPPER

Gillis, J., A. Claeys, and J. Hoste. Mededel. Koninkl. Vlaam. Acad. Wetenschap., Belg., Klasse Wetenschap. **9**, No. 11, 13 pp. (1947); CA **42**, 3279 (1948).

Treat drop test paper MN640W with 1 drop of 0.1% o-hydroxyphenylfluorone solution slightly acidified with hydrochloric acid. Dry at room temperature, place 1 drop of the unknown solution on it, add 1 to 2 drops of 20% potassium fluoride solution (in 0.5 N hydrochloric acid) and 2 or 3 drops of 0.5 N sulfuric acid. Germanium gives an orange color, molybdenum a carmine-red. Ceric, permanganate, and chromate ions destroy the reagent.

Glycidic Group

1—NEW COLOR REACTION FOR GLYCIDIC GROUP INCLUDING CELLULOSE, ITS ETHERS AND ESTERS

Mano, Eloisa Biasotto and Luiz Carlos A. Cunha Lima.

Rev. quim. ind. (Rio de Janeiro) **25,** No. 290, 17-19 (1956); CA **51,** 4215 (1957).

A colorimetric method of analysis is proposed for the identification of cellulose plastics. The plastic substance is warmed with 1 cc of benzene and 1 cc of an 8 to 1 solution of concentrated sulfuric acid and warmed for 2 minutes. One or two cc of ethyl alcohol is added. An intense green or blue coloration indicates a positive test. . . . Cellulose, cellulose nitrate, acetate, acetate-butyrate, methylcellulose, and carboxymethylcellulose, give a green or blue color. Ethylcellulose producing an unexplained violet color is an exception. *This reaction modified for use in field detection work.*

Halogenated Hydrocarbons

1—METHODS FOR THE DETECTION OF TOXIC GASES IN INDUSTRY. ORGANIC HALOGEN COMPOUNDS

Anon. Dept. Sci. Ind. Research, London, Eng., Leaflet No. **12,** 7 pp (1940).

The leaflet describes the detection of organic halogen compounds with a "Halide Detector Lamp," a form of blow lamp which burns pure alcohol in a supply of the air under test. The heat of the flame decomposes the organic halide, which then reacts with a copper screw in the nozzle of the lamp to form the corresponding copper halide; the copper halide colors the flame green. The test is of variable application. Add. Ref.: CA **35,** 1355 (1941).

2—SOLVENTS AND THINNERS USED IN PAINT AND VARNISHES FOR ARTICLES OF DAILY USE

Beythien, A. Paint Varnish Production Mgr. **21,** 81-82 (1941); CA **35,** 3836 (1941).

Methods of trichloroethylene detection are discussed.

3—TESTING FOR HYDROGEN CHLORIDE, ACID CHLORIDES AND CHLORINE-CONTAINING ORGANIC COMPOUNDS IN THE AIR

Anger. Vinzenz. Ger. (Pat. No.) 733,761, Mar. 4, 1943 (Cl. 42 **1.**4.06); CA **38,** 934 (1944).

The air sample is aspirated through a chromic acid-sulfuric acid solution kept at 160-170 degrees. The gas produced by the reaction is tested for chromyl chloride by passing the gas through a solution of diphenylcarbazide or diphenylcarbazone or over paper saturated with one of these solutions.

4—GAS TESTER

Wilner, Torsten. Tek. Tid. **80,** 553-554 (1950); CA **44,** 8704 (1950).

The author describes an apparatus originally designed for the detection of small quantities of combat gas which can be used for the determination of halogen-substituted compounds, such as carbon tetrachloride, trichloroethylene, chlorobenzene, and cooling agents of the Freon type. A small electric fan drives the air to be tested through a small catalyst tube containing an electrically heated platinum spiral, where the substance to be detected or determined is decomposed. The acid decomposition products cause a very distinct red color change on a specially impregnated test paper. The color change fades away rather rapidly after completion of the test. Weak acids do not react with the paper. This eliminates the sensitivity to a whole series of substances which could otherwise have an interfering effect. Chlorine-containing compounds can be detected in quantities as small as 1 mg per cc of air. The color change occurs on passage of 10^{-7} to 10^{-8} g through the catalyst tube. The sensitiveness is lower for halogen-free sulfur compounds, whose decomposition products are not effectively absorbed by the test paper. The construction of the apparatus is described in detail. Add. Ref.: IHD **15,** 624 (1951).

5—A FIELD METHOD FOR THE DETERMINATION OF HALOGENATED HYDROCARBONS

Braid ,P. E. and Kingsley Kay. Can. J. Technol. **29,** 159-169 (1951); CA **45,** 8940 (1951).

In a small portable field instrument for determining methyl bromide in air, a squeeze bulb forces measured amounts of test air through a reaction tube containing oxidizing agent. Prepare the oxidizer by mixing 3.5 of dehydrated iodine pentoxide with 9.5 g of pumice, and add 12 g of fuming sulfuric acid (56% free sulfur trioxide). Bring the air containing the liberated free bromine into contact with a fluorescein-treated test disk in a specially designed holder. Prepare the fluorescein solution by dissolving 0.1 g fluorescein in 5 ml of 10% sodium hydroxide and diluting to 100 ml with water. Dilute 6 ml of this solution to 100 ml with water. Compare the color produced on the test disk with the colors on a standard color card (concentration range, 0 to 150 ppm by volume). For chlorinated compounds, such as trichloroethylene and carbon tetrachloride, modify the apparatus by replacing the squeeze bulb with a pump which delivers 500 ml per stroke, and use 0.05% o-tolidine solution on the test disk as the sensitive reagent for chlorine. *Oxidizing and reducing agents in the air, which are not converted to a stable state, will interfere with the final color.*

6—A COLOR REACTION FOR DICHLOROETHANE

Kuznetsov, V. I. and Z. M. Pimenova. Zhur. Anal. Khim. **7,** 89-91 (1952); J. Anal. Chem. (U.S.S.R.) (English translation) **7,** 103-105 (1952).

The tolerance limit for dichloroethane in Russian working establishments is 0.05 mg per liter of air. Dichloroethane is detected by drawing air through a glass tube 10-12 cm.

long and 0.5 cm in diameter, containing 1 mm silica gel which is held in place with glass wool plugs. The tube is then treated with several drops of quinoline; the formation of a red color in 2 or 3 minutes confirms the presence of dichloroethane. One to two liters of air is sufficient to detect a concentration of 1 mg dichloroethane per liter of air. The procedure is relatively specific in that ethyl bromide, ethyl iodide, ethyl chloride, and 1,2-dibromoethane are the only compounds reported to give the same reaction. The same type of reaction can be used for the qualitative determination of dichloroethane in commercial solvents, by adding several drops of the solvent to quinoline in a test tube and heating. A deep red color forms immediately. Add. Refs.: IHD **17**, 414 (1953); CA **47**, 1533 (1953).

7—FLUORINE CHEMISTRY. II THE DETECTION OF TRACES OF SAFETY REFRIGERANTS

Mueller, Richard and H. Fischer. Chem. Tech. (Berlin) **5**, 298-301 (1953); CA **48**, 13537 (1954).

The pyridine-sodium hydroxide method previously used for the detection of chlorinated hydrocarbons was successfully applied to the detection of safety refrigerants. The limits of sensitivity for Eskimon 11, 12, 22 and 113 are described.

8—NEW METHOD OF DETECTION AND DETERMINATION OF CHLORINATED ETHYLENIC SOLVENTS IN AIR

Berton, Alain. Compt. rend. **245**, 1317-1318 (1957); AA **5**, 3176 (1958).

The method described is specific for the detection of chlorinated ethylenic solvents in air. The technique depends on the conversion of the di-, tri-, and tetrachloroethylenes into phosgene and chloroacetyl chlorides by ultraviolet light. The air sample is aspirated by a micropump into a container illuminated by a low-pressure, mercury-vapor lamp and is then directed against a filter paper impregnated with p-dimethylaminobenzaldehyde and dimethylaniline. The paper becomes yellow changing to blue, the intensity of which increases with solvent concentration. Since the micropump has constant discharge, the concentration of solvent can be calculated from the time needed to obtain a standard tint. The sensitivity of the method is 0.1 mg of trichloroethylene or tetrachloroethylene per liter of air. Add. Ref.: CA **52**, 2652 (1958).

9—REPORT ON THE DRAEGER GAS DETECTOR. TRICHLOROETHYLENE AND OTHER HALOGEN HYDROCARBONS

American Conference of Governmental Industrial Hygienists (A.C.G.I.H.). Transactions of the Twenty-first Annual Meeting, p. 126 (1959).

The Draeger detector tubes show wide variations in response to prepared concentrations in the range of 50-1200 ppm. No consistent percentage of error is found and at 100 ppm results were found to range from 1-4 times the known concentration. The tubes appear to read high at lower concentrations. As the concentration increases the indicated value becomes less than the true concentration. Perchlorethylene and methylene chloride calibrations indicated similar results. In the range of the threshold limit value the tubes tend to read above the true value.

10—AN INDICATOR TUBE FOR THE DETERMINATION OF TRICHLOROETHYLENE IN AIR

Gage, J. C. Analst **84**, 509-515 (1959).

To detect trichloroethylene in air, draw the air sample through two indicator tubes joined in series. The first tube contains a layer of silica gel impregnated with acid permanganate; the second tube contains silica gel impregnated with acidified o-tolidine, and serves to measure chlorine liberated by the first tube. Remove impurities from 50 to 60 mesh silica gel by boiling the gel under reflux with nitric acid for 1 to 2 hours, then washing in a stream of boiling water until free from nitrate. After drying in air, heat the granules for 6 hours at 150°C, then at 240°C for another 6 hours. Prepare the acidified permanganate for impregnating the silica gel by mixing 4 ml of a 40% w/v aqueous solution of orthophosphoric acid with 10 ml of a 5% w/v aqueous solution of potassium permanganate. Disperse 5 ml of this mixture into 25 g of silica gel by shaking in a stoppered flask. Fill into specially cleaned tubes (12" long by 3.4 to 3.6 mm i.d.) so that the acid permanganate-silica gel columns are 25 mm long; plug each end with acid-washed glass wick, and seal. For the second tube, grind 0.25 g of o-tolidine and 5 ml of concentrated hydrochloric acid into a paste, wash into a 250 ml volumetric flask with an additional 20 ml of concentrated hydrochloric acid, and dilute to the mark with water. Add 12.5 ml of this solution to 50 g of the purified silica gel and shake vigorously in a stoppered flask until the granules flow freely. Let the impregnated silica gel age for 2 weeks before use, then fill columns 60 mm long into the same size tubes as the permanganate mixture, plug, and seal. Just before use, snap off the ends of the tubes and join the tubes with a silicone rubber sleeve. Determine the concentration of trichloroethylene from the length of the deep orange stain in the o-tolidine tube after the test air has passed through the permanganate tube. With 3 strokes of a handpump, the tube will detect from 50 to 400 ppm of trichloroethylene; more than 5 pump strokes will detect concentrations below 50 ppm. The shelf life of the prepared tubes is about 9 months. Perchloroethylene, chlorine, and hydrochloric acid vapor interfere. Add. Ref.: CA **54**, 2830 (1960).

11— NEW METHOD FOR DETECTION AND DETERMINATION OF ETHYLENE CHLORIDES IN THE AIR

Berton, Alain. Compt. rend. **245**, 1317-1318 (1957); CA **52**, 2652 (1958).

The air sample containing di-, tri-, or perchloroethylene is pumped into a container illuminated by a mercury vapor lamp, then blown onto paper treated with p-dimethyl-aminobenzaldehyde and dimethylaniline. On the presence of the various ethylene chlorides, a yellow color changing to blue can be seen. The depth of the blue color is a measure of the concentration present. The method is quantitative by using a constant rate pump and noting time to obtain standard shade. Perchloroethylene or trichloroethylene at 0.1 mg per liter of air can be detected.

12—A RAPID SEMI-QUANTITATIVE METHOD FOR DETERMINING CHLOROBENZENE IN AIR

Russkikh, A. A. Nauch. Raboty Khim. Lab. Gor'kovsk. Nauch.-Issledovatel. Inst. Gigieny Truda i Professional. Boleznei, Sbornik 1957, No. 6, 59-60, CA 53, 22644 (1959).

The method is a modification of the Salova method for benzene. A solution is prepared from 5 ml commercial 40% formaldehyde in 100 ml concentrated sulfuric acid. Five ml of the solution is placed in a small vessel, and air is drawn through it at a rate of 10 liters per minute. The presence of chlorobenzene causes turbidity and a reddish brown coloration. Colorimetric standards are prepared by filling colorimeter tubes with 0.2, 0.5, 1, 2, and 3 ml of chlorobenzene in ether (1 mg per ml); the ether is evaporated carefully (below 30°) to 1 or 2 drops, and the tubes closed. The standards are prepared just before the air samples are completed by quickly adding the formalde-hyde-sulfuric acid solution to the prepared tubes. The tubes are shaken and compared with the air samples. Standards change rapidly and must be freshly prepared for each test. As little as 0.2 mg chlorobenzene in 50 to 100 ml air is detected. The test requires 15 minutes.

13—VAPOR-FORMING REAGENTS IN THE SMALL TEST TUBE TECHNIQUE FOR THE DETERMINATION OF ORGANIC VAPORS AND GASES

Grosskopf, Karl. Z. anal. Chem. 170, 271-277 (1959); CA 54, 2836 (1960).

In the author's apparatus, the test air is passed over a volatile reagent, then both the air and the reagent pass to a second reagent; all 3 react to form a color. The length of the colored layer is proportional to the amount of test substance present in the air. Carbon tetrachloride (5 to 100 ppm) is determined with sulfur trioxide + an aromatic amine + an aromatic aldehyde. *This system might possibly be applied in a field detector.*

See Section One
For reference 90.

Halogens

1—COPPER ABSORBER FOR HALOGENS AND HYDROGEN SULFIDE IN THEIR DETERMINATION IN AIR

Sadovskii, P. M. Zhur. Anal. Khim. 9, 58-59 (1954); CA 48, 6910 (1954).

Copper filings which have been screened or elutriated to remove any dust present is an effective absorbent for halogens.

2—COPPER ABSORBER FOR HALOGENS AND HYDROGEN SULFIDE IN THEIR DETERMINATION IN AIR

Sadovskii, P. M. J. Anal. Chem., U.S.S.R. 9, 67-68 (1954) (English translation); CA 49, 4451 (1955).

Same as above.

(The two abstracts above are included, not as a detector method, but rather as a procedure for removing contaminants from detector systems.)

3—DETECTING HALOGENS IN GASES

Draeger, Otto Heinrich (trading as Draegerwerk, Heinrich u. Bernahrd Draeger). Brit. (Pat. No.) 872,671, July 12, 1961; CA 55, 26866 (1961).

A modification of the Beilstein test is described as a method for the detection of halogen compounds. The sample is mixed with a combustible gas and passed over heated copper and burned in excess air. The amount of halogen coloring the flame is determined photometrically.

See Section One
For reference 72.

Hexane

1—GAS ANALYSIS BY MEANS OF DETECTOR TUBES. X. RAPID METHOD FOR THE DETERMINATION OF HEXANE VAPOR

Kobayashi, Yoshitaka and Tetsuzo Kitagawa. J. Chem. Soc. Japan, Ind. Chem. Sect. 56, 809-811 (1953); CA 48, 13545 (1954).

Silica gel granules, treated with chromium trioxide and sulfuric acid, are dried and placed in glass detector tubes. Hexane vapor drawn through the detecting column changes the silica gel from orange-yellow to dark green. The authors include temperature corrections as well as graphs for correlating hexane concentration with the length of the color change in the detector tube.

2—REPORT ON THE DRAEGER GAS DETECTOR. HYDROCARBONS

American Conference of Governmental Industrial

Hygienists. Transactions of the Twenty-first Annual Meeting, p. 127 (1959).

The Draeger detector for hydrocarbons is examined for accuracy. The tubes were checked using n-hexane. Concentrations below 1000 ppm were found to be difficult to determine because color changes produced are too faint to read. The result showed that at 2000 ppm the tubes produced values that were higher than true values.

Hydrocarbons

1—COMPOSITION FOR THE DETECTION OF HYDRO-CARBONS

Grosskopf, Carl (to Otto H. Draeger). U. S. (Pat. No.) 2,800,460, July 23, 1957; CA **51,** 16212 (1957).

A carrier, preferably silica gel, is impregnated with selenious acid and charged with sulfud trioxide. The reagent, in contact with vaporous hydrocarbons, changes color from yellow to brown.

2—ANALYZING FOR HYDROCARBONS

Anon. Chem. and Eng. News **35,** No. 21, 82-83 (1957).

A simple field apparatus, which can be operated by untrained personnel, will determine in 5 minutes the concentration of aliphatic or alicyclic hydrocarbons in the range 0 to 5000 ppm, with a maximum error of $\pm$ 20%. A special calibration scale is fitted to a standard squeeze bulb assembly, a tube containing iodine pentoxide and 65% fuming sulfuric acid on silica gel is placed in the holder beside the scale, and an air sample is drawn through the tube with 1 squeeze of the bulb. The hydrocarbon concentration, read directly from the scale, is proportional to the length of the brown iodine stain in the tube. Olefins, aromatics, aldehydes, alcohols, and carbon monoxide do not interfere.

See Section One
For reference 72.

Hydrogen

1—DEVICE FOR HYDROGEN DETECTION

Arendt, M. and E. V. Brown. U. S. (Pat. No.) 1,467,911, Sept. 11, 1922; CA **17,** 3631 (1923).

The authors describe an indicating element which can be constructed of palladiumized asbestos provided with a heater to prevent atmospheric changes from affecting its hydrogen-indicating properties.

2—DETERMINATION OF HYDROGEN BY MEANS OF SILVER PERMANGANATE SOLUTIONS

Hein, Fr. and W. Daniel. Z. anal. Chem. **99,** 385-390 (1934); CA **29,** 1360 (1935).

Silver permanganate is reduced by hydrogen and may be used as a detecting reagent for the gas. Test conditions must be accurately controlled.

3—THE USE OF SOLID INDICATORS FOR DIRECT DETECTION OF PHOTO-DISSOCIATION PRODUCTS

Neuimin, H. Compt. rend. acad. sci. U.S.S.R. **16,** 447-450 (1937); CA **32,** 1580 (1938).

A layer of molybdenum trioxide is more effective for detecting hydrogen than are other reagents, although tungstic anhydride and palladous chloride may be used. Hydrogen turns a 0.1 to 0.2 mm thick layer of molybdenum trioxide intensely blue (molybdenum indigo is formed). *This reaction is too sensitive to other reducing substances for simple hydrogen detection.*

4—SIMPLE TEST FOR THE IDENTIFICATION OF HYDROGEN GAS

Pesez, M. Bull. soc. chim. **1946,** 692; CA **41,** 2658 (1947).

The author describes a method for the identification of hydrogen. Five ml of an aqueous solution containing 10 mg methylene blue per 100 ml is placed in a test tube. A solution of palladium chloride (0.2 ml) is added. The air sample is bubbled slowly through the blue solution. If hydrogen is present the palladium chloride is reduced to palladium and a leuco derivative of methylene blue is formed. The decolorization requires about 20 ml of pure hydrogen. Air mixed with half as much hydrogen requires 80 to 100 ml. A mixture of equal parts of air and hydrogen gives no decolorization but 20 to 30 ml of a mixture of equal parts nitrogen and hydrogen gives the test.

5—DETECTION OF HYDROGEN

Campbell, Evan E. Unpublished data (1953).

Prepare the detecting medium by mixing 50 g of pure, dry silica gel (6-18 mesh) with 20 ml of 5% nitric acid saturated with picric acid containing 0.02 g palladium chloride. Spread the mixture on a large watch glass, oven dry at 100°C for 1 hour, then allow to stand at room temperature, uncovered, for at least 4 hours before use. For detecting hydrogen the silica gel may be placed in open containers, or made to adhere to any type of surface with adhesives such as alkyd resin, Krylon, or oil paint. Alternatively, fine silica gel (150-200 mesh) may be rubbed into filter paper or fiber glass disks. The detecting medium is stable indefinitely and the sensitivity is independent of the mesh size of the silica gel, although a larger mesh size requires more solution. Hydrogen turns the reagent black, and the time required for the black to appear on the surface of the silica gel is proportional to the hydrogen concentration.

6—ANALYTICAL PROCEDURE FOR THE DETECTION OF GASES

Guatelli, Manuel A. Rev. asoc. bioquim. arg. **18**, 3-40 (1954).

Treat 200 ml of 0.1 N silver nitrate with ammonia to dissolve the silver oxide formed. Place 20 g silica gel and 20 ml formaldehyde in the solution, let stand several minutes, then filter. Next, prepare 2 solutions: (1) 300 ml saturated potassium permanganate and (2) 46 g silver nitrate made to 50 ml with distilled water. Mix the 2 solutions, add to the silver silicate, filter, dry the treated gel in a desiccator, and store in a brown bottle. The silica gel so prepared will react with 3 liters of hydrogen. Add. Ref.: CA **48**, 8124 (1954).

See Section One

For reference 72.

Hydrogen Chloride
Hydrochloric Acid

Hydrochloric acid mists are detected readily by dry litmus or other indicator papers; the vapor form is detected more easily with moist indicator paper. Buffered papers and buffered solutions with indicators are useful only when the atmosphere contains a single acid contaminant.

1—TESTING FOR HYDROGEN CHLORIDE, ACID CHLORIDES AND CHLORINE-CONTAINING ORGANIC COMPOUNDS IN AIR

Anger, Vincenz. Ger (Pat. No.) 733,761, March 4, 1943 (Cl. 41 1.4.06); CA **38**, 934 (1944).

Pass the air sample through a chromium trioxide-sulfuric acid mixture at 160-170°C. Test the ensuing gas for chromyl chloride by passing it through a water-alcohol solution of diphenylcarbazide or diphenylcarbazone, or over paper saturated with one of these solutions.

2—ABSORPTION OF HYDROGEN CHLORIDE IN AIR ANALYSIS

Pimenova, Z. M. Gigiena i Sanit. **13**, No. 11, 31 (1948); CA **48**, 8971 (1949).

Hydrogen chloride can be absorbed by water at 95 degrees. This method of sample collection is applicable to hydrogen chloride gas as well as for hydrogen chloride aerosol. The determination is made nephelometrically with

silver nitrate. *An instrument such as the Hellige comparator may be calibrated for this test.*

See Section One

For references 6, 7, 8, 90, 93, 125.

Hydrogen Cyanide
Hydrocyanic Acid

1—THE EMPLOYMENT OF PHTHALOPHENONE PAPER AS A REAGENT FOR HYDROCYANIC ACID

Thiery, M. J. pharm. chim. (6) **25**, 51-53 (1907); CA **1**, 972 (1907).

Immerse strips of Berzelius paper in a solution of copper sulfate (1-2000), dry, and cut into small strips. Prepare an alkaline solution of phthalophenone by dissolving 0.5 g phenolphthalein in 30 ml absolute alcohol, diluting with water, and adding 20 g of sodium hydroxide. Place the mixture in a porcelain capsule and add powdered aluminum in small portions until the red color disappears. Add distilled water (previously boiled and cooled without access of air) to dilute the solution to 150 ml, then filter. To detect hydrocyanic acid moisten a strip of the copper sulfate paper with a few drops of the suspected liquid and add a few drops of the alkaline phthalophenone. Hydrocyanic acid turns the reagent paper pink. The author finds these reagents more rapid and much more delicate for the detection of minute amounts of hydrocyanic acid than the picrosodic paper previously employed for the test.

2—THE DETECTION AND DETERMINATION OF CYANOGEN AND HYDROGEN CYANIDE

Rhodes, F. H. J. Ind. Eng. Chem. **4**, 652-655 (1913); CA **7**, 1468 (1913).

Hydrogen cyanide can be absorbed in a silver nitrate solution slightly acidified with nitric acid. This reaction produces a product of silver cyanide. Cyanogen, on the other hand, is not absorbed and can be completely expelled by a current of air. Small amounts of cyanogen can be detected by removing the hydrogen cyanide with silver nitrate. *This is not directly applicable to air analysis; however, the technique of removing the hydrogen cyanide from the cyanogen is a means of handling a mixed atmosphere.*

3—THE DETECTION OF GASEOUS HYDROCYANIC ACID IN AIR

Sieverts, A. and A. Hermsdorf. Z. angew. Chem. **34**, Aufsatsteil 3-5 (1921); CA **15**, 1269 (1921).

Moisten a strip of filter paper with a solution of copper acetate-benzidine acetate and expose to the contaminated air for exactly 7 seconds. A faint blue color on the paper indicates over 15 mg hydrocyanic acid per cubic meter. A deep blue indicates over 60 mg per cubic meter, a concentration fatal to humans. Ammonia and formaldehyde do not interfere with the test; oxidizing gases interfere but are unlikely to be present under ordinary conditions. Prepare the copper acetate (2.86 g per liter) and benzidine acetate (475 ml cold saturated benzidine acetate solution diluted to 1 liter) solutions separately, store away from light, and mix equal parts just before use.

4—HYDROGEN CYANIDE POISONING IN INDUSTRIAL PROCESSES AND THE DETECTION OF HYDROGEN CYANIDE IN THE AIR ABOVE ELECTROPLATING BATHS

Koelsch, F. and G. Seiffert. Z. Hyg. Infektionskrankh. **101**, 190-196 (1923); CA **18**, 3552 (1924).

The authors use filter paper moistened with a copper acetate-benzidine acetate solution (Pertusi and Gastaldi's reaction) to detect hydrogen cyanide in air. The gas turns the reagent paper blue. If the color appears in less than 1 minute, the authors consider that ventilation is needed, and that possibly too strong a current is passing through the electroplating bath.

5—TESTS FOR HYDROCYANIC ACID GAS IN THE AIR

Katz, S. H. and E. S. Longfellow. J. Ind. Hyg. **5**, 97-104 (1923); CA **17**, 2686 (1923).

It is often desirable to determine the residual hydrogen cyanide concentration in a tank, fumigated vessel or building after it has been aired. The Bureau of Mines has developed a simple technique for this purpose. Tests are made with papers containing (1) sodium picrate (2) guaiacum and copper solution, and (3) phenolphthalein and copper solution. With the first reagent the color is yellow in the absence of hydrocyanic acid but varies from yellow-orange, tan to brown as the hydrocyanic acid content increases. With the second reagent a blue color develops and with the third a pink or bluish pink shade. The results obtained by these field tests agree within 20% of the values obtained by chemical analysis.

6—A DEVICE FOR THE DETERMINATION OF THE SMALLEST QUANTITIES OF HYDROCYANIC ACID IN THE AIR BY THE BENZIDINE-COPPER ACETATE REACTION

Deckert, Walter. Z. Desinfekt. **22**, 81-86 (1930); Chem. Zentr. **1930**, I, 1833; CA **25**, 4489 (1931).

A 25 cc air sample is passed through a filter which has been wetted with a benzidine-copper acetate solution. The tint is compared with a color scale. 0.002 mg hydrocyanic acid can thus be detected and 4-600 mg per cubic meter can be determined with an accuracy of plus or minus 25%.

7—CHEMICAL DETECTION OF RESPIRATORY POISONS

Smolczyk, E. and H. Cobler. Gasmaske **2**, 27-33 (1930); Wasser u. Abwasser **28**, 95 (1930); CA **26**, 1214 (1932).

The authors describe an apparatus which will indicate the composition and concentration of a gas. Sensitized filter strips are used. The reactions occurring and the sensitivity for hydrogen cyanide are given.

8—A RAPID MODIFIED METHOD OF DETECTING AND ESTIMATING HYDROCYANIC ACID SUITABLE FOR FIELD TESTS

Adriano, F. T. and L. Ynalvez. Philippine J. Agr. **3**, 105-110 (1932); CA **27**, 553 (1933).

The authors modify a picric acid test paper, used in agricultural chemistry, so that it can be used for field detection of hydrocyanic acid.

9—DETERMINATION OF HYDROCYANIC ACID IN AIR AND IN AIR-CARBON DIOXIDE MIXTURES

Cupples, H. L. Ind. Eng. Chem., Anal. Ed. **5**, 50-52 (1933); CA **27**, 865 (1933).

The authors describe an apparatus and a procedure for the rapid determination of hydrocyanic acid in mixtures with air or air-carbon dioxide, suitable for the field or laboratory work.

10—THE MICRO-DETECTION OF GASES AND VAPORS

Blank, Eugene W. J. Chem. Education **11**, 523-525 (1934).

Paper moistened with a solution of benzidine acetate and cupric acetate turns blue on exposure to hydrogen cyanide. The test is not specific and may be misleading. Pertusi and Gastaldi claim the test is specific in the presence of disodium phosphate. For confirmation, absorb the hydrogen cyanide in a drop of silver nitrate solution and examine for crystals of silver cyanide. The silver cyanide forms as tiny, highly refractive, short, stout prisms or rods, or sheaves of slender needles. Alternatively, the hydrogen cyanide may be absorbed in ammonium sulfide. If hydrogen cyanide has combined with the ammonium sulfide to form ammonium thiocyanate, a drop of ferric chloride will form blood red ferric thiocyanate. Add. Ref.: CA **28**, 6392 (1934).

11—THE SILVER IODIDE TEST FOR HYDROCYANIC ACID

Fox, Denis L. Science **79**, 37 (1934).

Although Guignard's test with sodium picrate is very delicate for detecting traces of hydrocyanic acid in the air, it is not highly specific. To confirm the presence of hydrocyanic acid, place 1 drop of 5% potassium iodide solution, 1 drop of freshly prepared 0.01 N silver nitrate (0.00025 N for very faint traces of hydrocyanic acid) and 1 ml of 5% potassium hydroxide in a small clean test tube. A faint bluish cloud of silver iodide will form. Draw the suspected air through the liquid, and if hydrocyanic acid is present in the air, the silver iodide turbidity will disappear. With 0.00025 N silver nitrate, this simple delicate and specific test will detect 1 part of hydrocyanic acid in 2,000,000. Add. Ref.: CA **28**, 990 (1934).

12—FUMIGATION OF THE LARGEST GERMAN PASSENGER SHIP (THE BREMEN)

Smolczyk, Eduard. Gasmaske **7**, 32-36 (1935); CA **29**, 4862 (1935).

The article describes an operation in which hydrocyanic acid containing a warning agent and a chemical stabilizer absorbed in an inert carrier was used.

13—PROBLEMS OF PASSIVE DEFENSE AGAINST THE DANGER OF CHEMICAL GAS ATTACKS

Harsovescu, C. Antigaz (Bucharest) **9**, No. 9/10, 22-34 (1935); Chem. Zentr. **1936**, I, 4240; CA **31**, 7141 (1937).

A review of the properties and possibilities of recognizing hydrogen cyanide are described. Methods for preventing contact of foods and drink with war gases are discussed.

14—THE DETECTION OF TOXIC GASES AND VAPORS

Leroux, Lucien. Rev. hyg. et med. prevent. **57**, 81-112 (1935).

The author discusses various techniques for detecting hydrogen cyanide. Prepare copper guaiac test papers by immersing strips of filter paper in a 1% copper sulfate solution and drying, then treating with a fresh 3.4% alcoholic guaiac solution just before use. For Pertusi-Gastaldi paper, mix equal parts of 0.25% copper nitrate solution and 0.25% benzidine acetate solution, and impregnate strips of filter paper with the mixture. The paper turns pale blue with 0.005 mg hydrogen cyanide per liter of air, blue with 0.008 mg per liter, and deep blue with 0.012 mg per liter. Alternatively, dissolve 2.68 g copper acetate in 1 liter of water (solution 1). Dilute 475. ml of saturated (at room temperature) benzidine acetate to 1 liter with water (solution 2). Impregnate strips of filter paper with a mixture of equal parts of solutions 1 and 2. Hydrocyanic acid changes sodium picrate paper from yellow to orange pink. Deniges reagent consists of 2 ml ammonium hydroxide, 1 drop of 5 to 10% potassium iodide, 20 ml water, and 1 drop of 1.5 to 2% silver nitrate. Test contaminated air for cyanide by waving a glass rod coated with sodium hydroxide in the air, then dipping the rod into 2 or 3 ml of Deniges reagent. If hydrocyanic acid is present, the opalescent reagent clears. Add. Ref.: CA **29**, 3627 (1935).

15—THE USE OF INDICATORS FOR THE DETECTION OF POISONOUS GASES AND VAPORS

Heering, D. Gasmaske **8**, 88-89 (1936).

A concentration of 0.062 mg hydrogen cyanide per liter of air will turn benzidine acetate paper blue in 7 seconds, while 0.011 mg per liter will form a dark to bright blue in 6 to 40 seconds, and 0.0011 mg will produce a just visible blue tint in from 25 to 60 seconds. Add. Ref.: CA **30**, 7059 (1936).

16—SIMPLE METHODS FOR THE DETECTION AND DETERMINATION OF POISONOUS GASES, VAPORS, SMOKES, AND DUSTS IN FACTORY AIR

Weber, Hans H. Zentr. Gewerbehyg. Unfallverhuet. **23**, 177-180 (1936).

Reagent preparation: For reagent I dissolve 0.286 g copper acetate in 100 ml water. For reagent II add 52.5 ml water to 47.5 ml saturated (at room temperature) benzidine acetate solution. For use mix equal parts of I and II. Separately, the reagents keep well stored in the dark; mixed, they keep a maximum of 2 weeks. Just before testing, and outside the contaminated atmosphere, moisten half the length of strips of filter paper with the reagent mixture and place in a stoppered glass vial. Expose the impregnated strips to the contaminated air for 7 seconds. The strips turn dark blue with more than 0.06 mg per liter of hydrocyanic acid; medium to light blue with approximately 0.04 mg per liter; and very pale blue with 0.015 to 0.022 mg per liter. The reaction is independent of temperature. Ammonia and formaldehyde do not interfere except to give the color a greenish tinge. Oxidizing agents such as chlorine and nitrogen oxides give a blue color with the benzidine acetate solution alone. Add. Ref.: CA **32**, 1609 (1938).

17—DETERMINATION OF FUMIGANTS. IV. DETECTION AND DETERMINATION OF RESIDUES OF HYDROGEN CYANIDE

Page, A. B. P. and F. P. Gloyns. J. Soc. Chem. Ind. **55**, 209-213T (1936); CA **30**, 7498 (1936).

The authors investigated the conditions necessary for the detection of hydrogen cyanide by the benzidine acetate-copper acetate test paper method. The reaction with iodine was considered most satisfactory for determination of small quantities of hydrogen cyanide. A vessel containing 0.0005 N iodine solution in carbon tetrachloride is evacuated to 100 mm mercury. On opening the vessel to the atmosphere containing hydrogen cyanide, the iodine solution is decolorized if more than the equivalent amount of hydrogen cyanide is drawn in.

18—CHEMICAL REACTIONS OF WAR GASES

Hennig, H. Gasschutz u. Luftschutz **7**, 18-21 (1937); CA **31**, 2311 (1937).

Detect hydrocyanic acid qualitatively on test papers moistened with a fresh mixture (less than 2 weeks old) of equal parts of the following solutions: Solution I, 2.86 g cupric acetate monohydrate in 1 liter of water; Solution II, 475.

ml of a saturated (at room temperature) aqueous solution of benzidine acetate plus 525. ml of water. If no blue color develops in 7 seconds there is no danger of hydrocyanic acid poisoning.

19—SHORT SCHEME OF ANALYSIS FOR THE DETECTION OF POISON GASES

Studinger, J. (With Notes on Their Odour and Irritant Action by R. Mueller). Chem. and Ind. (London) **15**, 225-231 (1937). Translated by F. G. Crosse from the original article in Mitteilungen aus dem Gebiete der Lebensmitteluntersuchung und Hygiene **27**, 8-23 (1936) (see CA **31**, 6367 (1937)).

Mix equal parts of the following: Solution A: 2.86 g copper acetate in 1 liter of water; Solution B: 475. ml of saturated benzidine acetate solution and 525. ml water. Strips of filter paper moistened with the mixture turn blue when exposed to hydrocyanic acid. The reaction is not specific. Add. Ref.: CA **31**, 3588 (1937).

20—METHODS FOR THE DETECTION OF TOXIC GASES IN INDUSTRY. HYDROGEN CYANIDE VAPOUR

Anon. Dept. of Scientific and Industrial Research, London, England. Leaflet No. 2 (1938) 9 pp.

The leaflet describes the following tests for detecting small quantities of hydrogen cyanide vapor: 1) Prussian Blue Test: The gas reacts with an alkaline ferrous sulfate solution containing ferric chloride; on acidifying, dark Prussian blue forms. This test is specific but insufficiently sensitive for low concentrations of hydrogen cyanide. 2) Benzidine-Copper Acetate Test Paper: The gas reacts with a mixed solution of copper acetate and benzidine acetate, the benzidine being oxidized to a blue compound. This test is specific and is sensitive to 1 part in 100,000, but bromine, chlorine, hydrogen chloride, sulfur dioxide, and hydrogen sulfide interfere. Prepare the benzidine-copper acetate paper by mixing, just before making the test, 25 ml of 1% benzidine acetate solution with 2 ml of 3% copper acetate solution. Immerse 2″ wide strips of extra thick white filter paper for 1 minute, drain, and dry in a warm atmosphere until the strips are just moist. Cut off and discard 1″ from the top and bottom of each strip. Use the strips immediately. 3) Congo Red-Silver Nitrate Test Paper: Prepare the papers fresh just before use. Immerse extra thick, 2″ wide strips of filter paper in a 0.05% solution of Congo red and dry thoroughly. Next, immerse the strips in a 5% solution of silver nitrate and dry quickly away from light. Cut off and discard 1″ from the top and bottom of each strip. Hydrogen cyanide stains the dry paper blue. (Hydrogen cyanide is too weak an acid to color the Congo red alone, but with silver nitrate present the gas forms nitric acid, which then produces the stain.) This test is sensitive (1 part in 100,000) but is affected by any acid or alkaline gases; the latter can be removed by first passing the gas through Congo red paper without

silver nitrate. The person making the test should not smoke at or near the point tested. The Congo red-silver nitrate test and the benzidine-copper acetate reaction have been made quantitative and have been developed as standard tests for hydrogen cyanide in industry. To estimate the concentration of hydrogen cyanide, draw air through the test paper with a specified number of strokes of a hand pump, and compare the depth of the stain produced with the stains on a standard color chart. 4) Sodium Picrate Test Paper: A test paper impregnated with a solution of picric acid and sodium carbonate turns brick-red with hydrogen cyanide. This test is neither specific nor sensitive. 5) Phenolphthalein Test: Hydrogen cyanide, with copper salts as catalysts, re-oxidizes phenolphthalein to a bright red color. Any other oxidizing gases will interfere. 6) Guaiacum Test: Similar to the benzidine-copper acetate test. Hydrogen cyanide oxidizes a guaiacum solution, in the presence of copper acetate, to a blue compound. Any other oxidizing gases interfere. 7) Thiocyanate Test: Hydrogen cyanide is converted to thiocyanate, with subsequent colorimetric estimation of the latter as ferric thiocyanate. Any other oxidizing gases interfere. Approximately 0.12 mg per liter of hydrogen cyanide is dangerous within 1 hour, while approximately 2.5 mg per liter is fatal. Add. Ref.: Analyst **63**, 658 (1938).

21—THE VENTILATION OF HOUSES AFTER FUMIGATION WITH HYDROGEN CYANIDE

Page, A. B. P., O. F. Lubatti, and F. P. Gloyns. J. Hyg. **39**, 12-34 (1939); CA **33**, 3046 (1939).

Detailed recommendations are made for house ventilation after hydrogen cyanide fumigation. The recommendations include a test for hydrogen cyanide by the benzidine acetate-copper acetate method.

22—THE SENSITIVITY OF THE PICRATE PAPER TEST (GUIGNARD TEST) FOR HYDROCYANIC ACID

Steyn, Douw G. J. S. African Vet. Med. Assoc. **10**, 65-68 (1939); CA **34**, 50 (1939).

Picrate paper is sensitive to about 0.00052 mg of hydrogen cyanide in 5 ml of solution. The test is more sensitive at high temperatures than at low temperatures. The picrate test is unreliable with materials containing reducing substances, and the more reliable and more sensitive ferric thiocyanate test should be used instead.

23—THE DETECTION OF TOXIC GASES AND VAPORS IN INDUSTRY

Vallender, R. B. Chem. and Ind. (London) **58**, 330-333 (1939).

The British recommend 2 detector papers for hydrogen cyanide. The first is a benzidine acetate-copper acetate paper which turns blue with air concentrations as low as 1 part in 100,000. The second is a paper impregnated first with Congo red and then with silver nitrate, which relies on the liberation of nitric acid to produce color changes of various shades of reddish-purple and blue. Concentrations as low as 1 part in 50,000 have produced symptoms. Add. Ref.: CA **33**, 4907 (1939).

24—IDENTIFICATION OF WAR GASES

Liberalli, Marcelo Robertson. Rev. quim. farm. (Rio de Janeiro) **4**, 49-53 (1939).

Paper, impregnated with a solution of 1% picric acid and 10% sodium carbonate, then dried, turns red when exposed to hydrogen cyanide. For a more sensitive paper, impregnate with an alcoholic copper sulfate-gum guaiac reagent, which turns intensely blue with hydrogen cyanide. Add. Ref.: CA **33**, 7921 (1939).

25—CASE HISTORIES AS RELATED TO FUMIGATION PROCEDURES

Horsfall, J. L. Pests **8**, No. 4, 19-23 (1940); CA **34**, 3400 (1940).

The author recommends the use of methyl orange-mercuric chloride test paper for residual hydrogen cyanide analysis.

26—DETERMINING HYDROCYANIC ACID IN GAS MIXTURES SUCH AS AIR

McAllister, Robert W. (to Mine Safety Appliances Co.) U. S. (Pat. No.) 2,176,462, Oct. 17, 1940; CA **34**, 964 (1940).

A method for the determination of hydrocyanic acid is described. The sample is passed through a column containing silica gel impregnated with a color-forming material such as a benzidine acetate-cupric acetate solution sensitive to hydrocyanic acid. The length of the colored stain is proportional to the concentration of hydrocyanic acid present. Add. Refs.: Mine Safety Appliances Co. (Pittsburgh, Pa.). Catalog of Industrial Safety Equipment 7-B, 3rd Ed., Sec. 3, p. 27 (1957); also Bull. 0811-1 (1959).

27—HYDROGEN CYANIDE GAS FUMIGATION

O'Donnell, J. E., H. W. Mundt, W. N. Knudsen, and Philip H. Delano. J. Ind. Hyg. Toxicol. **22**, 253-275 (1940).

1) Impregnate Whatman No. 40 filter paper with a mixture of 10 ml of 0.5% mercuric chloride, 5 ml of 0.25% methyl orange, and 1 ml of glycerine, drain, and dry the paper. The test paper, which is affected by light, may be stored for as long as 2 weeks in closed containers containing saturated sodium chloride solution. Hydrogen cyanide gas turns the orange-colored paper pink in 2 minutes at concentrations of from 10 to 14 ppm, with a range up to 200 ppm. 2) Saturate strips of filter paper with a 10% solution of gum guaiac and dry. For use, moisten the test paper with 0.25% copper sulfate, which will turn blue if hydrogen cyanide is present. The test is sensitive to at least 0.8 ppm of hydrogen cyanide. Other oxidizing gases interfere. Add. Ref.: CA **35**, 821 (1941).

28—DETECTION OF WAR GASES

Fenton, Paul F. J. Chem. Education **21**, 92 (1944).

Aspirate air contaminated with hydrogen cyanide through a detector tube filled with silica gel mixed with ferrous sulfate, then wet the tube with 20% sodium hydroxide solution, heat over a match, and finally treat with a mixture of equal parts of 5% ferric chloride solution and concentrated hydrochloric acid. Prussian blue forms if cyanide is present. Add. Ref.: CA **38**, 1811 (1944).

29—DETECTION OF WAR GASES

Fenton, Paul F. J. Chem. Education **21**, 488-489 (1944).

To a small portion of the contaminated silica gel (see Ibid., Section I), add several granules of ferrous sulfate and 2 drops of 20% potassium hydroxide. Stir, add 2 drops of alcohol, and ignite. Then add 2 drops of ferric chloride solution (equal parts of 5% ferric chloride and concentrated hydrochloric acid.) Prussian blue forms if cyanide is present. Add. Ref.: CA **39**, 135 (1945).

30—THE QUANTITATIVE DETERMINATION OF CYANIDE IN AIR

Lester, David. J. Ind. Hyg. Toxicol. **26**, 61-63 (1944).

The method is based on the colorimetric measurement of the amount of cyanide derivative formed from methemoglobin exposed to air containing cyanide. One ppm can be determined in a 1 liter air sample (0.0011 mg per liter), with an error of 0.1 ppm. For concentrations of 10 ppm and higher, the error is $\pm$ 2%. Make the solution of methemoglobin either from dried hemoglobin or from freshly shed whole blood; add 0.2 g of the former or 1 ml of the latter to 100 ml of M/15 phosphate buffer (pH 6.6). For whole blood, add 10 ml of 2% solution of saponin to complete the laking of the cells. To convert the hemoglobin to methemoglobin, add 0.4 ml of 20% solution of potassium ferricyanide to the hemoglobin solution. Add. Ref.: CA **38**, 3926 (1944).

31—A SENSITIVE, PORTABLE, SELF-CONTAINED PHOTOTUBE COLORIMETER FOR THE FIELD DETERMINATION OF CYANIDE IN AIR

Lester, David and Philip F. Ordung. J. Ind. Hyg. Toxicol. **26**, 197-200 (1944).

The colorimeter measures the change in light absorption of a methemoglobin solution in which a part of the methemoglobin is transformed to the cyanide derivative. Draw the cyanide-containing gas sample through the solution of methemoglobin with an aspirating pump; read the light absorption of the solution before and after passage of the gas. (See previous reference for preparation of the methemoglobin solution.) Add. Ref.: CA **38**, 5114 (1944).

32—A RAPID AND SIMPLE METHOD FOR MEASURING SMALL AMOUNTS OF CYANIDE GAS IN AIR

Robbie, W. A. and P. J. Leinfelder. J. Ind. Hyg. Toxicol. **27**, 136-139 (1945).

Bubble a known volume of the gas-air sample through a mixture of 3 parts of 0.005 M dibasic (hydrous) sodium phosphate and 1 part of a reagent made by adding 1 ml of 0.5% phenolphthalein in absolute ethanol to 99 ml of 0.01% copper sulfate (pentahydrate) solution. Add 1 part of 0.1% potassium hydroxide and after 1 minute measure the red color with a photoelectric colorimeter at 550 mu. Calculate the amount of hydrogen cyanide in the sample from a curve of readings of standard potassium cyanide solutions. The method is rapid, simple, and sensitive to 1 part of hydrogen cyanide in 50,000,000 reproducibly, and 1 gamma in 20 ml with a maximum error of 5%. Free halogen gases, hydrogen sulfide, and phenol interfere. The sample must not contain a higher concentration of hydrogen cyanide than the reagent can handle. Add. Ref.: CA **39**, 4813 (1945).

33—DETECTION AND ESTIMATION OF MICROQUANTITIES OF CYANIDE

Gettler, A. O., and L. Goldbaum. Ind. Eng. Chem., Anal. Ed. **19**, 270-271 (1947).

The sensitivity of the Prussian blue test is increased by aerating a sample solution containing hydrogen cyanide and conducting the gas through a specially prepared test paper. Dissolve 5 g of hydrated ferrous sulfate in 50 ml distilled water; filter off any insoluble residue. Immerse Whatman No. 50 filter paper in the solution for 5 minutes, remove the paper, and suspend it in the air until dry. Dip the dry paper into 20% sodium hydroxide solution, and air-dry again. Compare the unknown stain with a series of standard stains, which may be preserved indefinitely if they are mounted between glass plates. The test paper is specific for hydrogen cyanide and no other substances interfere. Its limiting sensitivity is 0.1 μg of hydrogen cyanide.

34—RAPID METHOD FOR THE DETERMINATION OF HYDROCYANIC ACID IN AIR

Fomicheva, N. I. Zavodskaya Lab **13**, 172-174 (1947) (in Russian); CA **42**, 1151 (1948).

A reagent for the determination of hydrogen cyanide is prepared by mixing equal volumes of (A) a solution of 0.2 g benzidine in 100 ml water, heated with a few drops of acetic acid, and (B) a 0.3% solution of copper acetate. 20 grams of silica gel are stirred into the liquid and then dried. The reagent should be used within a few hours after preparation. Owing to rapid change of the color, comparison standards are preferably prepared in water colors on paper; air should be sucked through the silica gel at a rate of 600-700 ml per minute. The method is suitable for the determination of 0.0004 to 0.05 mg hydrogen cyanide per liter.

35—TEST PROCEDURES AND METHODS IN AIR POLLUTION CONTROL

Air Pollution Control District, County of Los Angeles, California, Gordon P. Larson, Director. (Book carries no date, no publisher's name.)

The book details ways of handling air pollution samples. It includes complete procedures for the compounds mentioned, with the techniques employed in air analysis, and additional pertinent data such as particle sizes, air filtration rates, testing procedures, and stack sampling methods. The only analysis suitable for field use is that for hydrogen cyanide. It is based on the Gettler and Goldbaum Prussian blue method (see above).

36—HYDROGEN CYANIDE AS AN INDUSTRIAL HAZARD. METHODS OF DETECTION AND CONTROL

White, Norman G. Am. Ind. Hyg. Assoc. Quart. **9**, 81-84 (1948).

The author describes a device which uses a rubber bulb to draw a known volume of air through 10 ml of reagent in a midget impinger until the color of the reagent matches that of the standard. For the reagent, mix 0.166 g phenolphthalein in 75 ml of ethyl alcohol with 0.33 g copper sulfate pentahydrate in 100 ml of water, and dilute the mixture to 200 ml; dissolve 2.5 g trisodium phosphate dodeca hydrate in 1 liter of water. Place 2 ml of the phenolphthalein-copper solution in 98 ml of the phosphate solution. The author discusses the validity of this method over the usual alkali-producing reaction on free hanging paper and over the Prussian blue test. The method can detect 10 ppm of hydrogen cyanide in 2000 ml of air, but chlorine, bromine, iodine, phenol, and high concentrations of hydrogen sulfide interfere.

37—A COMPLEMENTING REACTION FOR THE IDENTIFICATION OF HYDROCYANIC ACID BY SODIUM PICRATE PAPER

Deniges, George. Rev. asoc. bioquim. arg. **15**, 192-193 (1948) (in French); CA **43**, 5701 (1949).

When hydrogen cyanide reacts with sodium picrate paper a red isopurpurate is formed while hydrogen sulfide, phosphine, and arsine (arsenous hydride) reduce the sodium picrate paper to a reddish picramate. Acetic acid 1:9 destroys the reddish picramate but not the red isopurpurate. The article refers to Guignard, Bull. sci. pharmacol. **5**, 415 (1906).

38—IDENTIFICATION OF HYDROCYANIC ACID BY SODIUM PICRATE PAPER

Deniges, Georges. Bull. soc. pharm. Bordeaux **87**, 5-9 (1949); CA **46**, 1390 (1952).

See 1948 article by the same author, above.

39—DETECTOR OF HYDROGEN CYANIDE IN AIR

Carhart, Homer W. and John A. Krynitsky. U. S. (Pat.

No.) 2,534,229, Dec. 19, 1950; CA **45**, 1467 (1951). Cloth plugs are used to section off a glass tube into 4 compartments. One central section is filled with activated coconut charcoal, 40 to 60 mesh, which was equilibrated with air at 40° and 80% relative humidity.The other central section is filled with a hydrogen cyanide-sensitive reagent prepared as follows: 1.5 g of copper sulfate pentahydrate is dissolved in 100 ml of distilled water. To this solution is added 110 g of iron-free, 40 to 60 mesh, silica gel, and the mixture well stirred. The impregnated gel is dried in a vacuum oven for 16 hours at 85° and then for 2 hours under 5 to 15 mm of mercury. 0.1 g tetramethyldiaminodiphenylmethane and 0.5 g dihydroxybenzaldehyde are dissolved in 120 ml of c.p. acetone and added to the dried gel, the mixture is stirred and dried at 65° for 4 hours and then for 2 hours under 5 to 15 mm of mercury. The final product has a pale greenish-blue cast and is very stable in storage. When the end of the tube is broken and air containing hydrogen cyanide is passed over it, the reagent becomes intensely blue, depending on the concentration of hydrogen cyanide. It is calculated to show 5 μg of hydrogen cyanide in 200 ml of air. A red or pink dye, e.g., DuPont TLA 35, in small amounts, may be added to the impregnated gel to give it a grayish tint. In place of the above amine diphenylamine or bis(p-methylaminophenyl) methane may be used also but these are not quite as stable.

40—THE BENZIDINE ACETATE-COPPER ACETATE TEST FOR HYDROGEN CYANIDE

Brown, W. Burns. Chemistry Industry **1952**, 124-126; CA **46**, 6038 (1952).

Filter paper is dipped into a mixture of equal volumes of a 0.3% copper acetate solution and 0.6 ml solution of acetic acid and 45 g of benzidine in 100 ml of water. The filter paper is then introduced into the hydrogen cyanide-air mixture for exactly 10 seconds. In the presence of hydrogen cyanide a blue color develops.

41—A SIMPLE DEVICE FOR AIR ANALYSIS

Gisclard, J. B., J. H. Rook, W. V. Andresen and W. R. Bradley. Am. Ind. Hyg. Assoc. Quart. **14**, 23-25 (1953).

The device described is a 100 ml syringe mounted on a plywood frame. The air sample is drawn through 2 side arm test tubes containing the reagent to be used. Hydrogen cyanide is determined by the method described by Norman G. White (see above). The absorbing solution and reagent is a buffered phenolphthalein and copper salt solution. Add. Ref.: CA **47**, 10768 (1953).

42—ANALYTICAL PROCEDURE FOR THE DETECTION OF GASES

Guatelli, Manuel A. Rev. asoc. bioquim. arg. **18**, 3-40 (1954).

The author proposes a scheme for analyzing air by testing with sensitive papers. The detector papers he discusses for hydrogen cyanide include: starch iodide paper (sensitive to 1 part per cubic meter), Schoenbein's paper, copper-guaiac paper, sodium picrate paper, and copper-phenolphthalein paper. A British modification of Gastaldi's copper-benzidine test is Whatman No. 40 filter paper impregnated with copper-helianthine reagent, made by mixing 10 parts of solution A (1.25 g mercuric chloride in 250 ml of water) with 5 parts of solution B (0.6 g helianthine in 250 ml of water), and adding 1 part of glycerine for a humectant. The paper is stable for 30 days. A color table is prepared for comparing with test papers in the field. Add. Ref.: CA **48**, 8124 (1954).

43—DETECTION OF CYANIDES

McConnaughey, Paul W. (to Mine Safety Appliances Co.) U. S. (Pat. No.) 2,728,639, Dec. 27, 1955; CA **50**, 5470 (1956).

The author describes a simple, rapid and reliable method for detecting the presence of hydrogen cyanide or acrylic nitrile in air. A reagent consisting of silica gel mixed with a reagent consisting of 0.02 g o-tolidine, 0.02 g anhydrous copper sulfate, and 2.5 g glycerol is prepared. When this reagent contacts cyanide a color change to blue or a blue-green occurs. This reagent will detect 0.54 μ of hydrogen cyanide per liter of air. The method can also be used for the quantitative determination of these cyanides. A measured volume of the air or other gas to be tested is passed through a tube containing the above reagent, and the stain length affords a direct measure of the cyanide concentration.

44—SAMPLING AND ANALYZING AIR FOR CONTAMINANTS IN WORK PLACES

Silverman, Leslie. Encyclopedia of Instrumentation for Industrial Hygiene, edited by Yaffe, Charles D., Dohrman H. Byers, and Andrew D. Hosey. (Univ. of Michigan, Inst. of Industrial Health, Ann Arbor, Mich., 1956) pp. 7-25.

S and S No. 598 filter paper impregnated with 1% benzidine acetate and 3% copper acetate turns light blue to dark blue with 10 to 50 ppm of hydrogen cyanide. Chlorine, bromine, and hydrogen chloride interfere. Whatman No. 40 filter paper impregnated with 0.5% mercuric chloride and 0.25% methyl orange turns pink to red in the range of 20 to 200 ppm hydrogen cyanide. The paper should be stored protected from light.

45—PAPER FOR DETECTION OF HYDROGEN CYANIDE

Johnson, John E. and Erston P. Poor (to U.S.A. as represented by Sec. of the Navy) U. S. (Pat. No.) 2,753,248, July 3, 1956; CA **50**, 15352 (1956).

Filter paper impregnated with alkali and p-nitrobenzaldehyde or its derivatives and wetted with an organic solvent produces color changes in the presence of hydrogen cyanide. p-Nitrobenzaldehyde changes color from pale yellow to purple. 4,4'-Dinitrobenzil gives the same color change while p-nitrobenzil changes from yellow to reddish-brown. An amount of 0.01 mg hydrogen cyanide per liter of air can be detected.

46—CRAYON MARK'S COLOR CHANGE IS POISON GAS WARNING

Anon. Chem. Processing, April, 1957; personal communication (Aromil), July 1957.

Hydrogen cyanide detector crayon pairs, available commercially from Aromil Chem. Co., Baltimore 7, Md., are sensitive to hydrogen cyanide when one is applied over the other. Ten ppm hydrogen cyanide in the atmosphere turns the mixed crayon mark reddish-pink after 5 minutes; on standing, the pink color darkens to purple or blue.

47—DETECTION OF HYDROCYANIC ACID

Draegerwerk Heinrich u. Bernhard Draeger. Ger. (Pat. No.) 962,476, April 25, 1957 (Cl 42.1. 4.06); CA 53, 7866 (1959).

Hydrocyanic acid in air is detected by reduced phenolphthalein in alkaline solution buffered with phosphate (pH 10 to 11). The reagent is in small test tubes, and the tubes also contain a layer of ceramic materials impregnated with ferrous oxide for preliminary purification of the air sample. Directions are given for preparing the indicator material; it should be stored in the absence of oxygen.

48—SENSITIVE DETECTOR CRAYONS FOR PHOSGENE, HYDROGEN CYANIDE, CYANOGEN CHLORIDE, AND LEWISITE

Witten, Benjamin and Arnold Prostak. Anal. Chem. 29, 885-887 (1957).

Hydrogen cyanide is converted to cyanogen chloride, then detected with the cyanogen chloride detector crayon plus a second crayon consisting of 14% chloramine T and 86% blanc fixe, neutral, amorphous, dry. This crayon makes white marks upon which are superimposed the cyanogen chloride detector crayon marks. Hydrogen cyanide turns the mixed marks red-blue. The concentration-time equivalent of about 5 mg minute per cubic meter is equivalent to detecting 5 ppm (5 mg per cubic meter) in 1 minute. The chloramine T crayon is stable for at least 3 years at room temperature, but is unstable at 65°C. Dibromantin (1,3-dibromo-5,5-dimethylhydantoin), stable at 65°C, may be substituted for the chloramine T. Add. Refs.: CA 51, 11915 (1957); IHD 21, 904 (1957).

49—A FIELD METHOD FOR THE RAPID DETERMINATION OF HYDROGEN CYANIDE IN AIR

Dixon, B. E., G. C. Hands, and A. F. F. Bartlett. Analyst 83, 199-202 (1958).

A field test for determining specifically small amounts of

hydrogen cyanide in industrial atmospheres is based on the formation of permanent Prussian blue stains on 4″ by 3″ Whatman No. 50 filter paper strips impregnated with 10% aqueous ferrous sulfate and 20% aqueous sodium hydroxide, then dried. Draw the test air through the paper at not more than 6 ml per second until 360 ml have been drawn, then immerse the paper in 30% sulfuric acid in a dish. Hydrogen cyanide turns the paper blue in from 30 seconds to 1 minute. Determine the amount of hydrogen cyanide by comparing the test stain with the stains on a standard stain chart. The test can detect up to about 500 ppm and is sensitive to slightly less than 1 ppm with an error of plus or minus 10% to 20%. Properly prepared and stored test papers remain active for about 10 months. Add. Refs.: IHD 22, 1175 (1958); AA 5, 3175 (1958); CA 52, 13527 (1958).

50—DETECTION OF HYDROGEN CYANIDE

Lichtenberg, Heinz. Arch. Kriminol. (Germany) 122, 177-178 (1958); CA 53, 10857 (1959).

Pass air samples containing cyanide through a modified Draeger leak detector which contains a cyanide ion sensitive reagent. Detect the hydrogen ions released in the reaction with a suitable indicator. The sensitivity of the method is 0.1 μg per liter of cyanide.

51—COLORIMETRIC DETERMINATION OF HYDROGEN CYANIDE WITH INDICATOR PAPER

McConnaughey, Paul W. (to Mine Safety Appliances Co.). U. S. (Pat. No.) 2,855,280, Oct. 7, 1958; CA 53, 2002, 13896 (1959).

As paper is dispensed from a strip, necessary reagents are deposited on it for detection and determination of hydrogen cyanide (i.e., copper sulfate pentahydrate, methylene-bis (N,N-dimethylaniline), and water).

52—SPOT TEST FOR N-CYANO COMPOUNDS

Feigl, Fritz and Vicente Gentil. Mikrochim. Acta 1, 44-46 (1959) (in English); CA 54, 24091 (1960).

Treat 1 drop of the test solution or solid unknown, in a test tube, with zinc and dilute hydrochloric acid, and heat in boiling water. The hydrogen cyanide evolved will give a blue color with a reagent (2.86g copper acetate, 675 ml saturated aqueous solution of benzidine acetate, and 525 ml water) on filter paper at the mouth of the tube. The method will detect 10 μg dicyandiamide in 0.05 ml, 8 μg cyanamide, or 20 μg potassium cyanourea.

53—TEST TUBE FOR DETECTING HYDROCYANIC ACID

Auergesellschaft G.m.b.H. (by Hermann Heidrich). Ger. (Pat. No.) 1,105,199, April 20, 1961 (Cl. 42 1); CA 55, 26571 (1961).

A detector tube containing silica gel impregnated with silver chloride, mercurous chloride, palladium chloride and an indicator such as bromothymal blue or bromocresol green is described for the determination of hydrocyanic acid. The prepared tubes are insensitive to oxygen and are stable for several years.

54—SPOT TESTS. VOL. II. ORGANIC APPLICATIONS

Feigl, Fritz, translated by Ralph E. Oesper. Elsevier Publishing Co., Houston, Texas (1954). 4th Ed., p. 338.

Impregnate filter paper with an alkaline solution of palladium dimethylglyoxime (precipitate an acid solution of palladium chloride with dimethylglyoxime, wash, shake with 3 N sodium hydroxide, and filter); or put a drop of the solution on filter paper. Hold the moist paper over the suspected gas, then spot the exposed part with a solution of nickel chloride (0.5 N nickel chloride saturated with ammonium chloride). A pink to red stain appears at once, the depth of color depending on the gas concentration.

Most of the reactions for hydrogen cyanide are applicable to aliphatic cyanides or nitriles with varying degrees of sensitivity and accuracy. Most of the chalks are unsatisfactory because by the time they react the high concentration of the cyanide gas has passed the breathing zone.

See Section One

For references 6, 25, 27, 29, 35, 48, 52, 54, 69, 81, 85, 86, 104, 106, 109, 112, 120, 125.

Hydrogen Fluoride
Hydrofluoric Acid

1—MODERN METHODS OF DETECTION AND DETERMINATION OF INDUSTRIAL GASES IN THE ATMOSPHERE

Leclerc, E. and R. Haux. Rev. universele mines **12**, 293-298 (1936).

To detect hydrogen fluoride, draw the air sample into a paraffin-lined flask filled with water. Add first a solution of a titanium salt, then hydrogen peroxide; if the water contains fluorine compounds, a yellow color will develop. Add. Ref.: CA **30**, 6672 (1936).

2—AUTOMATIC DETERMINATION AND WARNING OF DANGEROUS CONCENTRATIONS OF HYDROGEN FLUORIDE IN AIR

Chemodanova, L. S. Zavodskaya Lab. **8**, 1248-1253 (1939); CA **34**, 5785 (1940).

The authors describe a photocolorimetric method for the determination of hydrogen fluoride utilizing the decolorization of ferric thiocyanate as described by Foster. (CA **27**, 357, 4607 (1933)). The stability of the coloration of the iron solution is improved by the addition of potassium persulfate. The method is suitable for determining 0.025-0.35 mg of hydrogen fluoride in 25 ml. The chloride and nitrate ions decolorize the solution to a limited extent. Sulfate ion has also a weak effect but greater than that of chloride. Nitrate and phosphate ions decolorize the solution strongly. The solution is also decolorized by silicon hexafluoride. The determination is not effected by sulfur dioxide in amounts over 10-20 times that of hydrogen fluoride. For the continuous determination of hydrogen fluoride the automatic photoelectric colorimeter described in CA **34**, 49 (1940) was used. The range of determinations was 0.001-0.015 mg hydrogen fluoride in 1 liter of air. The results are tabulated and graphed.

3—DETECTING HYDROFLUORIC ACID VAPOR IN AIR

Marconi's Wireless Telegraph Co., Ltd. and Christopher P. Fagan. Brit. (Pat. No.) 566,389, Dec. 28, 1944; CA **41**, 666 (1947).

An absorbent material, such as filter paper or sintered glass plates is impregnated with a mixture of 3 parts of a 45% solution of zirconium nitrate in distilled water and 2 parts of a solution containing 1.2 g alizarin S in 100 ml of ethyl alcohol. This reagent is dried at 80°. The prepared reagent has a light pink color. In the presence of hydrofluoric acid the color changes to bright yellow.

4—REPORT ON QUALITATIVE TEST FOR FLUORINE

Harrigan, Mary C. J. Assoc. offic. Agr. Chemists **36**, 743-744 (1953).

Dip filter paper in a chloroform solution of aluminum oxinate, dry the paper, and expose it to hydrogen fluoride vapor. The surface in contact with the hydrogen fluoride will not fluoresce in ultraviolet light, and as little as 0.05 mg of fluorine can be detected. Prepare the aluminum oxinate reagent by warming to 50-60° C a solution of 2.22 g of aluminum ammonium sulfate dodecahydrate and 3 drops of hydrochloric acid in 250 ml water; add an excess of an acetic acid solution of the reagent (5% 8-hydroxy-quinoline in 2 N acetic acid). Add a 2 N solution of ammonium acetate slowly until a permanent precipitate forms, then add 20 to 25 ml more for complete precipitation. When the precipitate has settled filter it through a fritted glass filter, wash with cold water, dry at 120 to 140°C, and store in a desiccator. The reagent keeps for several weeks. Add. Ref.: CA **48**, 9864 (1954).

5—ANALYTICAL PROCEDURE FOR THE DETECTION OF GASES

Guatelli, Manual A. Rev. asoc. bioquim. arg. **18**, 3-40 (1954).

Prepare zirconium alizarin sulfonate test paper for detecting hydrogen fluoride by dissolving zirconium oxide in hydrochloric acid and combining this with a saturated solution of alizarin sulfonate. Extract the mixture with ether and impregnate paper with the aqueous layer, warming the solution on a water bath. Dry the papers and store protected from acid fumes. The sensitivity is 1 μg of fluoride ion. Add. Ref.: CA **48**, 8124 (1954).

6—COMPOSITION FOR DETERMINING HYDROFLUORIC ACID AND FLUORIDES

Auergesellschaft Akt.-Ges. (by Hermann Heidrich). Ger. (Pat. No.) 1,000,170, Jan. 3, 1957 (Cl. 42.1); CA **54**, 2096 (1960).

The detector tube for the determination of hydrofluoric acid and fluorides contains silica gel which is impregnated with ferric thiocyanate and contains a small amount of hydrochloric acid. The reagent was prepared by mixing 10 g silica gel and 10 cc of a 0.5% ethereal ferric thiocyanate solution with 3 drops concentrated hydrochloric acid. The mixture was stirred and held until the color turned slightly yellowish-red. The ferric thiocyanate solution was prepared by dissolving 0.95 g ferric chloride hexahydrate and 0.8 g ammonium thiocyanate in 100 cc water. The 2 solutions were combined, and the ferric thiocyanate was extracted with ether.

7—FIELD TYPE COLORIMETRIC TESTERS FOR GASES AND PARTICULATE MATTER

McConnaughey, Paul W. Presented at the annual meeting of the Am. Ind. Hyg. Assoc., Atlantic City, N.J., 1958. (Author's abstract).

Hydrogen fluoride in air can be detected quantitatively in concentrations of ½ to 5 ppm by a spot test procedure using Whatman No. 1 filter paper and dimethylaminoazophenyl arsonic acid-zirconium oxychloride suspension in alcohol, hydrochloric acid, and water solution. It was found that a sensitive test for hydrogen fluoride could be obtained by placing the newly prepared reagent on test paper and waving it in the atmosphere, but the speed at which it came in contact with the air sample affected the rate of the stain formation. An apparatus, using an aspirator bulb for sampling, was designed to control the exposure time between the reagent and a measured air sample to obtain a color of fixed intensity. The measured air sample passes slowly by the test reagent on the test paper. The air sample does not pass through the test paper but is channeled around it. The sample volume necessary to produce a color change from light brown to a deep pink tain similar to the color standard determines the concentration of hydrofluoric acid.

8—SPOT-TESTING SOLUTIONS, ESPECIALLY FOR DETECTION OF LEAD AND HYDROGEN FLUORIDE

McConnaughey, Paul W. (to Mine Safety Appliances Co.). U. S. (Pat. No.) 2,839,368, June 17, 1958; CA **53**, 989 (1959).

The author describes a technique for obtaining a uniform color test in spot testing analysis. The method essentially consists of depositing a suspension of a colorimetric reagent on a porous carrier. The detection of hydrogen fluoride using this procedure is described. One drop of a suspension prepared by mixing 10 parts by weight of a solution of 0.1 g zirconyl chloride in 100 ml 1 N hydrochloric acid with 1 part of a solution of 0.5 g p-(p-aminophenylazo) benzenearsonic acid in 45 ml ethyl alcohol containing 5 ml concentrated hydrochloric acid and 17 ml glycerol forms a red stain in the presence of hydrogen fluoride.

9—HYDROGEN FLUORIDE DETECTOR

Mine Safety Appliances Co. 201 N. Braddock Ave., Pittsburgh, Pa. Bull. 0811-10 (1959).

The hydrogen fluoride detector consists of a rubber bulb aspirator, a filter holder, a reagent kit of 4 syrettes, and filter papers. Place the filter paper in the filter holder, add 1 drop of the reagent to the exposed area, and draw the air sample. With 10 aspirations the sensitivity is 0.5 ppm hydrogen fluoride and with 1 aspiration the sensitivity may be greater than 5 ppm. The unique preparation of the chemicals gives them an indefinitely long shelf life.

10—AN AUTOMATIC HYDROGEN FLUORIDE RECORDER PROPOSED FOR INDUSTRIAL HYGIENE AND STACK MONITORING

Adams, Donald F. Anal. Chem. **32**, No. 10, 1312-1316 (1960).

High fluoride levels in the range of 0.1 to 200 mg per cubic meter are determined by measuring the color change produced by the reaction between a green iron-ferron (8-hydroxy-7-iodo-5-quinoline-sulfonic acid) complex and fluoride ions. Details of the reagent preparations are given, together with the effects of interfering ions. The manual method may be applicable to detector systems on a visual comparison basis. Add. Refs.: Anal. Chem., Anal. Reviews **33** No. 5, 3R-13R (1961). CA **54**, 24092 (1960).

11—THE RAPID DETERMINATION OF HYDROGEN FLUORIDE IN THE ATMOSPHERIC AIR BY THE METHOD OF INDICATOR TUBES

Bulycheva, A. I., Ts. A. Gol'dina, and T. I. Sergeeva. Fiz.-Khim. Metody Issledovan. Vozdushn. Sredy, Vsesoyuz. Tsentral. Nauch.-Issledovatel. Inst. Okhrany Truda **1961**, 65-62; CA **56**, 10509 (1962).

Grind porcelain powder, sift to a fineness of 390 to 247 μ, wash with cold, then with hot distilled water, and dry at 105°. Mix 1 ml of a 1% alcoholic solution of bromophenol blue with 0.15 ml of 0.1 N sodium hydroxide. Mix 5 g of the porcelain powder with 1 ml of the indicator solution, let stand in the dark for 40 minutes, then dry at 30 to 35° for 30 minutes. In a glass tube 50 mm long and 2.4 to 2.5 mm inside diameter place a 30 mm column of the powder, plug both ends with cotton and secure with an enameled wire spring. Pass 1 liter of contaminated air through the tube in 5 to 6 minutes and compare the length of yellow stain with that of a similarly prepared standard. The sensitivity is 0.0005 mg of hydrogen fluoride per liter of air. Other acid fumes interfere.

See Section One
For references 106, 125.

Hydrogen Peroxide

1—TESTING TUBE FOR QUANTITATIVE DETERMINATION OF HYDROGEN PEROXIDE VAPORS AND MISTS

Auergesellschaft Akt.-Ges. (by Hermann Heidrich). Ger. (Pat. No.) 1,019,484, Nov. 14, 1957 (Cl. 42.**1**); CA **54**, 16948 (1960).

A solution is prepared consisting of 1 g titanium dioxide in 8 cc of concentrated sulfuric acid. This mixture is boiled until a white vapor evolves. The resulting brownish solution is cooled and added to 190 cc of ice water. Approximately 60 cc of this solution is added to dry silica gel. The mixture is dried and introduced into the detector tubes.

NOTE: Most reagent systems for detecting oxidizing substances will detect hydrogen peroxide. Because hydrogen peroxide decomposes to hydroxyl ions, systems based on alkalinity also are suitable for detecting the peroxide.

See Section One
For reference 6.

Hydrogen Sulfide

1—COLORIMETRIC ESTIMATION OF SMALL AMOUNTS OF HYDROGEN SULFIDE

Mecklenburg, W. and F. Rosenkraenzer. Z. anorg. Chem. **86**, 143-153 (1914?); CA **8**, 1938 (1914).

Methylene blue is produced by the action of ferric chloride and dimethyl-p-phenylenediamine sulfate upon an aqueous solution of hydrogen sulfide containing free hydrochloric acid. The intensity of the color developed is proportional to the amount of hydrogen sulfide present, and the color is stable for several weeks. Variations in the amounts or order of addition of the reagents alter the intensity of the color. The standards solutions must be prepared from known amounts of hydrogen sulfide. Satisfactory results were obtained with quantities of hydrogen sulfide as little as 10 μg per liter.

2—CHEMICAL DETECTION OF RESPIRATORY POISONS

Smolczyk, E. and H. Cobler. Gasmaske **2**, 27-33

(1930); Wasser u. Abwasser **28**, 95 (1930); CA **26**, 1214 (1932).

An apparatus indicating the composition and concentration of gas is described. Sensitized paper strips are used and their reaction and sensitivity to hydrogen sulfide are given.

3—THE MICRO-DETECTION OF GASES AND VAPORS

Blank, Eugene W. J. Chem. Education **11**, 523-525 (1934).

Hydrogen sulfide is detected with lead acetate paper, or by a more delicate test with sodium plumbate. Add. Ref.: CA **28**, 6392 (1934).

4—AUTOMATIC DETECTION AND CONTROL OF HYDROGEN SULFIDE

Roberts, S. and G. Minors. Chem. and Ind. (London) **1934**, 526-529; CA **28**, 4941 (1934).

The authors describe an automatic detection and control device for hydrogen sulfide. Between 2 compartments, one containing an electric lamp and the other a photoelectric cell, an amplifying valve and a potentiometer, is a removable slide carrying a strip of filter paper impregnated with a 20% solution of lead acetate containing 10% glycerol. The paper is in contact with the gases. The change in current due to change in optical transparency causes an alarm to ring and sets an auxiliary pump in action. Details of construction are given.

5—A DETECTOR FOR LOW CONCENTRATIONS OF HYDROGEN SULFIDE

Littlefield, J. B., W. P. Yant, and L. B. Berger. Bur. Mines, Rept. of Investigations No. 3276, 13 pp (1935); CA **29**, 5382 (1935).

A rubber bulb or hand pump aspirates air to be tested for hydrogen sulfide through sensitized granules in a glass tube. Granules of activated aluminum trioxide (20-24 mesh) coated with silver cyanide or lead acetate satisfactorily estimated 0.0025 to +0.05% by volume of hydrogen sulfide, at temperatures from −22 to +25°. Tubes filled with silver cyanide-coated granules retained their sensitivity and usefulness after 18 months' storage. The detector indicates the amount of hydrogen sulfide either by the length of the dark stain produced by a constant sample volume, or by the volume of sample required to produce a standard length stain. Carbon monoxide, carbon dioxide, sulfur dioxide, chlorine, hydrogen chloride, natural gas, gasoline, benzene, ethyl and methyl alcohols do not react. Mercaptans interfere.

6—THE DETECTION OF TOXIC GASES AND VAPORS

Leroux, Lucien. Rev. hyg. et med. prevent. **57**, 81-112 (1935).

Immerse strips of filter paper in 20% neutral lead acetate solution, and dry at moderate temperature. In 30 seconds 0.00034% hydrogen sulfide blackens the paper, 0.0034%

blackens it in 2 seconds, and 0.34% immediately. Arsine and phosphine interfere. Add. Ref.: CA **29**, 3627 (1935).

7—IBID.

To an aqueous solution of the gas, add 1/50 its volume of hydrochloric acid, a small amount of paraphenylenediamine, and 1 drop of ferric chloride. A violet color indicates hydrogen sulfide; the test is sensitive to 0.01 mg per liter.

8—IBID.

One part in 100,000 of hydrogen sulfide may be detected by the very energetic reduction of a mixture of iodine pentoxide and sulfuric acid, with the liberation of free iodine. *(This has possible application to a tube-type field detector.)*

9—A REVERSIBLE INDICATOR FOR THE DETECTION OF SMALL QUANTITIES OF HYDROGEN SULFIDE IN THE ATMOSPHERE

Bell, J. and W. K. Hall. Chem. and Ind. (London) **1936**, 89-92; CA **30**, 2875 (1936).

The authors describe a method for the detection of hydrogen sulfide. The method depends on various colors produced by hydrogen sulfide in a solution of 0.5 g per liter sodium nitroprusside, 3.7 g per liter sodium carbonate and 1.9 g per liter sodium bicarbonate. The colors produced are respectively pink, mauve, and deep violet. The rate of color production is proportional to the concentration per unit time. This is controlled by varying the air volume and the solution volume. Three types of apparatus are described.

10—THE USE OF INDICATORS FOR THE DETECTION OF POISONOUS GASES AND VAPORS

Heering, D. Gasmaske **8**, 88-89 (1936).

Lead acetate paper, used wet, turns brown-black in 2 seconds at 0.047 mg hydrogen sulfide per liter; 0.0017 mg per liter reacts with the paper in 30 seconds. Add. Ref.: CA **30**, 7059 (1936).

11—MODERN METHODS OF DETECTION AND DETERMINATION OF INDUSTRIAL GASES IN THE ATMOSPHERE

Leclerc, E. and R. Haux. Rev. universelle mines **12**, 293-298 (1936).

The classical method for detecting hydrogen sulfide with lead acetate impregnated paper is sensitive to 1 part in 20,000. Inert granules can be treated with the lead acetate; alternatively, the granules can be treated with aluminum oxide and silver cyanide for the detection of hydrogen sulfide. In an automatic apparatus a photoelectric cell registers the variation in density of an indicator paper impregnated with lead acetate and glycerine. Add. Ref.: CA **30**, 6672 (1936).

12—THE SCIENTIFIC APPROACH TO THE POISON-GAS QUESTION

Anderson, P. H. Textile Colorist **58**, 805-806 (1936); CA **31**, 2708 (1937).

The author presents a review of the methods for detecting and estimating hydrogen sulfide concentrations in air.

13—A SIMPLE DEVICE FOR THE AUTOMATIC QUANTITATIVE INDICATION OF HYDROGEN SULFIDE IN THE ATMOSPHERE

Kraus, R. Chem. Fabrik **1936**, 241-242; CA **30**, 4726 (1936).

An apparatus for the automatic determination of hydrogen sulfide is presented. The apparatus is 16 cm in diameter and consists of a clock-driven dial which contains a filter paper with the hours printed on the edge. The paper is wetted with a lead solution containing glycerol. The glycerol prevents drying of the reagent. A narrow slit in the metal cover of the apparatus exposes the filter to the atmosphere and causes a discoloration in the presence of hydrogen sulfide. Directions for standardizing and interpreting the results are given.

14—SOME METHODS FOR THE DETECTION AND ESTIMATION OF POISONOUS GASES AND VAPORS IN THE AIR (A Practical Manual for the Industrial Hygienist)

Zhitkova, A. S., translated by J. B. Ficklen. (Service to Industry, Box 133, West Hartford, Conn., 1936), pp. 55-62.

Strips of filter paper moistened with a lead acetate solution turn light brown in the presence of hydrogen sulfide. High concentrations of the gas may turn the paper to metallic black, the depth of color being roughly proportional to the hydrogen sulfide concentration. Add. Refs.: CA **31**, 632 (1937); J. Ind. Hyg. Toxicol. **18**, 681 (1936).

15—SIMPLE METHODS FOR THE DETECTION AND DETERMINATION OF POISONOUS GASES, VAPORS, SMOKES, AND DUSTS IN FACTORY AIR

Weber, Hans H. Zentr. Gewerbehyg. Unfallverhuet. **23**, 177-180 (1936).

Hydrogen sulfide is detected with moistened lead acetate paper. With the technique of Smolczyk and Cobler (see above), 0.47 mg hydrogen sulfide per liter stains the paper immediately, and 0.047 mg per liter in 2 seconds. Add. Ref.: CA **32**, 1609 (1938).

16—COLORIMETRIC DETERMINATION OF HYDROGEN SULFIDE IN AIR

Smirnov, K. A. Zavodskaya Lab. **6**, 240 (1937); CA **31**, 6135 (1937).

Air is aspirated through 25 cc of a solution containing 2 cc of a 1% sodium nitroprusside and a few drops of am-

17—DETERMINATION OF TRACES OF HYDROGEN SULFIDE IN THE AIR

Quitmann, E. Z. anal. Chem. **109**, 241-246 (1937); CA **31**, 6580 (1937).

Estimations of hydrogen sulfide based on its darkening of lead acetate paper are compared with results of iodiometric titration of the calcium sulfide precipitate formed by the reaction of hydrogen sulfide with cadmium acetate solution.

18—A NEW APPARATUS FOR TRACES OF GAS. I. DETECTION OF HYDROGEN SULFIDE

Kraus, R. Z. anal. Chem. **112**, 1-7 (1938); CA **32**, 3669 (1938).

The automatic instrument previously described by the author, in which hydrogen sulfide is detected on lead acetate paper (see above) has been improved.

19—HYDROGEN SULFIDE AND PHENOL IN THE AIR. THEIR DETECTION WITH THE HELP OF THE BELL METHOD

Liesegang, Wilhelm. Gesundh.-Ing. **61**, 320-322 (1938); CA **32**, 8984 (1938).

A method for the detection of hydrogen sulfide existing as an air pollutant is described. The method depends upon the darkening of a filter paper moistened with lead acetate and stretched over a bell glass. An exposure time of 24 hours is required.

20—DETERMINATION OF HYDROGEN SULFIDE IN AIR

Maevskaya, V. P. Zavodskaya Lab. **7**, 181-183 (1938); CA **32**, 4469 (1938).

Mecklenburg and Rosenkraenzer's modification (see above) of the Fischer method is applied to the colorimetric determination of hydrogen sulfide in air.

21—THE DETECTION OF TOXIC GASES AND VAPORS IN INDUSTRY

Vallender, R. B. Chem. and Ind. (London) **58**, 330-333 (1939).

The British method (lead acetate and a hand pump) detects hydrogen sulfide, and concentrations as low as 1 part in 150,000 produce stains with only 5 pump strokes. Although some workers report that the lower detectable odor limit is 1 part in 7 million, the gas, in a concentration of only 1 part in 10,000, will paralyze the olfactory nerve so it cannot detect the odor. Odor alone, therefore, is insufficient for detecting harmful concentrations of hydrogen sulfide. Add. Ref.: CA **33**, 4907 (1939).

22—A COMMENT ON THE DETECTION OF HYDROGEN SULFIDE BY LEAD ACETATE PAPER

Johnsen, William and E. B. Colegrave. Chem. and Ind. (London) **17**, 726-727 (Correspondence) (1939).

The British hydrogen sulfide detector (Methods for the Detection of Toxic Gases in Industry, Leaflet No. 1, Hydrogen Sulfide, see below) is unreliable in the presence of sulfur and water vapor, because together they produce the same stain as hydrogen sulfide. Add. Refs.: CA **34**, 3619 (1940); CA **31**, 7002 (1937).

23—SODIUM NITROPRUSSIDE TEST PAPERS FOR THE DETECTION OF SULFUR DIOXIDE AND HYDROGEN SULFIDE

Sciacca, N. and E. Solarino. Ann. chim. applicata **30**, 246-247 (1940); CA **35**, 1353 (1941).

Filter papers impregnated with a solution of 4% sodium nitroprusside and 2% sodium carbonate will detect 1 part of hydrogen sulfide in 5,000,000.

24—TUBE FOR THE DETECTION OF POISONOUS SUBSTANCES

Chema, Ltd. and Jan Sigmund. Brit. (Pat. No.) 519,-957, April 10, 1940; CA **36**, 589 (1942).

The small detector tube for hydrogen sulfide contains 1 or more detecting layers, such as silica gel impregnated with the catalyst copper sulfate, then treated with benzodiacetate solution.

25—DETECTION OF TRACES OF HYDROGEN SULFIDE IN GASES CONTAINING SULFUR DIOXIDE

Fischer, J. Die Chemie **56**, 301 (1943); CA **38**, 1979 (1944).

Cuprous or mercurous nitrate solutions are recommended for the determination of hydrogen sulfide in the presence of sulfur dioxide. The reagents are impregnated into silica gel or filter paper.

26—METHODS FOR THE DETECTION OF TOXIC GASES IN INDUSTRY. HYDROGEN SULFIDE

Anon. Dept. Sci. Ind. Research, London, Eng., Leaflet No. **1**, 7 pp (1943).

In the method adopted as standard, a hand pump draws a known volume of air sample through a lead acetate test paper. Prepare the test papers, 2″ x 4″ strips of Whatman No. 1 filter paper, by immersing them for 1 minute in reagent. (Dissolve 10 g lead acetate in 90 ml distilled water, add 5 ml of glacial acetic acid and 10 ml of pure glycerol.) Drain the test papers and dry, suspended vertically, as completely as possible at room temperature in a hydrogen sulfide free atmosphere. Store in glass-stoppered, airtight containers, and prepare fresh every two weeks. Compare the stain (light to dark brown) produced on the paper by hydrogen sulfide with the stains on a standard chart, within 10 minutes, and preferably sooner. The test will detect 1 part of hydrogen sulfide in 150,000 parts of air by volume. (One part by volume of hydrogen sulfide in 1,000 parts of air is equivalent to 1.52 mg per liter.) (This edition revised in 1952.)

monium chloride until the solution becomes definitely colored.

27—AUTOMATIC DETECTION AND CONTROL OF HYDROGEN SULFIDE

Clough, J. J. Soc. Chem. Ind. **63**, 210-213 (1944); CA **38**, 6138 (1944).

An automatic sampler with an alarm system uses a lead salt impregnated paper to detect hydrogen sulfide.

28—RAPID METHOD FOR DETERMINING HYDROGEN SULFIDE IN AIR

Verokhobin, I. G. and E. D. Filyanskaya. Zavodskaya Lab. **14**, 106-107 (1948); CA **43**, 971 (1949).

The authors describe an apparatus for the determination of hydrogen sulfide in air. The apparatus consists of a 100 ml capacity pump with a scale graduated in mg hydrogen sulfide per liter. Glass tubes filled with porcelain particles treated with a 10% solution of lead acetate in 1.0% acetic acid are used. Hydrogen sulfide concentrations from 0.05-0.3 mg per liter can be detected within ±3-4% of the true value.

29—RAPID METHOD OF ESTIMATION OF HYDROGEN SULFIDE. I. HYDROGEN SULFIDE DETECTOR

Kitagawa, Tetsuzo. Repts. Tokyo Ind. Research Inst. Lab. **44**, 1-19 (1949); CA **44**, 1851 (1950).

One part of lead acetate solution is sprayed on 3 parts of silica gel dried at 65°. After preparing this reagent it is packed in a glass tube and 100 ml of sample is aspirated through the tube at the rate of 10 to 20 ml per second. The length of the stain produced is proportional to the amount of hydrogen sulfide.

30—DETECTION OF PHOSPHINE AND HYDROGEN SULFIDE IN ACETYLENE

Kitagawa, Tetsuzo and Tadahiko Ogawa. J. Electrochem. Soc. Japan **19**, 258-261 (1951); CA **46**, 1920 (1952).

Silica gel impregnated with lead salts detected 0.005-0.18% hydrogen sulfide in acetylene.

31—APPARATUS FOR THE RAPID DETERMINATION OF HYDROGEN SULFIDE IN AIR

Kirpatovskii, I. Novosti Neftyanoi Tekh., Neftepererabotka **1951**, No. 3, 22-24; CA **50**, 3806 (1956).

A method for the determination of hydrogen sulfide is presented. Hydrogen sulfide can be determined in 1 to 3 minutes by aspirating air through indicator tubes with a spring-actuated hand pump. The glass detector tubes are filled with powdered porcelain treated with a 1% acetic acid solution containing 7.5% lead acetate and 1% barium chloride. A 230 ml sample is used to determine concentrations ranging from 0.002 to 0.06 mg per liter while a 30 ml sample is used for the 0.05 to 0.4 mg per liter range. Two concentration comparison scales are provided with the apparatus.

32—INDICATOR AND RECORDER OF HYDROGEN SULFIDE CONCENTRATION IN GASEOUS MIXTURES

McClendon, Ernest A. (to Phillips Petroleum Co.). U. S. (Pat. No.) 2,554,414, May 22, 1951; CA **45**, 5984 (1951).

A continuous filter strip is wetted with aqueous sodium plumbate and the color changes occurring when the hydrogen sulfide contacts the reagent are photoelectrically recorded.

33—CONTINUOUS MULTIPOINT HYDROGEN SULFIDE DETECTOR

Aldred, L. and J. Clough. Ind. Chemist **29**, 515-520 (1953); IHD **18**, 1161 (1954).

In the instrument air drawn continuously from 6 sampling points passes through a sodium nitroprusside solution. Hydrogen sulfide causes a reversible color change in the solution, which is measured photoelectrically, while a recorder registers changes in concentration. *Although this procedure is photometric, the technique is suitable for visual comparison.* Add. Ref.: CA **48**, 3200 (1954).

34—SIMULTANEOUS DETERMINATION OF SMALL QUANTITIES OF HYDROGEN SULFIDE AND CARBON DISULFIDE IN AIR

Sonnenschein, W. and K. Schaefer. Z. anal. Chem. **140**, (1), 15-25 (1953); AA **1**, 1246 (1954).

A rapid and simple method for the determination of hydrogen sulfide and carbon disulfide is described. Hydrogen sulfide is determined by the colorimetric estimation (at 670 mμ) of the methylene blue formed when hydrogen sulfide reacts with a 0.1% solution of dimethyl-p-phenylenediamine hydrochloride in 18% hydrochloric acid and 0.5% ferric chloride hexahydrate in 4% hydrochloric acid. As little as 0.2 μg of hydrogen sulfide can be measured with an accuracy of ±20%. Colloidal zinc sulfide is a stable standard for the hydrogen sulfide calibration graph. Add. Ref.: CA **48**, 1200 (1954).

35—A SIMPLE DEVICE FOR AIR ANALYSIS

Gisclard, J. B., J. H. Rook, W. V. Andresen and W. R. Bradley. Am. Ind. Hyg. Assoc. Quart. **14**, 23-25 (1953).

A 100 ml syringe mounted on a plywood frame draws the air sample through 2 side-arm test tubes containing reagent. Hydrogen sulfide is determined by air titration of the 0.0001 N iodine solution with starch as indicator. The device and the absorbing solutions or reagents fit conveniently into a small carrying case. Add. Ref.: CA **47**, 10768 (1953).

36—METHODS FOR DETERMINING HYDROGEN SULFIDE IN GASES

Risenfield, F. C. and H. K. Orbach. Petroleum Eng.

25, No. 6, C32-38 (1953); CA **49**, 12197 (1955).

A review with 41 references.

37—ANALYTICAL PROCEDURE FOR THE DETECTION OF GASES

Guatelli, Manuel A. Rev. asoc. bioquim. arg. **18**, 3-40 (1954).

Lead acetate paper detects hydrogen sulfide. Any environment in which the color of the paper changes within 1 minute, should be considered dangerous. Add. Ref.: CA **48**, 8124 (1954).

38—A SIMPLIFIED TECHNIQUE FOR ATMOSPHERIC HYDROGEN SULFIDE STUDIES

Chanin, Gerson, John R. Elwood, and Edward H. Chow. Sewage and Ind. Wastes **26**, 1217-1230 (1954); CA **49**, 9848 (1955).

Hydrogen sulfide can be determined semiquantitatively by exposure of test tiles to the suspected atmosphere. The degree of blackening of the unglazed tiles (previously dipped in a solution of acetice acid, lead acetate, and glycerol, and dried) is proportional to the hydrogen sulfide in the air. Add. Ref.: IHD **19**, 113 (1955).

39—GAS ANALYSIS BY MEANS OF DETECTOR TUBES. XII. RAPID METHOD FOR THE DETERMINATION OF HYDROGEN SULFIDE IN THE PRESENCE OF SULFUR DIOXIDE

Kobayashi, Yoshitaka and Tetsuzo Kitagawa. J. Chem. Soc. Japan, Ind. Chem. Sect. **57**, 613-614 (1954); CA **49**, 8739 (1955).

Hydrogen sulfide can be determined in the presence of sulfur dioxide concentrations of less than 6 volumes per cent. A detector tube containing silica gel impregnated with a solution of ammonium molybdate and palladium sulfate is used for the analysis. The light yellow color of the silica gel reagent changes to dark-blue in the presence of hydrogen sulfide. The sample flow rate is 1 cc per second. Carbon monoxide, acetylene, hydrocarbons, arsine, phosphine, methyl acrylate, and nickel carbonyl interfere.

40—AN AUTOMATIC HYDROGEN SULFIDE ANALYZER

Maslennikov, B. M., and F. A. Kavitskaya. Khim. Prom. **1954**, 485-487; Chem. Tech., Berlin 7 (11), 682-683 (1955); CA **49**, 8637 (1955).

The apparatus described indicates a dangerous concentration of hydrogen sulfide in the air and sounds an alarm if the safety factor is exceeded. The device is actuated by the darkening of a paper strip saturated with a solution of 20% lead acetate, 12% glycerol, and 0.2% acetic acid in 67.8% water. Add. Refs.: IHD **19**, 1140 (1955); AA **3**, 1955 (1956).

41—ANALYSIS OF MEDICALLY IMPORTANT GASES USING SPOT TESTS

Massmann, W. Arch. Gewerbepathol. Gewerbehyg. **13**, 262-275 (1954).

The method for hydrogen sulfide detection is similar to that described for arsine. Prepare the reagent by dissolving 3.75 g ammonium molybdate in 25 ml cold water and filtering through dry filter paper into a 50 ml volumetric flask. Wash the filter with 30% sodium acetate solution and dilute the filtrate to volume. The reagent is unstable and must be made fresh just before use. Immerse papers in this solution, dry, and store in a tightly stoppered bottle. Draw air or gas samples through the paper at 4 liters per hour. The author gives the method of standardization and the conversion of sodium sulfide to hydrogen sulfide. The sensitivity is 10 ppm. Large quantities of some substances interfere, viz.: Sulfur dioxide, no interference below 200 ppm; Hydrogen cyanide, no interference below 200 ppm; Oxides of nitrogen, no interference below 80 ppm; Ammonia, no interference below 450 ppm. Carbon disulfide, carbon monoxide, carbon dioxide, and arsine do not interfere. Add. Ref.: IHD **19**, 599 (1955).

42—A LOW COST SAMPLER FOR MEASUREMENT OF LOW CONCENTRATIONS OF HYDROGEN SULFIDE

Sensenbaugh, J. Deane and W. C. L. Hemeon. Air Repair **4**, 5-7 (1954); CA **48**, 9122 (1954).

The American Iron and Steel Institute automatic smoke sampler was used, with particulate removed by a CC-6 filter. Whatman #4 filter paper was impregnated with a 5% solution of lead acetate and 5% glycerol, and dried. The optical density of the spots formed by the hydrogen sulfide was measured and the gas concentration determined from calibration charts.

43—CHARACTERIZATION OF CARBON DISULFIDE-ENDANGERED ACTIVITIES

Demus, Heinrich. Faserforsch u. Textiltech. **5**, 65-67 (1954); CA **48**, 11250 (1954).

A method for the determination of carbon disulfide is described. The method is used to determine exposure concentrations of workers in work rooms containing carbon disulfide and hydrogen sulfide vapors. A known volume of air is passed over a filter strip impregnated with a weighted quantity of lead acetate, and then through a solution containing 0.1 g copper acetate, 1 ml diethylamine and 20 ml of triethanolamine in 100 ml of 85% ethyl alcohol. The quantity of hydrogen sulfide is determined by comparing the degree of blackening of the filter strips with standard strips. The carbon disulfide concentration is determined from data obtained from the copper acetate solution. Add. Ref.: IHD **18**, 1327 (1954).

44—COPPER ABSORBER FOR HALOGENS AND HYDROGEN SULFIDE IN THEIR DETERMINATION IN AIR

Sadovskii, P. M. Zhur. Anal. Khim. **9**, 58-59 (1954); CA **48**, 6910 (1954).

The author describes an absorbent for the collection of halogens and hydrogen sulfide. Copper filings are prepared and freed of dust by screening or elutriation techniques. The absorbent is useful in preventing the change of titer of barium hydroxide during air analysis. Add. Refs.: J. Anal. Chem. U.S.S.R. **9**, 67-68 (1954) (English translation); CA **49**, 4451 (1955). *This abstract is included not as a detector method but rather as an aid in removing contaminants from detector systems.*

45—FIELD TESTS FOR THE DETERMINATION OF LEAD DUST AND HYDROGEN SULFIDE IN AIR

Komada, Taro, Senji Suenaga, and Sadako Osada. Bull. Inst. Pub. Health (Tokyo) **4**, No. 3, 32-36 (1955) (English summary); CA **49**, 15132 (1955).

Pomeroy's method (CA **35**, 6711 (1941)) with vanadyl color standards is used to determine hydrogen sulfide in air. These comparator color standards may be used also with a spectrophotometer.

46—DETERMINATION OF TOXIC GAS COMPONENTS IN AIR BY THE REICH STOP-METHOD

Kraus, E. Chem. Tech. (Berlin) **7**, 552-555 (1955); CA **50**, 12750 (1956).

The author describes a method for the determination of traces of hydrogen sulfide, sulfur dioxide, chlorine, ammonia, and hydrogen chloride based on the Reich method for the estimation of sulfur dioxide in roast gases.

47—DETERMINATION OF HYDROGEN SULFIDE IN THE ATMOSPHERE

Lang, W. and E. Mader. Z. anal. Chem. **145**, 179-184 (1955); CA **49**, 7447 (1955).

A good way to determine 10 to 30 μg of hydrogen sulfide is to pass the air through a dilute solution of iodo-starch and measure the extinction of color.

48—ANALYZER-RECORDER FOR MEASURING HYDROGEN SULFIDE IN AIR

Offutt, E. B. and L. V. Sorg. Anal. Chem. **27**, 429-432 (1955).

Hydrogen sulfide will darken on contact the exposed surface of 16 mm motion picture film (either blank or cleared) coated with a film of buffered lead acetate. Measure the density of the dark stain by photoelectric transmission in a continuously recording apparatus. The sensitivity is 1 ppm in the range of 1 to 25 ppm, 2 ppm in the range of 25 to 50 ppm, and about 5 ppm in the range of 50 to 100 ppm. Add. Refs.: CA **49**, 7293 (1955); IHD **19**, 598 (1955).

49—THE DETERMINATION OF VERY LOW CONCENTRATIONS OF HYDROGEN SULFIDE IN GAS. I.

Prince, C. G. T. J. Appl. Chem. (London) **5**, 364-374 (1955).

The author has revised the calibration of the methylene blue method for determining very low concentrations of hydrogen sulfide in gas and has demonstrated the new calibration's validity. He passes the gas through thick, white absorbent papers impregnated with 10% w/v lead acetate, and, using the methylene blue method as a primary standard, relates the sulfur content of the lead sulfite stains on the papers to the optical density of the stains. The author recommends that the stains be measured in a photoelectric densitometer rather than in a comparator, because results with the latter are low and subject to the personal errors of the operator who matches the depth of color. In the official (British) test for hydrogen sulfide in gas, 6 test papers impregnated with lead acetate are exposed to the gas and hydrogen sulfide is considered present if all the papers are unmistakably darker in any part than the comparison slip. Add. Refs.: CA **50**, 4714 (1956); APCA VII, No. 10 4305 (1962).

50—A METHOD FOR THE SIMULTANEOUS DETERMINATION OF TRACES OF HYDROGEN SULFIDE AND CARBON DISULFIDE IN AIR

Sonnenschein, W. and K. Schaefer. Z. anal. Chem. **153** (2), 107-112 (1956); AA **4**, 1043 (1957).

It is now shown that the results for the determination of hydrogen sulfide (cf. article by same authors cited previously) depend on the volume of air over the liquid. A modification of the method and apparatus to improve the analytical method is described.

51—SAMPLING AND ANALYZING AIR FOR CONTAMINANTS IN WORK PLACES

Silverman, Leslie. Encyclopedia of Instrumentation for Industrial Hygiene, edited by Yaffe, Charles D., Dohrman H. Byers, and Andrew D. Hosey. (Univ. of Michigan, Inst. of Industrial Health, Ann Arbor, Mich., 1956) pp. 7-25.

Granules impregnated with silver cyanide turn from white to black in the presence of hydrogen sulfide. Mercaptans interfere. Whatman No. 1 filter paper impregnated with a solution containing 10 g lead acetate, 90 ml water, 5 ml acetic acid, and 10 ml glycerol, turns light tan to dark brown with hydrogen sulfide. Mercaptans also interfere with this reaction.

52—ULTRAMICRODETERMINATION OF SULFIDES IN AIR

Jacobs, Morris B., M. M. Braverman, and Seymour Hochheiser. Anal. Chem. **29**, 1349-1351 (1957).

Hydrogen sulfide and other sulfides can be determined in the part per billion range in air if the air be bubbled through an alkaline suspension of cadmium hydroxide in a Greenburg-Smith impinger. The concentration of the absorbed sulfides is estimated by the methylene blue method. The authors detail the laboratory procedure and state that the method is adaptable for field use. Add. Ref.: CA **52**, 2652 (1958).

53—A POCKET INDICATOR FOR HYDROGEN SULFIDE CONCENTRATION IN MINES

Maslennikov, B. M. and F. A. Kavitskaya. Khim. Prom. **1957**, 177-191; CA **51**, 17266 (1957).

Heat to 60° a solution of 19.15 g sodium bicarbonate and 312.26 g pure glycerol in 1000 g water, then add 30 to 40 g sodium nitriferrocyanide. Filter paper tape saturated with this mixture turns a weak violet-red color with 0.001% hydrogen sulfide, an intense violet-red with 0.005%, and blue-violet with 0.01% or more of hydrogen sulfide in air. The colored stain persists for 3 minutes, and the papers remain stable for up to 2 years.

54—M.S.A. HYDROGEN SULFIDE DETECTOR

Mine Safety Appliances Co. Catalog of Industrial Safety Equipment, Catalog 7B, Section 3, p. 25 (3rd ed., 1957); Bull. 0805-1 (1961).

The detector comprises a rubber bulb aspirator, adapter, detector tubes, and a rack for spare detector tubes. A movable, calibrated cylinder, with the scale reading directly in percent hydrogen sulfide, is attached to the barrel of the pump. The detector tubes contain silver cyanide, on inert granules, which turns dark gray on contact with hydrogen sulfide, beginning at the end where the sample enters. After 10 squeezes of the bulb, the length of the dark stain is proportional to the hydrogen sulfide concentration in the air sample.

55—AIR SANITATION. VIII. ASSAY OF SULFUR DIOXIDE AND HYDROGEN SULFIDE IN AIR BY THE SPOT REACTION

Ishizaka, Otoharu, Hideo Nagano, Kazuko Okamura, Masami Saburi, Saeko Koide, and Michiko Goto. Nagoya Shiritsu Daigaku Yakugakubu Kiyo **5**, 14-20 (1957); CA **52**, 4076 (1958).

Cf. CA **51**, 6747 (1957). The coloration of potassium iodate-starch paper by sulfur dioxide or hydrogen sulfide gas is applied on a spot of the filter paper, and a measuring formula is introduced. Error is less than ± 5% for 5 to 50 ppm of sulfur dioxide or hydrogen sulfide under the condition of 0 to 40° and 40 to 80% humidity.

56—PHOTOELECTRIC GAS ANALYSIS

Offutt, Elmer B. and Leonard V. Sorg. U. S. (Pat. No.) 2,800,397, July 23, 1957; CA **51**, 18572 (1957).

A light-stable, gas-impermeable tape is pretreated with a mixture of 1 M lead acetate and 1 M sodium acetate maintained at pH 6 and with a gelatin coating, dried, and reeled. Zero to 500 ppm of hydrogen sulfide in the atmosphere may be detected directly, while higher concentrations require controlled dilutions of the influent sample stream for quantitation.

57—QUANTITATIVE DETERMINATION OF HYDROGEN SULFIDE AND CARBON DISULFIDE

Auergesellschaft Akt.-Ges. (by Hermann Heidrich). Ger. (Pat. No.) 1,031,545, June 4, 1958 (Cl. 42.1); C. Z. **1959**, 11024; CA **54**, 13992 (1960).

The authors describe a simultaneous, quantitative method for the determination of hydrogen sulfide and carbon disulfide in air, utilizing the reaction between plumbites or stannites and formaldehyde. The air is first aspirated through a layer of silica gel impregnated with lead salt which changes its color when absorbing hydrogen sulfide and then through a tube filled with silica gel impregnated with alcoholic or aqueous alkali solution and plumbite (or stannite), which is wetted with 40% formaldehyde solution shortly before the air is passed through. The latter is used for the carbon disulfide determination.

58—RAPID DETERMINATION OF SULFIDE SULFUR IN WATER BY MEANS OF A DETECTOR TUBE

Kobayashi, Yoshitaka. J. Chem. Soc. Japan, Ind. Chem. Sect. **61**, 48-52 (1958); AA **5**, 4331 (1958).

One hundred g of dried 40 to 60 mesh silica gel is mixed with 100 ml of a 0.5% lead acetate. The reagent is dried until the water content is about 30%. The product is packed in a glass tube which is kept sealed. For the analysis one end of the detector is immersed in the sample solution for 3 minutes. The length of the colored layer increases with the content of sulfur (2 to 1000 ppm) and is independent of the pH. The amount is determined by reference to an empirical table. The error is approximately 10%.

59—HYDROGEN SULFIDE-SENSITIVE TAPE

Sorg, Leonard V. and Elmer B. Offutt. U. S. (Pat. No.) 2,864,725, Dec. 16, 1958; CA **53**, 5777 (1959).

The patent describes a device for feeding gelatin coated tape or other strip material over a treating solution to impregnate the gelatin coating. The tape is used in the hydrogen sulfide analyzer-recorders described in U. S. (Pat. No.) 2,800,397, to Offutt and Sorg (see above) and in U. S. (Pat. No.) 2,895,807 to Sorg and Lamkin (see below).

60—GAS ANALYZER

Sorg, Leonard V. and John C. Lamkin. (to Standard Oil Co., Indiana). U. S. (Pat No.) 2,895,807, July 21, 1959; CA **53**, 16614 (1959).

An apparatus for the continuous recording of hydrogen sulfide concentrations in an air stream is discussed. The apparatus consists of a transparent tape coated with gelatin or agar containing lead acetate and sodium acetate. Variations in the intensity of the light being transmitted through the tape are related to the hydrogen sulfide concentration. The transmitted light is detected by a photoelectric cell below the tape.

61—AIR POLLUTION SAMPLING AND ANALYSIS WITH SPECIAL REFERENCE TO SULFATE PULPING OPERATIONS

Hendrickson, E. R. Tappi **42**, No. 5, 173A-176A (1959); CA **53**, 17392 (1959).

Hydrogen sulfide is absorbed in a zinc acetate solution containing a small quantity of sodium hydroxide. The precipitated zinc sulfide formed is redissolved in an acid solution and allowed to react with p-aminodimethylaniline sulfate in the presence of ferric chloride. Methylene blue is formed in direct proportion to the amount of sulfide in the solution, and the intensity of the color, when compared with standards, gives a measure of the hydrogen sulfide in the effluent.

62—FAST METHOD FOR DETERMINATION OF HYDROGEN SULFIDE IN AIR

Gernet, E. V. and A. A. Russkikh. Gigiena Truda i Professional. Zabolevaniya **3**, No. 3, 51-54 (1959); CA **54**, 7012 (1960).

A method for determining hydrogen sulfide in air is based on the colorimetric determination of the lead sulfide formed when air containing hydrogen sulfide is drawn through an opening containing filter paper saturated with lead acetate. The determination is possible at air temperatures from 8 to 40° and at relative humidities from 25% to 94%. The sensitivity of the method is 0.05 μg of hydrogen sulfide and the detection limit is 0.00014 mg per liter of air, with an accuracy of $\pm$ 9 to $\pm$ 18%.

63—TRACES OF HYDROGEN SULFIDE IN THE ATMOSPHERE OF DWELLINGS

Hoffmann, E. Australian Paint J. **4**, No. 7, 15-16 (1959); CA **54**, 13509 (1960).

Hydrogen sulfide, in the microgram per liter range, is determined in dwellings by means of lead acetate papers. Cooking and smoking were found to be the primary contributors of hydrogen sulfide.

64—CONTINUOUS DETERMINATION OF HYDROGEN SULFIDE IN AIR

Chetkowska, Maria, Joanna Gallus-Olender, and Irena Strzeszewska. Chemik (Gliwice, Poland) **14**, 384-386 (1961); CA **56**, 15777 (1962).

Air containing hydrogen sulfide is bubbled through a colorimetric reagent that can be regenerated by bubbling clean air through it. The color changes are: greenish yellow with 0.010, light pink with 0.015, dark red with 0.030, violet red with 0.05, and violet with 0.100 mg per liter of hydrogen sulfide in air. Discard the reagent when it darkens or turns bronze color.

65—MEASUREMENT OF TRACE QUANTITIES OF HYDROGEN SULFIDE IN INDUSTRIAL ATMOSPHERES

Smith, A. F., D. G. Jenkins, and D. E. Cunningworth. J. Appl. Chem. **11**, 317-328 (1961).

Industrial atmospheres usually contain much more sulfur dioxide than hydrogen sulfide, yet many methods for measuring traces of hydrogen sulfide in air ignore the effects of such interference. The authors appraise 5 published hydrogen sulfide detection methods (including the lead acetate-impregnated paper tape procedure) for sulfur dioxide interference, maximum flow rate, limit of detection, and accurate calibration to low levels. They suggest modifications to eliminate sulfur dioxide interference, and describe a simple, portable field apparatus for measuring hydrogen sulfide concentrations as low as 10^{-4} ppm in a 2 hour sample. Add. Ref.: "Particle Poop" (Gelman Instr. Co., 1962).

66—HYDROGEN SULFIDE DETERMINATION BY TILE DARKENING STUDIES

Gilardi, Edward F. and Raymond M. Manganelli. Ind. Hyg. News Rept. **5**, No. 7, July, 1962.

Non-porous ceramic tiles are coated with an aqueous solution of lead acetate, acetic acid, and glycerol. Hydrogen sulfide reacts with the coating to form colored lead sulfide on the tile surface. Dimethyl sulfide, dimethyl disulfide, and methyl mercaptan in concentrations higher than would be encountered in the outdoor atmosphere do not interfere with hydrogen sulfide measurement by the tile darkening method.

See Section One

For references 6, 7, 35, 59, 69, 76, 81, 87, 88, 96, 106, 109, 129.

Iodate
Iodine
Iodides

1—INSOLUBLE COLOR REAGENTS. COLOR REAGENT PAPERS FROM ION-EXCHANGE PAPERS

Sansoni, Bruno. Naturwissenschaften **46**, 228-229 (1959) (in German); CA **54**, 12879 (1960).

The authors describe hydroxy-type anionic-exchange papers which are impregnated with thiocyanate, sulfide, iodide, and permanganate ions as wells as with iodine and various acid-base indicators. The papers to be used are cut into 1 mm squares. The papers are subjected to the reactant and rinsed, and the color changes are observed under a microscope. A concentration of 4.7 g iodate was detected on iodide paper.

2—COLOR TESTS FOR CHLORIDES, BROMIDES, AND IODIDES

Kuznetsov, V. I. Doklady Akad. Nauk. U.S.S.R. **77**, 281-284 (1951); CA **45**, 6967 (1951).

The author shows that the following results can be obtained in color tests for the halide ions with organic reagents: 4-(8-hydroxy-5-quinolylazo)benzenesulfonic acid, silver complex at pH 6.5 to 7.0 which is pink originally and becomes yellow after addition of a halide. The reagent is usable to 0.5 μg iodide. 2-(8-hydroxy-5-quinolylazo)-5-nitro-benzenesulfonic acid plus a mercurous complex produces an orange-red to yellow coloration. A mercuric complex produces the same colors. Less than 0.3 μg iodine can be detected. The colors can be compared with standards and used for estimation of the halides. Mercuric nitrate solution appears to be most satisfactory for conversion of the sodium salts of the reagents into the complexes.

3—SEMIQUANTITATIVE DETERMINATION OF IODIDE

Meditsch, Jorge de Oliveira, Eng. Quim. 15(6), 7-8 (1963); CF Ibid. 13 No. 6, B (1961) CA 60, 8628, 1964).

Whatman No. 1 paper is impregnated with a saturated $HgCl_2$ solution and air dried. The paper is then treated with 10 μl samples of K1 solutions containing 10, 20, 30, 50, 70, or 100 μg of I. The width of the yellow ring produced is a measure of the iodine concentration. The error is $\pm$ 2% to $\pm$ 10%. The interfering ions are H_2S, $SnCl_2$, NaOH, NH_4OH, CN^-, SCN^-, Cl^-, and Br^-.

See Section One
For references 6, 94.

Iron

1—SPECIFIC SPOT TEST FOR IRON

Mallik, K. L., and S. Buddhadev, Anal. Chem. Acta 23(3), 225-6 (1960). CA **60**, 8629, (1964).

The authors describe two methods for the determination of iron. The first test involves mixing, on a spot plate, a drop of test solution, a drop of a reducing agent, and 2 drops of 1% phenyl 2-pyredylketoxime in 95% ethyl alcohol. The presence of iron is indicated by a violet color after the mixture is made alkaline with sodium carbonate. The second method involves placing one drop of the test solution on Whatman No. 40 paper. Added to this are 2 drops 10% ascorbic acid and 2 drops of the above reagent. The spot is exposed to ammonia fumes and a violet coloration indicates the presence of iron. Interfering ions are copper, cobalt and cyanide. The limit of identification is about 0.05 μg.

Isophorone

1—DETERMINATION OF SMALL QUANTITIES OF ISOPHORONE IN AIR

Kacy, H. W., Jr. and R. W. Cope. Am. Ind. Hyg. Assoc. Quart. **16**, 55-59 (1955).

Scrub air contaminated with isophorone through 20 ml of glacial acetic acid. Transfer 10 ml of this solution to a 25 ml graduate, add 1 ml of phosphomolybdic acid reagent (10% in glacial acetic acid, filtered), and mix. Heat in a boiling water bath for 45 minutes, cool, dilute to 15 ml with additional acetic acid, and measure the resulting molybdenum blue spectrophotometrically at 650 mu, against a calibration curve prepared from 98% pure isophorone in glacial acetic acid, and treated the same as the air sample. Add. Ref.: IHD **19**, 480 (1955). *Although this method is not described for field detection, the reagent will react at room temperature with elevated concentrations of isophorone.*

2—TECHNICAL ISOPHORONE

Carpignano, Rosarina. Ann. chim. (Rome) **45**, 81-87 (1955); CA **49**, 9194 (1955).

The author studied the colorimetric sodium nitroprusside reaction photocolorimetrically. It was determined that reproducible results could be obtained when the reagents were added in the following specific order: ethyl alcohol solution of isophorone, water, sodium nitroprusside, ammonia, and dilution with water to the required volume. Beer's law was obeyed between the concentrations of 0.02 to 0.08. *The abstract does not specify to what units the concentration figures refer; the reference is included for its possible application to a field detector.*

Lead
Lead Tetraethyl

1—A NEW METHOD FOR DETERMINING TETRAETHYL LEAD IN AIR

Bykhovskaya, M. S. Gigiena i Sanit. **10**, No. 9, 17-21 (1945); CA **41**, 1952 (1947).

The author describes a method for the determination of tetraethyl lead in air. An absorbent is prepared by igniting purified silica gel, moistening it with silver nitrate, and drying in the dark just prior to use. One hundred liters of air are aspirated through a tube containing the gel. Absorption of 1 μg of tetraethyl lead causes the gel to turn yellowish-brown, and the color deepens when ethyl alcohol is added. The color of the gel is compared with standards obtained similarly with known quantities of tetraethyl lead in air.

2—ANALYSIS OF AIR CONTAMINATED WITH TETRA-ETHYL LEAD

Ventura, Benedetto. Ann. chim. applicata **36**, 377-380 (1946); CA **41**, 5415 (1947).

The author describes a colorimetric method of analysis of tetraethyl lead based on the darkening produced by lead liberated with hydrogen sulfide.

3—DETERMINATION OF LEAD IN AIR. RAPID MICRO-METHOD FOR FIELD USE

Snyder, L. J., W. R. Barnes, and J. V. Tokos. Anal. Chem. **20**, 772-776 (1948).

Prepare the following reagents in the laboratory and take them to the field in small sealed bottles: (1) 10 ml of 1.0 N iodine solution (dissolve 250 g of postassium iodide in 750 ml of water; de-lead); (2) 30 ml of reagent (dissolve 10 g of potassium cyanide, 100 g of sodium sulfite, and 20 g of ammonium citrate in 550 ml of distilled water. De-lead but do not acidify after de-leading. Dilute with 1950 ml of lead-free concentrated ammonium hydroxide); (3) 10 ml of chloroform; (4) solid dithizone. Collect 4. cubic feet of air sample at 40 to 60 cubic feet per minute through specially constructed scrubbers containing the absorbing medium, solution 1; drain the lead-containing liquid into the alkaline reducing solution 2; mix by shaking. Add solutions 3 and 4, shake again, and compare the resulting cherry red color of the dithizone layer with permanent glass standards in a Hellige 605 comparator, using a special lead dithizonate disk 351-D, calibrated in micrograms per cubic feet. The method requires approximately 10 minutes, is accurate to better than 1 μg of lead per cubic foot of air, and all the equipment is contained in 2 portable cases. Add. Ref.: CA **42**, 8702 (1948).

4—DIRECT FIELD DETERMINATION OF LEAD IN AIR

Amdur, Mary O. and Leslie Silverman. Arch. Ind. Hyg. Occupational Med. **10**, 152-157 (1954).

Draw 10 to 20 liters of lead-contaminated air through a Yagoda Confined Spot Test paper in a suitable holder. Add 1 drop of 0.2% tetrahydroxyquinone in 95% ethyl alcohol, plus 1 drop of tartaric acid buffer of pH 2.79. Allow to stand 1 minute, blot, and compare with standards. Lead fumes produce a violet color on the filter paper. The reagent is active for at least 4 months at room temperature. Zinc, antimony, bismuth, copper, tin, and iron do not interfere with the reaction; cadmium interferes if its quantity is larger than that of the lead. The author's standard deviations from actual values were $\pm$ 1.4 μg. Add Refs.: CA **48**, 13528 (1954); IHD **18**, 1162 (1954). *This technique has been applied commercially by Mine Safety Appliances Co. (Bull. No. 0811-5 (1955)) (see below).*

5—FIELD TESTS FOR THE DETERMINATION OF LEAD DUST AND HYDROGEN SULFIDE IN AIR

Komada, Taro, Senji Suenaga, and Sadako Osada. Bull. Inst. Pub. Health (Tokyo) **4**, No. 3, 32-36 (English summary) (1955); CA **49**, 15132 (1955).

The authors describe a modification of Snyder's dithizone method for lead determination (previously abstracted) simplified for field work by utilization of cobalt chloride color standard solutions varying in concentration and stored in a series of sealed test tubes.

6—LEAD IN AIR

Mine Safety Appliances Co. Bull. No. 0811-5 (1955). The Lead in Air Kit contains a 500 ml hand pump, No. 1160 fiberglass filters, 2 reagents in glass vials sealed into polyethylene tubes, and 2 standard stain discs equivalent to 0.15 and 0.6 mg lead per cubic meter, respectively, for detecting lead in air by the Amdur and Silverman technique described above.

7—FIELD TYPE COLORIMETRIC TESTERS FOR GASES AND PARTICULATE MATTER

McConnaughey, Paul W. Presented at the annual meeting of the Am. Ind. Hyg. Assoc., Atlantic City, N.J., 1958.

The author presents an improved version of the Amdur-Silverman method described above. Equal quantities of the metals antimony, arsenic, bismuth, cadmium, chromium, copper, iron, silicon, tin, or zinc do not interfere, nor do chloride, iodide, or nitrate ions, if the acid buffer is at pH 2.8.

8—SPOT-TESTING SOLUTIONS, ESPECIALLY FOR DE-TECTION OF LEAD AND HYDROGEN FLUORIDE

McConnaughey, Paul W. (to Mine Safety Appliances Co.) U. S. (Pat. No.) 2,839,368, June 17, 1958; CA **53**, 989 (1959).

A colorimetric reagent in the form of a suspension in a volatile non-solvent is deposited on a porous carrier, to avoid the migration of the reagent to the periphery of the wetted area (and enhanced peripheral color intensity), and obtain a uniform color test. As little as 0.3 μg of lead per sq. cm of filter paper can be detected with 1 drop of a stable 1% suspension of disodium tetrahydroxybenzo-quinone in 95% ethyl alcohol followed by 1 drop of pH 2.79 buffer to produce a uniform red stain.

9—A FIELD METHOD FOR DETERMINATION OF LEAD FUME

Dixon, B. E. and P. Metson. Analyst **84**, 46-50 (1959).

A field test for determining small amounts of lead fume in industrial atmospheres in the presence of moderate amounts of lead dust, is based on the formation of a purple color when the lead fume is drawn through Munktell

00 filter paper strips, 2½″ x 1″, freshly impregnated with 0.2% ethanolic tetrahydroxy-p-benzoquinone. After collection on the test paper, dissolve any lead particles *in situ* with a spray composed of 1 volume of glacial acetic acid and 3 volumes of acetone. After 1 minute compare the uniform purple background stain formed by the lead fume with a standard color chart similarly prepared, or with permanent painted strips. Larger particles of lead dust may form isolated pinpoints of more intense color. The method is sensitive to 0.05 mg lead per cubic meter, and avoids the error, inherent in ordinary chemical methods, of including adventitious lead dust in the figure for lead fume. The efficiency of the Munktell paper is 90%. Interference by other metal fumes may be overcome in various way. Add. Refs.: IHD **23**, 389 (1959); AA **6**, 3927 (1959).

10—UNICO LEAD-IN-AIR DETECTOR

Union Industrial Equipment Corp., Port Chester, N.Y. Brochure (1959).

The Lead-in-Air Detector Kit includes a Uni-Jet Air Sampler with precision control valve that permits precise rate control, reagents, color standards for 0.1, 0.2, 0.3, 0.4 mg lead per cubic meter of air, carrying case, accessories, and a built-in, explosion proof power source. The procedure based on Quino's method (see below) involves 3 steps and takes less than 10 minutes.

11—FIELD METHOD FOR THE DETERMINATION OF INORGANIC LEAD FUMES IN AIR

Quino, Enrique A. J. Am. Ind. Hyg. Assoc. **20**, 134-137 (1959).

The author states that the 0.2% alcoholic solution of tetrahydroxyquinone of the Amdur and Silverman method (see above) does not retain its activity for longer than a day. McConnaughey's method, in which a stain is developed by adding to lead collected on a filter paper a drop of ethanol solution containing a suspension of sodium tetrahydroxyquinone and buffer solution (see above) does not produce uniform colorations on the filter paper, and lead determinations with the color standards show significant discrepancies from chemical analyses with the dithizone method. The author's method is based on the formation of a pink lead complex stain on a filter paper impregnated with tetrahydroxyquinone in an aqueous-acetone buffer. The precision and accuracy parallel the standard dithizone procedure, with interference only from high concentrations of cadmium. The complete unit is inexpensive and the sampling equipment needed is readily available in most industrial hygiene laboratories. A commercially available kit, the Unico Lead-in-Air Detector, is made by the Union Industrial Equipment Corporation (see above). Add. Ref.: CA **54**, 3811 (1960); Occ. Hyg. Abstr. **34**, No. 8, 787 (1959).

12—DETERMINATION OF PARTICULATE LEAD CONTENT IN AIR

Tufts, Barbara J. Anal. Chem. **31**, 238-241 (1959).

The author describes techniques for checking lead content in the atmosphere and differentiating between lead and nonlead-containing particles, by means of a micro spot test on membrane filters. The testing reagent is a saturated solution of tetrahydroxyquinone, in 50% aqueous ethyl alcohol, which forms a red precipitate with lead. The reagent is relatively unstable and must be prepared fresh each day. *The method could be expanded to detect higher concentrations.* Add. Ref.: CA **53**, 11730 (1959).

13—A FIELD METHOD FOR DETERMINING TOTAL AIRBORNE LEAD

Dixon, B. E. and P. Metson. Analyst **85**, 122-126 (1960).

Collect the sample on a test paper, then treat it in a graduated sample tube with cold dilute nitric acid containing hydrogen peroxide, to dissolve the lead dust and disintegrate the paper. Add successively measured amounts of ammoniacal cyanide-metabisulfite-citrate solution and a solution of dithizone in carbon tetrachloride, and extract the lead dithizonate at pH 11. Compare the color of the lower layer with aqueous color standards or with permanent glass color standards. The method is precise only between approximately 0.06 and 1. mg of lead per cubic meter, but the volume of the sample may be increased or decreased. The procedure requires neither heat nor skilled technique. Add. Refs.: Analyst **84**, 46-50 (1959) (see above); AA **7**, 4508 (1950); CA **54**, 20028 (1960); IHD **25**, 47 (1961).

14—DETERMINATION OF LEAD IONS WITH QUINALIZARIN

Neminovskaya, A. F., Tr Novocherk. Politekhn. Inst., 143, 45-53 (1963) CA **61** 25 (1964).

The author describes a method for the determination of lead ions using quinalizarin as the analytical reagent. This reagent reacts with lead ions to form a blue-violet color at pH 6.2-6.4 and a blue color at pH 8.2-8.8. A buffer (NH$_4$DAc) is added to the sample solution to maintain the proper pH. Quinalizarin solution (0.001%) is added and the mixture allowed to stand for 2-3 minutes. The color produced is compared to standards containing known amounts of lead.

See Section One
References 5, 98, 106, 115, 116.

Lewisite
(Beta-Chlorovinyldichloroarsine)

1—THE DETECTION OF TOXIC GASES AND VAPORS

Leroux, Lucien. Rev. hyg. et med. prevent. **57**, 81-112 (1935).

Methyl orange (0.05%) in amyl alcohol solution turns red with aliphatic arsines, e.g., lewisite. Mustard gas interferes with the reaction. Add. Ref.: CA **29**, 3627 (1935).

2—PROBLEMS OF PASSIVE DEFENSE AGAINST THE DANGER OF CHEMICAL GAS ATTACKS

Harsovescu, C. Antigaz (Bucharest) **9**, No. 9/10, 22-34 (1935); Chem. Zentr. **1936, I**, 4240; CA **31**, 7141 (1937).

The article describes a method of detecting organic arsines with copper iodide, based on the work of Paul Bruere (Practical Methods for the Protection from War Gases, Vigot, Paris, 1933, p. 18-25).

3—TESTS AVAILABLE FOR THE IDENTIFICATION OF SMALL QUANTITIES OF THE WAR GASES

Cox, H. E. Analyst **64**, 807-813 (1939).

Lewisite is identified by its decomposition products, which give reactions for acid, chloride, and arsenic. When passed into 1 ml of a 15% sodium hydroxide solution, the acetylene formed will produce a red stain on cuprous chloride paper. The arsenic will give a direct Gutzeit test. If excess hydrogen sulfide is avoided, the test is sensitive to 0.02 to 0.05 mg, according to S. Nametkin and W. Nekrassov (Z. anal. Chem. **77**, 285 (1929), this reference quoted in Cox's article). Add. Ref.: CA **34**, 541 (1940).

4—DETECTION OF LEWISITE

Froger, Christian. Compt. rend. **209**, 351 (1939); CA **33**, 8143 (1939).

After absorbing lewisite in a Draeger detector, add a few drops of osmic acid to the detector; a black ring of osmium dioxide appears. From 4 liters of air, 25 mg of lewisite per cubic meter can be detected, and the test is unaffected by vapors of ethyl alcohol, ethyl ether, acetone, or sulfur dioxide (provided the sulfur dioxide concentration is no more than 4 mg per cubic meter). Acrolein interferes.

5—IDENTIFICATION OF WAR GASES

Sharman, C. F. Chem. and Ind. (London) **18**, 741-742 (1940).

The author describes a modification of the Twiss-Neale lamp (see under "Mustard Gas"). When lewisite is decomposed over the incandescent filament the chlorine in the pyrolysis product reacts with o-tolidine (saturated solution in equal parts of alcohol and water) to give a bright yellow stain with a patch in the middle, turning green and then blue. The chlorine also will turn starch iodate test paper in the apparatus blue. Add. Ref.: CA **35**, 820 (1941).

6—VAPOR DETECTOR TUBES AND DETECTOR KIT FOR SOME CHEMICAL AGENTS USED IN GAS WARFARE

Fenton, Paul F. J. Chem. Education **20**, 564-565 (1943).

Aspirate contaminated air through silica gel in a type A tube and heat the tube over a match. Add a drop of strong alkali and a drop or two of Ilosvay reagent. Lewisite gives a red color; a blue or yellow color must be considered negative. For an alternate reaction, aspirate air through a type B tube containing a 1 to 2 cm column of a 50-50 mixture of silica gel and 20 mesh, arsenic-free zinc. Moisten one of the cotton plugs with mercuric bromide, and add through the other end of the tube enough concentrated hydrochloric acid to react with the zinc column in the silica gel. The arsine formed reacts with the mercuric bromide to stain the cotton plug brown. For the Bettendorf arsenic test, aspirate the contaminated air through pure silica gel in a type A tube. Convert the arsenic in the lewisite to sodium arsenite with a drop of strong alkali and heat from a match, neutralize with a drop of concentrated acid, then add stannous chloride to form the visible gray metallic arsenic. Add. Ref.: CA **38**, 898 (1944).

7—TETRAMETHYLDIAMINOTHIOBENZOPHENONE - COLOR TESTS WITH CW AGENTS

Brown, Weldon G. and R. G. Denkewalter. Natl. Defense Research Comm. (OSRD) Informal Rept. No. 80, Sect. 9-3-1 (1943).

Tetramethyldiaminothiobenzophenone reacts with all the common chemical warfare agents (except hydrogen cyanide and arsine) to give a blue or green color, either directly or, wth mustards, on heating. Although the sensitivity is excellent, the reagent is too unstable to use in prepared tubes. It might be applied in the field as a screening test for quick differentiation of toxic and nontoxic agents, but is too unstable, when impregnated on gels, for screening tests in a field detector kit. Florisil, freshly impregnated with the reagent and air dried, turns green directly with lewisite, with a sensitivity of 2.5 μg.

8—DETECTION OF WAR GASES

Fenton, Paul F. J. Chem. Education **21**, 488-489 (1944).

To overcome the instability of the Ilosvay reagent (see author's previous article, above) the author dissolves the components separately, each in 25 ml of distilled water (3 g copper sulfate, 3 g ammonium chloride, 5 g hydroxylamine hydrochloride, and 4 ml concentrated ammonium hydroxide), and at the time of the test mixes 1 drop of each soluton to make the reagent, then, in turn, mixes 1 drop of this reagent with 2 drops of 20% potassium hydroxide. Next, he moistens a portion of the contaminated silica gel (see Ibid., Section I) with a small drop of the alkalinized Ilosvay reagent. Lewisite turns the reagent purple. Add. Ref.: CA **39**, 135 (1945).

9—NOTE ON A NEW COLOR REACTION OF BETA-CHLOROVINYLDICHLOROARSINE

Mason, Howard S. J. Am. Chem. Soc. **67**, 2267-2268 (1945).

Silica gel impregnated with a chloroform solution of erogosterol turns violet immediately on contact with traces of b-chlorovinyldichloroarsine vapor, and changes to deep green with larger amounts of the vapor. Hydrochloric acid vapor changes the reagent color to deep rust brown. Add. Ref.: CA **40**, 1106 (1946).

10—ORGANIC REAGENTS FOR THE IDENTIFICATION OF CERTAIN VESICANTS

Yoe, John H. and Everett C. Cogbill. Mikrochemie ver. Mikrochim. Acta **38**, 492-497 (1951); CA **46**, 2443 (1952).

The authors list 15 organic reagents which give colors with lewisite and ethyldichloroarsine. Arsenical vesicants can be identified on a test paper impregnated with one of these reagents. Ten of the papers give colors with ethyldichloroarsine which distinguish it from lewisite and from the mustard vesicants, and 5 of the 10 also will differentiate lewisite from the other toxics. Two papers can identify lewisite alone. Three give identical tests with the 2 arsenicals but do not react with vesicants of the mustard type.

11—DETECTION SOLUTION FOR LEWISITE

Gehauf, Bernard and Melvin M. Falkof (to the U.S.A., as represented by the Secy. of War). U. S. (Pat. No.) 2,689,831, Sept. 21, 1954; CA **49**, 104 (1955).

Cuprous ions in aqueous alkaline solution turn brownish red with lewisite, then change to brilliant red if piperidine is added. Pulverize 0.2 g of cupric carbonate and 12 g of arsenic trioxide, and add, with 1 ml of piperidine, to 100 ml of water. Liquid lewisite and the oxide turn the reagent red.

12—SENSITIVE DETECTOR CRAYONS FOR PHOSGENE, HYDROGEN CYANIDE, CYANOGEN CHLORIDE, AND LEWISITE

Witten, Benjamin and Arnold Prostak. Anal. Chem. **29**, 885-887 (1957).

Lewisite gives a greenish color with 4,4'-bis (dimethylamino) thiobenzophenone. A crayon incorporates 5% of the reagent (from a benzene-chloroform solution), together with 95% of blanc fixe, neutral, amorphous, dry. The light tan marks of the crayon turn intensely blue green on contact with lewisite or with ethyldichloroarsine, and purple with high concentrations of phosgene. Chlorine and cyanogen bromide vapors turn the mark grayish. Add. Refs.: CA **51**, 11915 (1957); IHD **21**, 904 (1957).

See Section One

For references 25, 48, 52, 54, 64, 66, 86, 120.

Manganese

1—SPOT TEST FOR THE DETECTOR OF MANGANESE

Kadarmandalgi, S. G., J. Chem. Educ. 41 (8) 437-8 (1964) CA **61** 10019 (1964).

The detection of manganese involves adding 1-2 drops of 10% NH_4Cl, 1 drop of 4-6x NH_4OH and 2 drops of 0.2% resacetophenone oxime in 10% ethyl alcohol to 1 drop of the manganese containing test solution. A yellow to brown color indicates the presence of manganese. The limit of detection is 0.5 μg. Interferences are Cu, Fe^{+++}, C_2O_4, Ne, Co, Th, Pb, AC, Cr, Sn, Hg, PO_4, BO_3, CO_3, F and CrO_4.

Mercaptan

1—DETECTION AND ESTIMATION OF METHYL MERCAPTAN AND CARBON DISULFIDE IN AIR CONTAINING HYDROGEN SULFIDE

Reith, J. F. Rec. trav. chim. **53**, 18-23 (1934) (in English); CA **28**, 1955 (1934).

The authors present a method for the determination of methy mercaptan and carbon disulfide in the presence of hydrogen sulfide. It is necessary to first carry out a separation by means of solid lead acetate. The gas is aspirated through a series of 4 wash bottles. The first two are Jena wash bottles equipped with glass filter No. 83 G.1 and containing 20 cc of 0.5 N sodium hydroxide. The next 2 are very small with gas dispersers and each contains 2 cc of sodium hydroxide in ethyl alcohol. After absorption the contents of the first 2 wash bottles are united and 4 cc of 25% hydrochloric acid is added. These two bottles are connected to the apparatus for mercaptan detection. This consists of 2 tubes (20 x 9 cm) connected with a ground joint. The first contains calcium chloride and the second contains finely divided lead acetate (about 20 g). This second tube is connected with a small wash bottle containing 1 cc of isatin-sulfuric acid (10 mg in 100 cc sulfuric acid prepared fresh every day). Air is slowly drawn through the apparatus for 30 minutes. The hydrogen sulfide is absorbed by the lead salt and the mercaptan colors the isatin reagent a grass green. If desired, the quantity of mercaptan can be estimated colorimetrically (0.005 to 0.1 mg with an accuracy of about 0.01 mg).

2—A SPECTROPHOTOMETRIC METHOD FOR THE DE-TERMINATION OF MERCAPTANS IN AIR

Moore, Hezekiah, Harold L. Helwig, and Robert J. Graul. Am. Ind. Hyg. Assoc. J. **21**, 466-470 (1960).

For determining total mercaptans rapidly, collect air samples in 5% mercuric acetate solution, then treat with a special color-developing reagent. *This is included because of the possibility of preparing a set of standards for field use.* Add. Ref.: APCA **6**, 3661 (1961).

Mercury
Mercury Vapor

1—DETECTION OF TIN AND MERCURY BY MEANS OF SPOT TESTS

Tananaev, N. A. Z. anorg. allgem. Chem. **133**, 372-374 (1924); CA **18**, 1628 (1924).

Moisten a strip of filter paper with a drop of stannous chloride solution, add a drop of the solution to be tested for mercury, and follow with a drop of aniline.

2—DETECTION OF CHROMIUM, MANGANESE, MER-CURY, SILVER AND GOLD BY THE SPOT-TEST METHOD

Tananaev, N. A. and Tananaev, Iv. Z anorg. allgem. Chem. **170**, 113-127 (1928); CA **22**, 1930 (1928).

The authors list several additional spot tests for mercury, but say they are less characteristic than the one described above.

3—APPARATUS FOR DETECTING AND ESTIMATING MERCURY VAPOR IN AIR, FLUE GASES, ETC.

Nordlander, B. W. Brit. (Pat. No.) 264-820, Jan. 21, 1926; CA **22**, 188 (1928).

Mercury-sensitive selenium sulfide in a protective colloid, such as gelatin, is applied to a paper or other carrier. Directions are given for preparing the selenium sulfide, and the apparatus for using the reagent is described in detail.

4—SELENIUM SULFIDE—A NEW DETECTOR FOR MER-CURY VAPOR

Nordlander, Birger W. Ind. Eng. Chem. **19**, No. 4, 518-521 (1927).

A very sensitive indicator for mercury vapor is based on the reaction between active selenium sulfide and the vapor. Paper coated with the selenium sulfide blackens when exposed to mercury vapor, the degree of blackening being a function of time of exposure, concentration of the mercury, and other controllable factors. With the apparatus described, a wide range of concentrations can be measured.

5—DEVICE FOR DETECTING TRACES OF MERCURY VAPOR (WITH SELENIUM SULFIDE)

Anon. Gen. Elec. Rev. **30**, 442 (1927); CA **21**, 3491 (1927).

The article describes a method for the determination of mercury vapor in air in the range of 1 part in 20 million. The method is based on reaction between selenium sulfide and the mercury vapor. The reaction product is an easily observable colored substance. The darkening depends upon the concentration of mercury vapor, the time of exposure, and other controllable factors. The apparatus can be used to produce a continuous and automatic record of the mercury content. The photoelectric cell circuit may be arranged to furnish a warning signal when the mercury concentration becomes dangerously high.

6—DETECTION OF MERCURY VAPOR

Nordlander, Birger W. U. S. (Pat. No.) 1,711,742, May 7, 1929; CA **23**, 3190 (1929).

The apparatus described here is either the same as, or very similar to, the one described by the same author in a British patent (see above).

7—THE DETERMINATION OF MERCURY IN AIR AND IN URINE

Fraser, A. M. J. Ind. Hyg. **16**, 67-76 (1934).

The author uses the mercury vapor detector developed by Nordlander (see above), in which mercury-contaminated air is pumped against selenium sulfide coated paper, and the depth of color of the mercuric sulfide formed is compared with calibrated standards. If temperature and air speed are kept constant, the mercury concentration is directly proportional to the depth of color on the paper.

8—THE DETECTION OF TOXIC GASES AND VAPORS

Leroux, Lucien. Rev. hyg. et med. prevent. **57**, 81-112 (1935).

As little as 1 part of mercury in 20,000,000 parts of air will blacken a reagent paper impregnated with selenium sulfide. The greater the concentration of the mercury, the greater the blackening of the paper. For another procedure, draw filtered and dried air through warm tubes over iodine crystals. Crystals of mercuric iodide precipitate over the iodine crystals in the cooler part of the tube if mercury is present in the air current. Add. Ref.: CA **29**, 3627 (1935).

9—THE USE OF INDICATORS FOR THE DETECTION OF POISONOUS GASES AND VAPORS

Heering, D. Gasmaske **8**, 88-89 (1936).

Mercury vapor reacts with gold chloride and potassium iodide to give a red color at 0.003 mg per liter of air. Add. Ref.: CA **30**, 7059 (1936).

10—DETECTING FOREIGN SUBSTANCES IN THE AT-MOSPHERE

Establissements Luchaire. Fr. (Pat. No.) 816,128, July 30, 1937; CA **32**, 1984 (1938).

An apparatus for indicating poisonous gases is described, in which the gas is bubbled through the reagents. The presence of mercury vapor is indicated.

11—A METHOD FOR THE DETERMINATION OF SMALL QUANTITIES OF MERCURY IN AIR

Grosskopf, K. Draeger-Hefte #191, 3589-3591 (1937); CA **31**, 8427 (1937).

The author describes a method for the determination of mercury in air based upon the reduction of auric chloride by mercury. Silica gel impregnated with auric chloride which is dried and activated in a vacuum at elevated temperatures is the reagent used for the determination. An indicator tube is then filled with this reagent and used with a Draeger apparatus. When air containing mercury is passed through the tube, characteristic colorations are produced and the amount of mercury present can be determined by comparison with standard tubes. The method is sensitive to a concentration of 0.001 mg mercury per liter of air.

12—APPARATUS FOR DETECTING IMPURITIES IN THE ATMOSPHERE

The British Thomson-Houston Co. Ltd. Brit. (Pat. No.) 460,835, Feb. 4, 1937; CA **31**, 4541 (1937).

An apparatus for the detection of mercury in air is described. The apparatus consists of a chimney whose upper end contains a curved holder suitable for holding a piece of test material. The base of the chimney contains a heat source to keep the air at the optimum temperature for the reaction. The apparatus is particularly applicable to the detection of mercury, a selenium sulfide indicator as described in Brit. (Pat. No.) 264,820 (see above) being used.

13—APPARATUS FOR DETECTING HARMFUL QUANTITIES OF MERCURY VAPOR IN THE ATMOSPHERE

Swisher, Thomas H. (to General Elec. Co.) U. S. (Pat. No.) 2,073,531, Mar. 9, 1937; CA **31**, 2877 (1937).

A chimney shaft is used having an opening adjacent to its bottom, a selenium sulfide film sensitive to mercury mounted at its top, and a luminous heat source such as an incandescent lamp is mounted adjacent to the bottom of the shaft so that discoloration of the film indicates the amount of mercury present.

14—MERCURY VAPOR DETECTION

Biggs, L. R. J. Ind. Hyg. Toxicol. **20**, 161-168 (1938).

Selenium sulfide paper blackens when exposed to mercury. A mercury vapor detector uses this chemical indicator on a continuous strip of paper; the degree of darkening of the tape is proportional to the mercury concentration in the air for the period of exposure. Other apparatus using selenium sulfide includes a continuous monitor (lamp shade type) as developed by Swisher (see above), and a "sniffer", made by attaching the sensitive indicator paper to a hand vacuum cleaner. Two types of photoelectric detectors depend on the permeability of mercury vapor to ultraviolet light. Add. Ref.: CA **32**, 2864 (1938).

15—MERCURY POISONING AS A MINING HAZARD

Davenport, Sara J. and D. Harrington. U. S. Bur. Mines, Circ. **7180**, 27 pp. (1941); CA **36**, 1401 (1942).

The authors present a review of mercury mining hazards. Data is also presented on the toxicity and detection of mercury in air.

16—MERCURY VAPOR DETECTOR

Woodson, Thomas T. (to General Elec. Co.). U. S. (Pat. No.) 2,227,117, Dec. 31, 1941; CA **35**, 2377 (1941).

The author describes an apparatus for detecting mercury in air or other gas.

17—THE DETERMINATION OF MERCURY IN AIR

Barnes, E. C. J. Ind. Hyg. Toxicol. **28**, 257-261 (1946).

Draw air through an absorbing solution (0.25% iodine in 3% aqueous potassium iodide) in a standard impinger at 1 cubic foot per minute. Treat 5 ml of the sample with 1 ml of 10% copper sulfate solution, then with 2 ml of 3 N sodium sulfite. Prepare similarly a set of standards with which to compare the pink-orange color produced by mercury. The method is applicable to mercury vapor, dust, and organic mercury, and has been suitably modified for field use and detector techniques. The sensitivity is 3 μg mercury in the aliquot taken, and there are practically no interferences, while the overall efficiency of the impinger and the analytical method is better than 90%. Add. Ref.: CA **41**, 1574 (1947)

18—ANALYTICAL SELENIUM STRIP

Stitt, Fred (to the U.S.A., as represented by the Secy. of Agr.) U. S. (Pat. No.) 2,576,251, Sept. 11, 1951; CA **46**, 66 (1952).

Paper impregnated with aqueous potassium selenocyanate is exposed to hydrogen chloride for 30 minutes, then dried at 100° to produce an analytical strip in which the sole active agent is selenium.

19—SENSITIZED PAPER FOR THE ESTIMATION OF MERCURY VAPOR

Stitt, Fred and Yoshio Tomimatsu. Anal. Chem. **23**, 1098-1101 (1951).

The authors present a critical study of the selenocyanate reaction with mercury, including the effect of solution preparation, temperature, flow rate, and other factors. Soak sheets either of Whatman No. 1 or S and S 610 paper in a selenocyanate solution, prepared by shaking potassium cyanide solution with an excess of powdered selenium, drain carefully, dry, cut into strips, and place in special adapters. The paper reacts with mercury in the air at 65° or higher, and the length of the blackening is directly proportional to the concentration of the mercury, in the 60° to 200° range. The papers can be used conveniently with the portable instrument described by the authors for ethylene in Anal. Chem. **23**, 1138 (1951) Add. Ref.: CA **45**, 10127 (1951).

20—M. S. A. MERCURY VAPOR DETECTOR

Mine Safety Appliances Co., Pittsburgh, Pa. Bull. No. DO-1 (1953).

The commercial detector is based on the reaction of mercury with a strip of paper impregnated with selenium sulfide. Convection from a 25 watt lamp causes the air to pass by the paper. The paper then is removed and compared with standard color stains. The stain density is proportional to the concentration and exposure time. The sensitivity is 1 ppm or 0.082 mg per cubic meter.

21—RAPID DETERMINATION OF MERCURY VAPOR IN AIR

Yavorovskaya, S. F. Gigiena i Sanit. **1953**, No. 4, 48-49; CA **47**, 11072 (1953).

Silica gel impregnated with cuprous iodide and iodide is the reagent used for mercury determination. In the presence of mercury a pink coloration is produced. The intensity of the color is proportional to the concentration of mercury present. The adsorbent is prepared by soaking silica gel grains in saturated copper sulfate solution, followed by saturated potassium iodide solution, drying at 70-80°, and sifting. *The silica gel reagent lacks sensitivity and the relationship of the color change to concentration depends on the potassium iodide treatment.*

22—DETERMINATION OF MERCURY IN THE ATMOSPHERE

Aruin, A. S. Gigiena i Sanit. **1954**, No. 5, 46; CA **48**, 9861 (1954).

Sample air containing mercury into acid potassium permanganate solution, reduce the excess permanganate with oxalic acid, mix the solution with Reinecke salt solution, and compare the resulting red suspension with standards. *The procedure might be used in a field detector.*

23—SAMPLING AND ANALYZING AIR FOR CONTAMINANTS IN WORK PLACES

Silverman, Leslie. Encyclopedia of Instrumentation for Industrial Hygiene, edited by Yaffe, Charles D., Dohrman H. Byers, and Andrew D. Hosey. (Univ. of Michigan, Inst. of Industrial Health, Ann Arbor, Mich., 1956) pp. 7-25.

Mercury in the range of 0.1 to 70 ppm turns test paper impregnated with selenium or selenium sulfide from yellow to black.

24—IMPROVEMENTS IN OR RELATING TO THE DETECTION OF MERCURY VAPOR IN AIR OR OTHER GASES

Draeger, Otto H. Brit. (Pat. No.) 811,408, date appl. 2-4-57; Germany, date appl. April 17, 1956; AA **6**, 3236 (1957).

The air is aspirated through silica gel impregnated with mercuric bromide and auric bromide. Any mercury present in the sample reduces the mercuric bromide to mercurous bromide which then reduces the auric bromide to colloidal gold, which changes the color of the reagent from yellow to intense red-violet.

25—QUANTITATIVE DETERMINATION OF MERCURY

Auergesellschaft Akt.-Ges. (by Walter Lemcke). Ger. (Pat. No.) 1,007,082, April 25, 1957 (Cl 42.**1**); CA **54**, 176 (1960).

Silica or aluminum oxide gel is soaked with a solution of palladium chloride. This reagent is introduced into a glass tube and subsequently used for the determination of mercury. *See addition to this patent below.*

26—DETERMINATION OF MERCURY VAPOR IN GASES

Draegerwerk Heinrich u. Bernhard Draeger. Ger. Pat. No.) 1,018,646 (Cl. 42.**1**), Oct. 31, 1957; CA **54**, 24136 (1960).

Pass air or gases containing mercury vapor over kieselguhr impregnated with a mercuric salt and an indicator which can change color during reduction, e.g., gold chloride or other gold salt.

27—THE DETERMINATION OF MERCURY IN AIR

Sergeant, G. A., B. E. Dixon, and R. G. Lidzey. Analyst **82**, 27-33, (1957).

The authors describe a method for determining all forms of mercury in air at concentrations of about 100 μg per cubic meter. Iodized active carbon adsorbs the mercury vapor, and a mineral wool filter traps mercury-bearing dust. After heating the adsorbed mercury with active carbon and iron powder in a specially constructed ignition tube, transfer the mercury vapor to selenium sulfide test paper and compare the stain on the paper with a set of standard stains prepared from known amounts of mercury. Prepare the selenium sulfide test paper by impregnating Whatman No. 1 filter paper with 2% selenous acid solution, draining, and drying at 100°C. Just before use add 1 drop of a 5% ethyl alcohol solution of thioacetamide, and dry the paper for a few minutes. Add. Refs.: IHD **21**, 798 (1957); CA **51**, 9405 (1957); AA **4**, 2814 (1957).

28—FIELD TYPE COLORIMETRIC TESTERS FOR GASES AND PARTICULATE MATTER

McConnaughey, Paul W. Presented at the annual meeting of the American Industrial Hygiene Association, Atlantic City, N. J., 1958.

The length of the red stain, produced by mercury vapor in a detector tube containing cuprous iodide and glycerine impregnated on silica gel, is proportional to the quantity of the gas in the air sample, provided the given air sample volume was taken at a fixed rate.

29—INSOLUBLE COLOR REAGENTS. COLOR REAGENT PAPERS FROM ION-EXCHANGE PAPERS

Sansoni, Bruno. Naturwissenschaften **46**, 228-229 (1959) (in German); CA **54**, 12879 (1960).

The authors describe hydroxy-type anionic-exchange papers which are impregnated with thiocyanate, sulfide, iodide, and permanganate ions as well as iodine and various acid-base indicators. The papers to be used are cut into 1-mm squares. The papers are subjected to the reactant and rinsed, and the color changes are observed under a microscope. A concentration of 6.7 g of divalent mercury was detected on sulfide paper.

30—M. S. A. MERCURY VAPOR DETECTOR

Mine Safety Appliances Co., Pittsburgh, Pa. Bull. 0805-3 (1959).

The apparatus consists of a rubber bulb pump mounted on a holder, a rotating scale, and silica gel indicating tubes. The scale for measuring the stain length in the silica gel tube is calibrated for 25 aspirations, and the length of the stain measurement is accurate in the range from 0 to 1.0 mg per cubic meter.

31—REPORT ON THE DRAEGER GAS DETECTOR

American Conference of Governmental Industrial Hygienists. Transactions of the Twenty-first Annual Meeting, pp. 125-127 (1959).

The article indicates that large concentrations of mercury are easily detected but values near the threshold limit appear to be difficult to test as well as unreliable. The reliability of quantitative evaluations is also doubtful.

32—DETECTION OF MERCURY VAPOR

Draeger, Otto H. Brit. (Pat. No.) 811,408, April 2, 1959; CA **53**, 12958 (1959).

The author describes a more sensitive method for the detection of mercury in air. The reagent is prepared by impregnating pure silica gel having a grain size of 0.5 mm and a bulk weight of 500 g./l. with 0.001 g.-mole. auric bromide and 0.001 g.-mole mercuric bromide from an aqueous solution. The water is then evaporated in vacuo at 50° to a 10% residual and the resulting reagent activated several hours at 100°.

33—INFORMATION ON THE DRAEGER GAS DETECTOR

Draegerwerk Heinr. and Bernhard Draeger, Luebeck, Germany (distributed by New Jersey Safety Equipment Co., 299 Park Ave., East Orange, N. J.).

34—MERCURY DETECTOR TUBE. Information Sheet No. 33 (Jan. 1960).

The 0.1/a Mercury Detector Tube, to be used with the Draeger Multi-Gas-Detector, contains a preclensing layer and an indicating layer. The mercury detection is based on the reduction of a gold complex salt in the indicating layer to colloidal gold, with the sensitivity increased by the addition of a mercury II salt. The reaction is specific for mercury vapor, other contaminants in the air sample being retained in the pre-cleansing layer. (The detector tube does not measure organic compounds of mercury.) Carbon monoxide, if present in concentrations above 0.2%-volume, may interfere with the detection of small quantities of mercury. The test result is calculated from the number of strokes required to produce a discernible gray ring, characteristic for mercury vapor, at the line of demarcation between the white preclensing layer and the yellow indicating layer. The detector tube picks up an absolute quantity of approximately 0.2 μg of mercury. Since the bellows pump passes 0.1 liter per stroke, a quantity of 0.1 μg of mercury in 1 liter of air would be recognized by drawing 2 liters of air (= 20 pump strokes). The measuring range of the detector tube, therefore, is between 0.1 and 2. mg per cubic meter of air.

35—AUTOMATIC SAMPLING AND DETERMINATION OF MICRO-QUANTITIES OF MERCURY VAPOR

Hemeon, Wesley C. L. and George F. Haines, Jr. Am. Ind. Hyg. Assoc. J. **22**, 75-79 (1961).

The AISI smoke sampler containing paper impregnated with potassium iodide reagent is used to sample automatically for mercury vapor in air. After volatilization, the mercury is measured with a mercury vapor detector. Add. Ref.: APCA **VI**, 3655 (1961).

36—LINEAR COLORIMETRIC METHOD FOR DETERMINING MERCURY VAPORS IN AIR

Bregvadze, U. D. and M. N. Mirianashvili. Sb. Nauchn. Rabot Inst. Okhrany Truda, Vses. Tsentr. Sov. Prof. Soyuzov **1961**, No. 4, 120-125; CA **58**, 870 (1963).

The method, based on the reaction of mercury and copper diiodide, uses filter paper impregnated with Polezhaev's reagent. Mercury vapor concentration is determined from 1 of 2 scales: 0 to 1.4 μg per liter with 1 liter of air, and 0 to 0.15 μg per liter for 4 liters of air. Add. Ref.: Zh., Khim. **1962**, Abstr. No. 111344.

37—TEST TUBE FOR DETECTION OF MERCURY IN AIR

Auergesellschaft G.m.b.H. (by Hermann Heidrich). Ger. (Pat. No.) 1,096,644, Jan. 5, 1961 (Cl. 42.1); CA **55**, 23190 (1961).

This is an addition to Ger. (Pat. No.) 1,007,082 (abstracted previously). The sensitivity of the test is improved when ammonium molybdate is added in an amount of 10 to 15 times that of the palladium (or ruthenium) chloride.

38—M. S. A. MERCURY VAPOR DETECTOR

Mine Safety Appliances Co., Pittsburgh, Pa. 8B3621-1, Sect. 3, p. 14 (1962).

Air samples are drawn by an aspirator bulb through a replaceable "breaktip" glass indicator tube filled with an impregnated chemical which changes color if the air contains mercury vapor. An accompanying scale for comparing the length of the colored stain indicates the concentration of the mercury, in the range from 0 to 1.0 mg per cubic meter. (See abstract of earlier bulletin, above.)

39—RAPID METHOD FOR DETERMINING MERCURY VAPORS IN THE AIR

Gurvits, B. I., G. P. Chuklenkova, Metod. Materialy & Nauchchn. Soobshch. Vses. Nauchn.-Issled. Inst. Zheleznodor. Gigieny. 1962 (2) 21-7.

Two tests for the determination of mercury vapor in air are presented. One method is a line color procedure involving an indicator tube with a colored column from which the mercury concentration is read directly from the height of column in the tube. The second method involves the measurement of the color intensity produced on an indicator gel against a standard comparison scale. The same reaction is used in both methods. The indicator material is prepared by impregnating silica gel with an alcoholic suspension of copper iodide. In the presence of mercury a yellowish-rose color is produced. Sensitivity is 0.01 mg/m^3 of air.

40—ALLYL ALCOHOL AS A SENSITIVE AND SPECIFIC REAGENT FOR THE DETECTION OF MERCUROUS IONS

Qureshi, M., N. A. Abraham, K. G. Varshney. Anal. Chem. 36(10) 2040-1 (1964) CA **61** 11310 (1964).

The sample solution is made slightly acidic with 0.01 N nitric acid. One drop of 0.1 M silver nitrate and 1 drop of allyl alcohol are added. A black coloration indicates the presence of Hg_2^{+2}.

See Section One

For references 5, 6, 71, 72, 98, 106, 119.

Methane

1—INDICATING IMPURITIES IN GAS

Siemens and Halske A. G. Fr. (Pat. No.) 822,148, Dec. 21, 1937; CA **32**, 5265 (1938).

The authors describe an apparatus for automatically indicating the presence of combustible impurities in gases.

2—DETECTING FOREIGN SUBSTANCES IN THE ATMOSPHERE

Establissements Luchaire. Fr. (Pat. No.) 816,128, July 30, 1937; CA **32**, 1984 (1938).

The patent describes an apparatus for indicating poisonous gases, in which the gas, bubbling through reagents, indicates the presence of fire damp, etc.

3—IMPROVEMENTS IN OR RELATING TO TESTING AIR OR OTHER GASES TO DETERMINE THE METHANE CONTENT THEREOF

Draeger, O. H. Brit. (Pat. No.) 773,534, Mar. 10, 1954; AA **4**, 3787 (1957).

A method of analysis for methane in air or gases is presented. An indicator tube containing successive layers of an ozone-forming reagent (such as silica gel impregnated with sulfuric acid and a permanganate) and a formaldehyde indicating reagent such as chromotropic acid is used.

4—DETECTION OF METHANE

Draegerwerk Heinrich und Bernhard Draeger. Ger. (Pat. No.) 1,036,540 (Cl. 42.1), Aug. 14, 1958; CA **55**, 3308 (1961).

The authors describe a method for the detection of methane in air or other gases. Sulfur trioxide is added to the sample which is then passed over a mixture of sulfuric acid and permanganate, and finally over a reagent for the determination of carbon monoxide. The best method is to aspirate the gas through a test tube containing 1 g permanganate, e.g., potassium permanganate or silver permanganate, and either 25 cc sulfuric acid containing 5 to 15% free sulfur trioxide, or 50 cc 50% sulfuric acid per 5 g potassium permanganate. The layer capable of giving off sulfur trioxide may also contain iodine pentoxide, and the reagent for detecting carbon monoxide which is deposited on a carrier, e.g., silica gel, contains sulfuric acid containing free sulfur trioxide, and iodine pentoxide.

5—VAPOR-FORMING REAGENTS IN THE SMALL TEST TUBE TECHNIQUE FOR THE DETERMINATION OF ORGANIC VAPORS AND GASES

Grosskopf, Karl. Z. anal. Chem. **170**, 271-277 (1959); CA **54**, 2836 (1960).

In the author's apparatus, the test air is passed over a volatile reagent, then both the air and the reagent pass to a second reagent; all 3 react to form a color. The length of the colored layer is proportional to the amount of test substance present in the air. Methane (5 to 100 ppm) is determined with sulfur trioxide + potassium permanganate + iodine pentoxide-sulfuric acid. *This system might be applied in a field detector.*

Methanol

1—A SIMPLE AND RELIABLE METHOD FOR THE DETERMINATION OF METHYL ALCOHOL AND FORMALDEHYDE IN AIR

Ackerbauer, C. F. and R. J. Lebowich. J. Lab. Clin. Med. **28**, 373-377 (1942).

Draw air through a series of 4 bubblers containing, in the first bubbler, 75 ml of 1% phosphoric acid and 75 ml of 2% barium chloride, mixed; in the second bubbler, 200 ml of an alkaline solution of potassium permanganate, which removes by oxidation all of the methanol; in the third, 225 ml of modified Schiff's reagent of Wright; and in the fourth bubbler (which may be eliminated in the field) 200 ml of 2 N sodium bisulfite. Decolorize the permanganate in the second bubbler with oxalic-sulfuric acid mixture, and add Schiff's reagent. Compare the color with those in a set of standards, either visually, or, preferably, in a Hellige colorimeter. Add. Ref. CA **37**, 6592 (1943).

2—GAS ANALYSIS BY MEANS OF DETECTOR TUBES. VIII. RAPID METHOD FOR THE DETERMINATION OF ETHYL ALCOHOL AND METHANOL IN AIR

Kobayashi, Yoshitaka. J. Chem. Soc. Japan, Ind. Chem. Sect. **56**, 526-527 (1953); CA **48**, 11978 (1954).

Detector tubes containing silica gel impregnated with an aqueous solution of potassium dichromate acidified by sulfuric acid and dried at approximately 100° are used for the detection of ethyl and methyl alcohol. The charts and graphs expressing the relations of concentrations (0.5 to 5.0%) of ethyl alcohol and methyl alcohol with the length of the column which changes to blue-green are provided.

See Section One
For reference 105.

Methyl Acrylate
Methyl Chloroacrylate

1—THE DETERMINATION OF METHYL-alpha-CHLOROACRYLATE IN THE ATMOSPHERE

Haslam, J., S. M. A. Whettem, and W. W. Soppet. Analyst **76**, 628-634 (1951).

Draw a known volume of air, containing from 0.1 to 5 ppm (0.5 to 25 mg) of methyl-alpha-chloroacrylate per cubic meter of air, through 0.001N potassium permanganate, and compare the color produced either with empirical standard solutions or with standard color disks in a comparator. Add. Ref.: CA **46**, 859 (1952).

2—DETERMINATION OF SOLVENT VAPORS IN AIR. VI. METHYL ACRYLATE

Kobayashi, Yoshitaka. J. Soc. Org. Cynthet. Chem., Japan **12**, 503-505, (1954); CA **51**, 952 (1957).

The determination is carried out with the same reagent and apparatus as is used for the determination of propane. The useful range of the method is 10 to 3000 ppm.

Methyl Bromide

1—ANALYTICAL METHODS FOR METHYL BROMIDE

Stenger, V. A., S. A. Shrader, and A. W. Beshgetoor. Ind. Eng. Chem., Anal. Ed. **11**, 121-124 (1939).

Methods for determining methyl bromide in air include the well-known Beilstein test for organic halide vapors, in which a flame impinges on a copper strip; methyl bromide (or other halide vapor) colors the flame green or blue. The Frigidaire halide leak detector, using this procedure, can detect 50 to 500 ppm of methyl bromide. Add. Ref.: CA **33**, 2846 (1939).

2—METHODS FOR THE DETECTION OF TOXIC GASES IN INDUSTRY. ORGANIC HALOGEN COMPOUNDS

Anon. Dept. of Scientific and Industrial Research, London, England, Leaflet No. 12, 7 pp. (1940).

The leaflet describes the detection of organic halogen compounds with a "Halide Detector Lamp," the heat of whose flame decomposes the halide in the test air so it reacts with a copper screw in the nozzle of the lamp to form the corresponding copper halide, which colors the flame green. The lamp is not well suited to detect methyl bromide, because harmful concentrations of the gas may be too low to color the flame.

3—DETECTION AND DETERMINATION OF TRACES OF METHYL BROMIDE

Lubatti, O. F. Nature **155**, 109-110 (1945); CA **39**, 1819 (1945).

The author describes a method for the determination of small quantities of methyl bromide. The method depends on the catalytic combustion of traces of methyl bromide in air on a glowing platinum wire and the determination of the bromine liberated by the coloration of a test paper. The paper is moistened with a pale yellow solution of fluorescein, which is changed to the red eosin dye according to the amount of methyl bromide decomposed. A portable apparatus for making the test is described.

4—A FIELD METHOD FOR THE DETERMINATION OF HALOGENATED HYDROCARBONS

Braid, P. E. and Kingsley Kay. Can. J. Technol. **29**, 159-169 (1951); CA **45**, 8940 (1951).

In a small portable field instrument for determining methyl bromide in air, a squeeze bulb forces measured amounts of test air through a reaction tube containing oxidizing agent. Prepare the oxidizer by mixing 3.5 g of dehydrated iodine pentoxide with 9.5 g of pumice, and add 12 g of fuming sulfuric acid (56% free sulfur trioxide). Bring the air containing the liberated free bromine into contact with a fluorescein-treated test disk in a specially-designed holder. (Prepare the fluorescein solution by dissolving 0.1 g fluorescein in 5 ml of 10% sodium hydroxide and diluting to 100 ml with water. Dilute 6 ml of this solution to 100 ml with water.) Compare the color produced in the test disk with the colors on a standard color card (concentration range, 0 to 150 ppm by volume). For chlorinated compounds, such as trichloroethylene and carbon tetrachloride, modify the apparatus by replacing the squeeze bulb with a pump which delivers 500 ml per stroke, and use 0.05% o-tolidine solution on the test disk as the sensitive reagent for chlorine.

5—APPARATUS FOR THE DETERMINATION OF LOW CONCENTRATIONS OF METHYL BROMIDE AND OTHER GASES

Call, F. J. Sci. Food Agr. **3**, 463-470 (1952); CA **47**, 1007 (1953).

A medium hard filter paper of close texture is impregnated with 0.02 to 0.1% fluorescein. Bromine in combustion reacts with the fluorescein to produce a colored stain on the paper. The stain will be proportional to the concentration of the bromide under the conditions of rigid control described in the article. The method is applicable to hydrogen cyanide and carbon tetrachloride, and to other systems for which a suitable test paper can be prepared. Add. Ref.: IHD **17**, 190 (1953).

6—APPARATUS FOR THE DETERMINATION OF HIGH CONCENTRATIONS OF METHYL BROMIDE IN FUMIGATION

Loveday, D. J. Sci. Food Agr. **5**, 376-381 (1954); CA **48**, 12475 (1954).

An apparatus based on Call's method (see abstract above) determines 0 to 30 mg methyl bromide per liter of air. Bromine, liberated by combustion of the methyl bromide, is drawn along a strip of paper impregnated with fluorescein; the length of the colored stain on the paper is pro-

portional to the concentration of methyl bromide. A modification of this method uses buffered phenol red as an indicator.

7—SAMPLING AND ANALYZING AIR FOR CONTAMINANTS IN WORK PLACES

Silverman, Leslie. Encyclopedia of Instrumentation for Industrial Hygiene, edited by Yaffe, Charles D., H. Byers, and Andrew D. Hosey. (Univ. of Michigan, Inst. of Industrial Health, Ann Arbor, Mich., 1956) pp. 7-25.

S and S 598 Y filter paper impregnated with 0.006% fluorescein in 20% sodium hydroxide turns from greenish yellow to strong pink in the presence of 0 to 150 ppm of methyl bromide. A Hoolamite reaction tube should precede the unit. Some other brominated hydrocarbons interfere.

8—VAPOR-FORMING REAGENTS IN THE SMALL TEST TUBE TECHNIQUE FOR THE DETERMINATION OF ORGANIC VAPORS AND GASES

Grosskopf, Karl. Z. anal. Chem. **170**, 271-277 (1959); CA **54**, 2836 (1960).

In the author's apparatus, the test air is passed over a volatile reagent, then both the air and the reagent pass to a second reagent; all 3 react to form a color. The length of the colored layer is proportional to the amount of test substance present in the air. Methyl bromide (5 to 100 ppm) is determined with sulfuric acid + potassium permanganate + o-tolidine. *This system might be applied in a field detector.*

9—THE DETECTION AND ESTIMATION OF LOW CONCENTRATIONS OF METHYL BROMIDE IN AIR

Heseltine, H. K. Pest Technol. **1**, No. 10-11, 253-255 (1959); CA **54**, 13509 (1960).

A special pump draws air with low concentrations of methyl bromide through detector tubes containing a powder impregnated with sulfur trioxide. The sulfur trioxide, when released, activates a layer of potassium permanganate and fuming sulfuric acid on silica gel to react with methyl bromide and release bromine, which reacts with o-tolidine. The reaction product is absorbed on an indicating layer, giving a color change depending on the concentration. The detector tubes, which are available commercially, provide an easy and accurate means for deciding whether an area is safe to enter after use of methyl bromide.

See Section One
For reference 90.

Methyl Chloroformate
Methyl (or Ethyl) Chlorosulfonate

1—TESTS AVAILABLE FOR THE IDENTIFICATION OF SMALL QUANTITIES OF THE WAR GASES

Cox, H. E. Analyst **64**, 807-813 (1939).
Identify methyl chloroformate by passing the gas through an alcoholic solution of aniline; hydrochloric acid is produced and may be identified. Add. Ref.: CA **34**, 541 (1940).

2—IBID.

Methyl chlorosulfonate usually is admixed with dimethyl sulfate. It differs from the latter by being hydrolyzed in water to methyl sulfate and hydrochloric acid. Methyl chlorosulfonate may be recognized by the liberation of the hydrochloric acid and the formation of potassium sulfate and chloride when aspirated through alcoholic potassium hydroxide solution.
METHYL ETHER - see DIMETHYL ETHER

Methyl Dichloroarsine

1—TESTS AVAILABLE FOR THE IDENTIFICATION OF SMALL QUANTITIES OF THE WAR GASES

Cox, H. E. Analyst **64**, 807-813 (1939).
Methyl dichloroarsine gives an immediate gray precipitate of metallic mercury when passed into 1 ml of mercurous nitrate solution just acidified with nitric acid. Methyl dichloroarsine may be identified also by the sulfide reaction with hydrogen sulfide. Add. Ref.: CA **34**, 541 (1940).
See Section One
For references 36, 52.

Mineral Oil Vapors
See Section One
For reference 104.

Molybdenum

1—o-HYDROXYPHENYLFLUORONE AS SPECIFIC REAGENT FOR MOLYBDENUM AND COPPER

Gillis, J., A. Craeys, and J. Hoste. Mededel.
Koninkl. Vlaam. Acad. Wetenschap., Belg., Klasse Wetenschap. **9**, No. 11, 13 pp. (1947); CA **42**, 3279 (1948).
Treat drop test paper MN 640 W with 1 drop of 0.1% o-hydroxyphenylfluorone solution slightly acidified with hydrochloric acid. Dry at room temperature, place 1 drop of unknown solution on it, add 1 to 2 drops of 20% potassium fluoride solution (in 0.5 N hydrochloric acid) and 2 or 3 drops of 0.5 N sulfuric acid. The paper turns carmine-red if molybdenum is present. The sensitivity of this specific reaction is $1:3.10^4$. Ceric, permanganate, and chromate ions destroy the reagent.

Monoethanolamine

1—THE DETERMINATION OF MONOETHANOLAMINE AND AMMONIA IN AIR

Williams, D. D. and R. R. Miller. Anal. Chem. **34**, 225-227 (1962).
A method for the routine determination of parts per million quantities of ammonia and/or monoethanolamine (MEA) vapor in air uses the reagent ninhydrin which, supported on silica gel in a glass tube, reacts equally well with both contaminants. Orthoboric acid serves as a selective filter to remove MEA from the sampled air. Consecutive sampling through the tube in opposite directions permits the simultaneous determination of either or both contaminants. The tubes are 4-inch lengths of glass tubing drawn out and sealed at one end. Insert an end-holding plug of properly sized polyurethane foam or glass wool and position it at the sealed end of the tube, being careful to leave a flat interface. Add, in order, a 20 mm layer of impregnated silica gel, a separator plug, a 10 mm layer of 30 to 60 mesh calcium carbonate, another separator plug, a 10 mm layer of 30 to 60 mesh orthoboric acid, and a holding plug. Draw out and seal the open end of the tube, being careful to avoid heating the boric acid. Tamp the fillings enough to ensure firm layers of uniform density. Prepare the silica gel by adding to a weighed quantity (W) of pure white gel (dried at 110° C) 2% (0.02 W) of triketohydrindene hydrate (ninhydrin) dissolved in just enough distilled water to wet the gel completely. Stir, allow to stand 10 minutes, then remove excess water by passing a stream of filtered air or inert gas at a temperature of 20 to 25° C and relative humidity of 50 to 60% over or through the gel until equilibrium is attained. The gel should contain 25 to 30% by weight of water and should be free flowing. The interposition of the calcium carbonate layer prevents the transport of the boric acid to the active gel under ambient temperature fluctuations. The shelf life of the tubes is at least 18 months,

especially if they are refrigerated. Add. Refs.: APCA Abstr. **7**, No. 10, 4309 (1962); IHD **26**, 379 (1962).

See Section One
For reference 125.

Mononitrotoluene
See Section One
For reference 60.

Mustard Gas (Yperite)
(B,B'-Dichlorodiethyl Sulfide)

1—POSSIBILITIES OF DETECTION OF CHEMICALS USED IN WARFARE
Hoeriger, Max. Protar **1**, 197-201 (1935); Chem. Zentr. **1936**, I, 3952; CA **31**, 7141 (1937).

Mustard gas can be determined by reacting it with bleaching powder. The action product is a visible suffocating fume.

2—THE DETECTION OF TOXIC GASES AND VAPORS
Leroux, Lucien. Rev. hyg. et med. prevent. **57**, 81-112 (1935).

Paper impregnated with methyl red solution (0.05 gm dissolved in 100 ml alcohol at 60°) turns pink with mustard gas. The arsines give the same reaction because of the acid produced when they are hydrolyzed. The Grignard reaction, using a freshly prepared aqueous solution of potassium iodide, gives a specific precipitate, with a sensitivity of 1 part in 25,000. Flocculation occurs in cuprous iodide when as little as 0.05 mg yperite per liter of air bubbles through the reagent. As little as 0.05 mg mustard gas per liter liberates free selenium from selenous acid. Add. Ref.: CA **29**, 3627 (1935).

3—THE DETECTION OF RESPIRATORY POISONS
Stampe, Gerhard. Draeger-Hefte No. **180**, 2964-2966 (1935); CA **30**, 701 (1936).

A description of the apparatus and methods used in detecting the presence of poisonous gases is given. A new method, specific for mustard gas, is detailed. The analysis is based on the reaction of mustard gas with certain gold salts.

4—A SPECIFIC IDENTIFICATION OF DICHLORODIETHYL SULFIDE IN PRESENCE OF OTHER CHEMICAL WARFARE AGENTS
Obermiller, Martha. Angew. Chem. **49**, 162-164 (1936); CA **30**, 3115 (1936).

Auric chloride and palladous chloride give specific reactions with dichlorodiethyl sulfide. When filter papers are impregnated with these reagents characteristic colors are also obtained. Auric chloride produces a reddish-brown spot and palladous chloride produces a yellow spot. Auric chloride gives better results, especially with the filter paper test. The specific reaction is not influenced by the presence of other chemical warfare agents such as hydrogen cyanide, phosgene, lewisite, etc. The hydrogen chloride formed by hydrolysis of most agents in aqueous solution does not interfere with the reaction. Several convenient detecting devices are described which permit the detection of mustard gas in a concentration of 10 mg per cubic meter in a period of 4 minutes, with a required sampling rate of 4 to 40 liters per minute, depending upon the type of apparatus used. Compared with this procedure a concentration of 100 mg per cubic meter is required for the Grignard detection in a like period. 10 references.

5—DETECTING B,B'-DICHLORODIETHYL SULFIDE IN AIR
Draegerwerk Heinrich u. Bernhard Draeger. Ger. (Pat. No.) 625,094, Feb. 3, 1936 (Cl. 42.**1**. 4.06); CA **30**, 2884 (1936).

The air sample is led into a container together with air which has been passed over or through bleaching powder or a material containing bleaching powder. White crystals are deposited on the sides of the container if B,B'-dichlorodiethyl sulfide is present.

6—DETECTING THE PRESENCE OF MUSTARD GAS
Schroeter, Gustav-Adolf (to Otto H. Draeger). U. S. (Pat. No.) 2,054,885, Sept. 22, 1936; CA **30**, 7500 (1936).

A salt of gold, platinum, palladium, or univalent copper, such as the chloride, can be used as a detector because of the color changes these salts undergo in the presence of mustard gas.

7—THE SPECIFIC DETECTION OF B,B'-DICHLORODIETHYL SULFIDE BY MEANS OF THE ADSORPTION METHOD (GAS-DETECTING APPARATUS)
Schroeter, Gustav A. Angew. Chem. **49**, 164-165 (1936); CA **30**, 3116 (1936).

The author summarizes the reactions and methods for the detection of B,B'-dichlorodiethyl sulfide with particular emphasis on the auric chloride reaction. 12 references.

8—THE DRAEGER GAS DETECTOR (DS-APPARATUS)
Draegerwerk. Draeger-Hefte No. **186**, 3297-3301 (1936); CA **31**, 176 (1937).

A gas detector for minute amounts of mustard gas in air consists of a small cylinder filled with a colorless granulated adsorbent impregnated with gold chloride, and a hand pump to draw air through the adsorbent. Mustard gas may be detected in the presence of war gases and related gases, but allyl mustard oil, diphenylaminechloroarsine (chlorodihydrophenarsazine), ethyldichloroarsine, and thiodiglycol desensitize the reaction somewhat.

9—DETECTING DICHLORODIETHYL SULFIDE

Draeger, Otto H. Fr. (Pat. No.) 794,443, Feb. 17, 1936; CA **30**, 4434 (1936).

The sample is aspirated through a glass tube containing silica gel. The collected sample is treated with a heavy metal salt (e.g. gold chloride) solution containing hydrogen peroxide.

10—AN APPARATUS FOR DETECTING WAR GASES

Olivier, S. C. J. Chem. Weekblad **33**, 249 (1936); CA **30**, 4585 (1936).

The air sample is aspirated through an apparatus containing silica gel. After collection, the sample is treated with gold chloride and a reducing agent. In the presence of mustard gas a yellow color is produced.

11—SHORT SCHEME OF ANALYSIS FOR THE DETECTION OF POISON GASES

Studinger, J. (With Notes on Their Odour and Irritant Action by R. Mueller). Chem. and Ind. (London) **15**, 225-231 (1937). Translated by F. G. Crosse from the original article in Mitteilungen aus dem Gebiete der Lebensmitteluntersuchung und Hygiene **27**, 8-23 (1936) (see CA **31**, 6367 (1957)).

Mustard gas reacts with sodium iodoplatinate. When filter paper moistened with a 2% solution of sodium iodoplatinate is dipped into mustard gas or into an aqueous mixture of the gas the paper turns first purple-red and then blue. Another test for mustard gas uses a 0.1% gold chloride solution. The analysis can be carried out with a dry gold chloride test paper. The addition of mustard gas followed by moistening of the paper produces a yellow color. Add. Ref.: CA **31**, 3588 (1937).

12—CHEMICAL REACTIONS OF WAR GASES

Hennig, H. Gasschutz u. Luftschutz **7**, 18-21 (1937); CA **31**, 2311 (1937).

Determine dichlorodiethyl sulfide (mustard gas) qualitatively by means of gold chloride or palladium chloride, either in aqueous solution (0.1% or 0.05%, respectively) or on test paper (10% or 0.2% solution, respectively).

13—DETECTING POISONOUS GASES IN AIR

Auergesellschaft A.-G. Ger. (Pat. No.) 670,440, Jan. 18, 1939 (Cl. 42.**1**. 4.06); CA **33**, 3023 (1939).

The sample is drawn through an indicator tube containing a mixture of a colorless adsorbent, e.g., silica gel, and soluble starch. The mixture is then treated with hydriodic acid solution and if mustard gas is present a blue coloration is observed. A similar procedure, with appropriate colorless adsorbents and reagents, is adopted in testing for other gases.

14—TESTS AVAILABLE FOR THE IDENTIFICATION OF SMALL QUANTITIES OF THE WAR GASES

Cox, H. E. Analyst **64**, 807-813 (1939).

Mustard gas produces a deep yellow spot or stain on dried filter paper impregnated with 0.1% solution of gold chloride. For the Grignard test for mustard gas, dissolve in 200 ml of water 20 g of sodium iodide, 40 drops of 7.5% solution of copper sulfate, and 2 ml of 35% gum arabic solution. Mustard gas forms a yellow, colloidal precipitate of diiodoethyl sulfide. For a third test, dip filter paper into 2% solution of sodium platinum iodide. Mustard gas turns the paper purple first, then blue. Add. Ref.: CA **34**, 541 (1940).

15—DETECTION METHODS OF WAR MATERIALS PROPOSED IN LITERATURE

Dultz, George. Wien. Pharm. Wochschr. **72**, 548-552 (1939); CA **34**, 542 (1940).

The authors present a review dealing with B,B'-dichloroethyl sulfide. 20 references.

16—NO TITLE

Thomas, Garfield. Chem. and Ind. (London) **17**, 1072-1073 (1939). (Report of meeting of Birmingham Section, Society of Chemical Industry, Birmingham, England, Nov. 24, 1939.)

To sample for war gases in the field, a pump, drawing 100 ml of air at each stroke, is used in conjunction with a tube packed with glass wool and activated carbon. To detect mustard gas in soil, a glass tube packed with glass wool soaked in 5% acetic acid is attached to the pump. A cone containing the soil sample then is fitted to the tube and 4 liters of air aspirated through. The cone is removed and sodium iodide and 2 drops of platinum chloride are added, followed by a few drops of starch solution. A purple color indicates mustard gas. *This might be applied to air samples.*

17—IDENTIFICATION OF WAR GASES

Liberalli, Marcelo Robertson. Rev. quim. farm (Rio de Janeiro) **4**, 49-53 (1939).

Yperite turns sodium platinic iodide-impregnated paper from red to blue. The reagent is specific for mustard gas. Cotton wrapped in gauze, which has been impregnated with 0.05% alcoholic methyl red and dried, turns pink when exposed to mustard gas or to lewisite. Add. Ref.: CA **33**, 7921 (1939).

18—WAR GASES AND THEIR IDENTIFICATION

Twiss, D. F. and A. E. T. Neale. Chem. and Ind. (London) **18**, 13-14 (1940).

The author describes an ethyl alcohol lamp to detect halogen in war gases by the Beilstein method, and sulfur from sulfur dioxide in the combustion products. Identification of both substances help recognize mustard gas. Add. Ref.: CA **34**, 4828 (1940); Chem. and Ind. (London) **17**, 1073 (1939).

19—A CORRECTION

Thomas, Garfield. Chem. and Ind. (London) **18**, 30-31 (1940).

The test for mustard gas should use a reagent called iodoplatinate, made by mixing sodium iodide and platinic chloride. "The Detection and Identification of War Gases," published by H. M. Stationery Office (London, England) is the original source for the technique. (See previous article by the same author, above.)

20—WAR GASES AND THEIR IDENTIFICATION. MODIFICATION OF THE TWISS-NEALE LAMP TEST FOR MUSTARD GAS

Edwards, G. H. Chem. and Ind. (London) **18**, 239-240 (1940).

The author describes a modification if the Twiss-Neale lamp technique for identifying mustard gas (see above). After burning organic materials containing sulfur to sulfur dioxide, he identifies the sulfur dioxide on a test filter paper impregnated with phosphotungstate-phosphomolybdate solution and moistened with aqueous ammonia. The author details the preparation of reagent and test paper, mentions that the paper is light-sensitive, and claims that detection of sulfur dioxide with this paper, instead of with starch-iodate paper, eliminates interference by iodine from ethyl iodoacetate ("K.S.K."). Add. Ref.: CA **34**, 7475 (1940).

21—DETECTION OF DELETERIOUS GASES

Draegerwerk Heinrich u. Bernhard Draeger. Ger. (Pat. No.) 691,442, April 30, 1940 (Cl. 42.**1**. 4.06); CA **35**, 3928 (1941).

The air sample is aspirated through a glass detector tube filled with a colorless gel saturated with a suitable indicator, e.g., gold chloride for dichlorodiethyl sulfide. The gel is soaked in a nitrate solution of the metal-indicator, then dried and the metal reduced. The finely divided metal serves as indicator.

22—TEST FOR MUSTARD GAS

Draegerwerk Heinrich u. Bernhard Draeger. Ger. (Pat. No.) 692,375), May 23, 1940 (Cl. 42.**1**. 4.06); CA **35**, 4314 (1941).

The sample is aspirated through a silica gel detector tube. An aqueous solution of gold chloride followed by sodium thiosulfate is added to the collected sample. Dichlorodiethyl sulfide forms a brown complex with gold chloride. The gold chloride not tied up with the gas is rendered colorless by the sodium thiosulfate.

23—IDENTIFICATION OF WAR GASES

Sharman, C. F. Chem. and Ind. (London) **18**, 741-742 (1940).

The author describes a modification of the Twiss-Neale lamp (see above) in which an incandescent filament replaces the alcohol flame. The entire apparatus is enclosed in a small, portable box. If the air sample contains mustard gas, sulfurd ioxide will appear in the pyrolysis products and will color starch iodate paper blue. A confirmatory test for chlorine substitutes o-tolidine for the Twiss-Neale Beilstein procedure. Mustard gas gives a bright yellow stain with a patch in the middle immediately over the filament, turning green and then blue. Add. Ref.: CA **35**, 820 (1941).

24—QUALITATIVE STUDIES ON SOME REACTIONS OF THE ORGANIC SULFIDES AND PARTICULARLY OF DICHLOROETHYL-B,B'-SULFIDE

Ribas, I., A. Cano, and A. D. Contra. Anales fis. quim. **37**, 478-486 (1941); CA **37**, 54 (1943).

The author describes a more sensitive test than that of Obermiller (see previous abstract) to detect dichloroethyl-B-B'-sulfide in water or air. The method depends upon the cloudiness caused by the contaminant in an aqueous solution of a heteropoly acid, such as phosphotungstic acid, containing a few drops of gold chloride solution. The sensitivity is 1:200,000 and the reaction is specific. This reaction might be applied to the field detection of mustard gas.

25—TESTING FOR DICHLORODIETHYLSULFIDE

Deutches Reich (represented by the Oberkommando des Herres). Ger. (Pat. No.) 712,211, Sept. 18, 1941 (Cl. 61.b. 1.03); CA **37**, 4333 (1943).

Solutions of gold chloride are used to detect dichlorodiethylsulfide. Complex acids of heavy metals, from group V and VI of the Periodic Table, are used to stabilize the gold solutions.

26—INDICATOR FOR MUSTARD GAS

Draegerwerk Heinrich u. Bernhard Draeger. Ger. (Pat. No.) 704,314, Feb. 27, 1941 (Cl. 42.**1**. 4.06); CA **36**, 992 (1942).

The sample containing the mustard gas is contacted first with iodine trichloride and the resulting mixture is treated with a 4% aqueous solution of sodium N-chloro-p-toluene-sulfonamide. A brownish red color stable for several hours results in the presence of mustard gas. This indicator is sensitive down to 10 mg of mustard gas per cubic meter. For this content only 2 liters is required for the test.

27—TEST FOR WAR GASES, ESPECIALLY DICHLORO-DIETHYL SULFIDE

Draegerwerk Heinrich u. Bernhard Draeger. Ger. (Pat. No.) 721,094, April 23, 1942 (Cl. 42.1. 4.06); CA **37**, 2308 (1943).

Iodate and starch solutions are used as reagents for the determination of war gases.

28—MUSTARD GAS IN AIR. SENSITIVITY OF QUALITATIVE TESTS AND A ROUGH QUANTITATIVE DETERMINATION

Rieman, William, III. Ind. Eng. Chem., Anal. Ed. **15**, 411-412 (1943).

The author investigated the sensitivity of several qualitative tests for mustard gas in air. He bubbled the test gas through dilute acetic acid solution at 170 ± 20 ml per minute (a convenient rate for a field test when air is passed by means of a rubber bulb aspirator); the tests showed that absorption was nearly complete when the air velocity was small, but decreased with increased velocity. Reagents tested included Grignard solution (potassium cuprous iodide), chlorauric acid solution, B-naphthol solution, chlorauric acid impregnated filter paper (dried), and sodium iodoplatinate impregnated paper (moistened with water before use). The iodoplatinate solution was the most sensitive test under the conditions used; 0.01 μg of mustard gas per ml could be detected with a 5 minute absorption period. Oxidizing agents such as chlorine or nitrous fumes, and reducing agents such as large concentrations of arsenical vesicants, interfere with the iodoplatinate test. Add. Ref.: CA **37**, 4332 (1943).

See Section One

For references 37, 41, 42, 48, 52, 54, 64, 66, 86.

Naphthalene

1—DETERMINATION OF SMALL AMOUNTS OF NAPHTHALENE IN AIR

Leibov, Z. M. Lab. Prakt. (U.S.S.R.) **15**, No. 11, 22-23 (1940); CA **35**, 3561 (1941).

Naphthalene is nitrated (instantaneously) and reacted with alcoholic alkali to produce a color. As little as 0.003 mg of naphthalene can be detected and determined. *The method might be applicable to field detection.*

2—DETERMINATION OF NAPHTHALENE IN AIR

Robbins, M. Chain. Arch. Ind. Hyg. Occupational Med. **4**, 85-87 (1951).

The determination of naphthalene is based on its reaction with paraformaldehyde in a sulfuric acid-phosphoric acid solution. Sample the suspected air at 1.5 to 2 liters per minute into 10 ml of 95% ethanol in a midget fritted bubbler, using an M. S. A. midget impinger pump. To determine 0.5 to 10 ppm of naphthalene, react a suitable aliquot of the alcoholic naphthalene solution with 5 ml of reagent (made by dissolving 1 g of paraformaldehyde in 25 ml of concentrated sulfuric acid and diluting with agitation to 100 ml with 85% phosphoric acid). Measure the resulting color photometrically against standards of known concentrations of naphthalene. The sensitivity is 2 μg of naphthalene, with a reproducibility of $\pm 10\%$. The reagent must be fresh, and a set of standards must be run with each of unknowns. Benzene interferes with the reaction. Add. Refs. IHD **15**, 1032 (1951); CA **45**, 9425 (1951).

1-Naphthylamine

1—RAPID METHOD OF DETERMINATION OF SMALL AMOUNTS OF 1-NAPHTHYLAMINE IN AIR OF INDUSTRIAL ESTABLISHMENTS

Vaskevich, D. N. and T. I. Sergeeva. Gigiena i Sanit. **21**, No. 3, 41-44 (1956); IHD **20**, 1354 (1956).

The sample is aspirated through a solution of diazoaminobenzene in ethanol in the presence of 70% acetic acid. When 1-naphthylamine contacts this reagent a raspberry color is produced. The color is read against a standard scale in a photometer. The sensitivity is 0.3 μg in 3 ml and the limiting concentration is 1×10^{-7}. The standard scale maintains color for months. A three-fold excess of 2-naphthylamine does not interfere. Add. Ref.: CA **50**, 10312 (1956).

Nerve Gases
(Alkyl Fluorophosphates)

1—A NEW REACTION FOR THE DETECTION FOR THE METALLOID (NON-METAL-) LABILE HALOGEN LINKAGE

Schoenemann, R. B. R., translated by C. L. Wheeler. Office of Publication Board, U. S. Dept. of Commerce, P. B. 119,887 (ETF-550 G 1212) (Aug. 1944) 8 pp.

The Schoenemann process is based on the chemical reaction of sarin (isopropyl ester of methyl phosphonofluoridic acid) with o-toluidine and alkaline peroxide on paper. The sensitivity is 0.5 μg. Add. Ref.: *DETECTION AND ESTIMATION OF NERVE GASES BY FLUORESCENCE REACTION.* Gehauf and Goldenson. Anal. Chem. **29**, 276-278 (1957).

2—ALARMS AND ANALYZERS FOR NERVE GAS VAPORS

Cherry, R. H., G. M. Foley, C. O. Badgett, R. D. Eanes, and H. R. Smith. Anal. Chem. **30**, No. 7, 1239-1247 (1958).

Automatic alarms to warn of lethal concentrations of nerve gases (G-Agents, GA) use the Schoenemann reaction with indole in a buffer solution as the sensitive, stable reagent which reacts with the nerve gas to form the fluorescing indoxyl. The instrument can act as a continuous alarm, giving warning before any injury occurs, or as a calibrated analyzer, for GB, the isopropyl ester of methane phosphonyl fluoride, and for GA, the ethyl ester of dimethylamidocyanophosphoric acid. The automatic chemical processing system is combined with a fluorescence photometer, and data are presented for selecting the reagents of maximum sensitivity for a given photometer. Two separate solutions are used, together with acid-stabilized hydrogen peroxide and carbonate-bicarbonate buffering. Add. Refs.: AA **5**, 4376 (1958); Anal. Chem., Anal. Reviews **32**, No. 5, 54R-63R (1960).

3—PORTABLE AUTOMATIC ALARM FOR DETECTION OF TOXIC AGENTS IN ATMOSPHERE

Young, J. C., J. R. Parsons, and H. E. Reeber. Anal. Chem. **30**, 1236-1239 (1958).

The authors describe in detail the electrical and mechanical systems of a portable automatic alarm that will detect 0.02 ppm of GB (isopropyl methyl phosphonofluoridate) within 2 minutes, and concentrations above 2 ppm in 5 seconds. The apparatus draws air through a filter paper to remove dust, then through a cellulose tape wetted with o-dianisidine dihydrochloride and sodium pyrophosphate peroxide; the impregnated tape turns red in the presence of a G-agent. Chlorine, chlorosulfonic acid smoke, and nitrogen dioxide may interfere. The apparatus could be adapted to detect nitrogen dioxide, chlorine, hydrogen sulfide, sulfur dioxide, ammonia, and hydrochloric acid by using tape impregnated with suitable reagents for their detection. Add. Refs.: AA**5**, 4377 (1958); Anal. Chem., Anal. Reviews **32**, No. 5, 54R-63R (1960).

Nickel

1—THE APPLICATION OF SPOT REACTIONS IN QUALITATIVE ANALYSIS

Feigl, Friedrich and Rosa Stern. Z. anal. Chem. **60**, 1-43 (1921); CA **15**, 2600 (1921).

The test for nickel with dimethylglyoxime is more sensitive on filter paper than in a test tube.

2—QUALITATIVE ANALYSIS OF THE ELEMENTS OF THE FIRST TO THIRD GROUPS WHEN PRESENT TOGETHER, WITH SPECIAL REGARD TO SPOT TESTS

Tananaev, N. A. Z. anorg. allgem. Chem. **140**, 320-334 (1924); CA **19**, 1108 (1925).

Impregnate filter paper with ammonium phosphate solution, dry, treat with the solution to be tested, then with dimethylglyoxime, and expose to ammonia vapor. A red color indicates the presence of nickel.

3—NEW REAGENT PAPERS FOR POROSITY TESTING AND FOR THE DETERMINATION OF METALS

Kutzelnigg, Arthur. Metalloberflaeche **5**, B 113-115 (1951); CA **46**, 56 (1952).

Dimethylglyoxime, absorbed on filter paper, is useful in the determination of nickel. The paper should be moistened with water.

4—A RAPID DETERMINATION OF A SMALL AMOUNT OF NICKEL BY MEANS OF A DETECTOR TUBE

Kobayashi, Yoshitaka. J. Chem. Soc. Japan, Ind. Chem. Sect. **58** (10), 728-732 (1955); AA **4**, 123 (1957).

A detector tube was devised for a relatively rapid determination of nickel in the range of 0.01 to 3.0 mg per ml. One hundred g of silica gel (60 to 80 mesh) is mixed with an ethanolic solution of dimethylglyoxime (1%, 100 ml) and gently dried. The treated silica gel (0.9 g) is placed in a glass tube whose dimensions are 20 cm x 4.5 mm. One ml of the sample solution (pH 3 to 7), is passed through the tube and the length of the pink layer is measured. The concentration of nickel is calculated from an empirical table. Interference is caused by ferrous iron, copper, cobalt, vanadium, palladium, and platinum. Results are in good agreement with those obtained by the gravimetric method. Add. Ref.: CA **50**, 9934 (1956). (This is included as a detector because of its unique use for solution chemistry.)

5—A SPOT TEST ANALYSIS OF THE GROUP III CATIONS

Marion, Stephen P. and Isaac Zlochower. J. Chem. Education **36**, 378-380 (1959).

Paper spot test: Soak filter paper in 1% ethanolic dimethylglyoxime and dry. Add a drop of concentrated ammonia to the dimethylglyoxime paper, then add a drop of the test solution, then several more drops of ammonia. A bright pink stain on the outer edge, appearing usually within a minute, indicates nickel. Add. Ref.: CA **54**, 2093 (1960).

6—DETERMINATION OF MICROGRAM QUANTITIES OF NICKEL BY THE IMPREGNATED-PAPER METHOD

Kielczewski, W., J. Supinski, Chem. anal. (Warsaw) 10(4) 677-80 (1965) CA **64** 5745 (1966).

Strips of Whatman No. 1 paper are immersed in a solution of 0.2 g & nitroso-B-naphthol in 20 ml HOAc and 200 ml of 1 N Na₃PO₄ and dried at 70°. After this treatment the strips are passed through 0.5 N Ba (NO₃)₂. The test solution is placed on the impregnated paper which is immersed in water and subsequently dried at 70°. The area of the yellow spots are proportional to the concentration.

See Section One
For references 5, 94, 98.

Nickel Carbonyl

1—RAPID METHOD FOR THE DETERMINATION OF LOW CONCENTRATIONS OF NICKEL CARBONYL VAPOR

Kobayashi, Yoshitaka. Yuki Gossei Kagaku Kyokai-shi **15**, 466-471 (1957); CA **51**, 16204 (1957).

A detector tube is filled with silica gel impregnated with 0.5% gold chloride. One hundred cc of the test sample is aspirated at a rate of 1 cc per second. In the presence of nickel carbonyl the silica gel changes from a light yellow to bluish-violet. The relation between the concentration of nickel carbonyl and length of colored layer is described. The useful range for this determination to 200 to 600 ppm. When 30 cc of the test gas is used, the measuring range is 50 to 2000 ppm. By measuring the minimum volume of test gas needed to color the silica gel at a constant sampling rate, the concentration of nickel carbonyl down to 3 ppm can be determined. The effects of other factors such as diameter of the tube, temperature, and the presence of ethylene and carbon monoxide are discussed.

2—THE DETERMINATION OF MICROGRAM QUANTITIES OF NICKEL, NICKEL TETRACARBONYL, AND ITS SOLID DECOMPOSITION PRODUCTS IN AIR

Belyakov, A. A. Zavodskaya Laboratariya **26**, No. 2, 158-159 (1960); Industrial Laboratory (English trans.) **26**, 166-167 (1960).

Draw the test air at 0.5 liter per minute through an absorption tube containing one or two 15 mm diameter filter papers and then through 2 absorption vessels with porous plate, each containing 3 ml of a 1.5% solution of chloramine B in alcohol, acidified before removal of the sample with 1:1 hydrochloric acid. The chloramine B solution retains the nickel carbonyl vapor. Compare the colored solutions with standards. The sensitivity of the method is 1 μg of nickel carbonyl; the error does not exceed 10%. Samples should be analyzed within 6 to 8 hours.

Nitric Acid

See Section One
For references 6, 60, 88.

Nitrobenzene

1—COLORIMETRIC DETERMINATION OF VAPORS OF NITROBENZENE, AZOBENZENE, ANILINE, AND BENZIDINE IN AIR

Bykhovskaya, M. S. Org. Chem. Ind. (U.S.S.R.) **6**, 638-639 (1939); CA **34**, 5375 (1940).

Known methods of analysis for some benzene derivatives are described in detail. The sample is aspirated through a nitrating acid to convert nitrobenzene into dinitrobenzene and azobenzene into dinitroazobenzene. The later reacts with glucose and sodium hydroxide to produce an intense blue (Bose, CA **26**, 1877 (1932)). Dinitrobenzene in acetone reacted with sodium hydroxide produces a violet coloration (Stepanov, Sudebnaya Khim. **1929**). Benzidine vapors absorbed in water produce a blue coloration with ferric chloride and sodium hydroxide (Witt, Ber. **10**, 874 (1877)), and aniline reacted with sodium hypochlorite and phenol produces a pale-blue indo-phenol reaction (Alekseeva, CA **25**, 5877 (1931)).

2—DETERMINATION OF SMALL AMOUNTS OF NITROBENZENE IN AIR

Strafford, N. and D. A. Harper. J. Soc. Chem. Ind. **58**, 169-172 (1939) CA **33**, 6199 (1939).

Filter paper impregnated with absorbent carbon is sold for the purpose of decolorizing solutions but it is also adequate for the absorption of nitrobenzene in air. A paper exposed to laboratory air gained 0.04 mg in weight during 6 hours although only 0.2 part of nitrobenzene per million of air was present. When air containing nitrobenzene was passed through 2 of these papers, with an intervening air space, no nitrobenzene was found in the second paper. The quantity of absorbed nitrobenzene can be determined by reduction to aniline with titanium sulfate, addition of alkali hydroxide, isolation of aniline by steam distillation, followed by colorimetric determination by diazotization and coupling with an R salt. In this manner, 0.2 to 100 ppm of nitrobenzene in air can be determined in samples of 30 to 40 liters. Most other aromatic nitro compounds will yield the same test but the other compounds are equally poisonous and the test is recommended especially for testing air known to contain small quantities of nitrobenzene. *This abstract is included because of the unique technique for removing organic substances (e.g., nitrobenzene) from air before detecting other compounds.*

3—A FIELD TEST FOR NITROBENZENE VAPOR IN AIR

Hands, G. C. Analyst **85**, No. 1016, 843-845 (1960).

In a clean, dry, all-glass bubbler place 2 ml of Cellosolve (2-ethoxyethanol), and connect the bubbler to a pump via a trap. Take a 6-liter sample of suspected air at a rate of 1.5 liters per minute (or 50 strokes at a rate of 5 seconds per exhaust stroke with a hand pump). Detach the bubbler, and add to its contents 1 ml of liquid zinc amalgam and then 4 ml of dilute hydrochloric acid. Close the bubbler and shake for 1 minute; transfer 5 ml of the aqueous layer to a clean, dry specimen tube without including any of the zinc. Add 0.5 ml of sodium nitrite solution, shake gently, let stand for 2 minutes, add 2 ml of sodium carbonate solution, then immediately 0.5 ml of R salt solution. Shake to mix, add 2 ml of ammonia solution, shake again, and compare with aqueous color standards prepared from potassium dichromate and cobalt sulfate, or with glass standards from Tintometer Ltd. The method is sensitive to from 0.5 to 2.0 ppm by volume, with a precision of about ±20%. A complete determination, including sampling, takes 10 to 15 minutes. The author gives detailed directions for preparing the reagents and apparatus. Add. Ref.: APCA Abstr. **6**, No. 10, 3550 (1961).

Nitro Compounds, Aromatic

1—COLOR REACTION OF AROMATIC NITRO COMPOUNDS

Nisida, Sumi. Bull. Inst. Phys. Chem. Research (Tokyo) **20**, 20-24 (1941); Abstracts (in English) 1-2 (in Sci. Papers Inst. Phys. Chem. Research (Tokyo) **38**, Nos. 1004-1007); CA **35**, 7320 (1941).

The author describes various reactions of some aromatic nitro compounds. Nitro compounds (2-3 mg) in acetone (2-3 cc) often give colored solutions when treated with 2 N potassium or sodium hydroxide (3 drops). Mononitro compounds produce colorless or pale yellow solutions, 2,4-dinitro compounds yield blue solutions if position 1 is occupied by a methyl group and red colors with other groups at position 1. Dinitro and trinitro compounds with other arrangements of the nitro groups yield colorless or faintly colored solutions.

Nitrogen Mustard

See Section One

For references 64, 66, 86.

Nitrogen Oxides

1—THE DETECTION OF OZONE

Fischer, F. and H. Marx. Ber. **39**, 2555-2557 (1906); Analyst **31**, 417-418 (1906).

Paper moistened with alcoholic tetramethyl-p-diamido-diphenylamine turns violet in contact with ozone. Oxides of nitrogen color this moist tetramethyl base paper a straw yellow, while mixtures of nitrous oxides and ozone give dirty-brown intermediate shades. The test paper must be moist because ozone colors the dry paper yellow. If either the nitrous oxide or the ozone predominates in the gas mixture, the paper gives the color of the gas that is in excess. Paper colored violet by ozone turns yellow if exposed subsequently to nitrous oxides, and vice versa.

2—DETECTION OF NITROGEN OXIDES FORMED BY SPARKS DISCHARGED IN AIR

Sommerlad, Hermann. Z. physic. chem. Unterricht. **21**, 250-251; CA **3**, 2781 (1909).

The method depends upon the discharge of sparks in a Woulfe between 2 heavy copper wires which pass separately through 2 holes in the stopper. Through a third hole a filter paper soaked in sulfanilic acid, a-naphthylamine, or alcoholic diphenylamine solution is introduced.

3—CHEMICAL DETECTION OF RESPIRATORY POISONS

Smolczyk, E. and H. Cobler. Gasmaske **2**, 27-33 (1930); Wasser u. Abwasser **28**, 95 (1930); CA **26**, 1214 (1932).

The authors describe an apparatus which indicates the composition and concentration of gases. Sensitized paper strips are used for the analysis and their reaction and sensitivity to nitric oxide are given.

4—A SIMPLE SPOT-PLATE TEST FOR NITRATE NITROGEN IN SOIL AND OTHER EXTRACTS

Morgan, M. Francis. Science **71**, 343-344 (1930).

The author has applied the principle of the very sensitive diphenylamine color reaction with nitrates to a spot plate technique. The reagent is a freshly prepared solution of 0.05 g of diphenylamine in 25 ml of concentrated sulfuric acid. Place 1 drop of distilled water on a spot plate; add 4 drops of reagent, and stir with a glass rod for 2 minutes. If no blue color develops the reagent is satisfactory. Transfer 1 drop of the solution to be tested to the spot plate; add 4 drops of reagent, and stir with a glass rod until full color develops (about 2 minutes). The intensity of the blue color is an approximate quantitative measurement of the nitrate nitrogen in the sample, within the limits of from 1 to 25 ppm. Variations cannot be observed readily above 25 ppm; if above that concentration, dilute accurately to fall within the observable range. Prepare a chart of standard colors with water color paints, or use the color blocks in Ridgway's "Color Standards and Nomenclature," viz.:

Nitrate Nitrogen - ppm	Color
1	Pale forget-me-not blue
2	Pale violet blue
3	Light violet blue
5	Dull violaceous blue
7	Phenyl blue
10	Helvetia blue
15	Hays blue
20	Cyanine blue

(See article by Snell and Snell, below, for preparation of standards.)

5—SPOT TEST FOR NITRITE

Hahn, Friedrich L. Mikrochemie **9**, 31-33 (1931).
Filter paper, impregnated with specially prepared a-naphthylamine oxalate, gives a sensitive test for nitrite. Add. Ref.: CA **25**, 1181 (1931).

6—DETECTION OF SMALL QUANTITIES OF NITROUS ACID WITH INDIGOSOLS

v. Bigray, Emod. Chem.-Ztg. **57**, 94 (1933); CA **27**, 1592 (1933).
Five drops of a 10% indigosol 04B is added to 100 cc of solution and to this is added 5 cc of 7 N sulfuric acid. If 1 mg of nitrogen trioxide is present per liter a dark blue color will develop. A color appears slowly with even less nitrogen trioxide and with more nitrogen trioxide a blue precipitate is formed. *Indigosol 04 B (color index 1184) is a soluble form of tetrabromo indigo. Other soluble indigos may be used as well.* Add. Ref.: Z. anal. Chem. **96**, 443 (1934).

7—THE MICRO-DETECTION OF GASES AND VAPORS

Blank, Eugene W. J. Chem. Education **11**, 523-525 (1934).
Benzidine, after exposure to nitrogen dioxide, couples with b-naphthol to give a red dyestuff. *This might be used for a test paper.* Add. Ref.: CA **28**, 6392 (1934).

8—A STABLE REAGENT FOR THE DETECTION OF NITRITES

Stone, Irwin. Z. anal. Chem. **96**, 443 (1934).
A stable reagent for the detection of nitrites consists of 1 ml of aniline, 1 g of phenol, 15 ml of concentrated hydrochloric acid, and 150 ml of water. Add 0.5 ml of the reagent to the neutralized solution suspected of containing nitrites, and follow with sodium hydroxide to definite alkalinity; a deep yellow color develops in the presence of nitrites. A possible yellow color in the sample solution before addition of the reagents may be extracted with amyl

alcohol without affecting the reaction. The reaction will detect 0.01 mg nitrogen trioxide per ml. Add. Refs.: Chemist-Analyst **22**, 10 (1933); Chem. Centr. **104**, I, 1975 (1933).

9—THE DETECTION OF TOXIC GASES AND VAPORS

Leroux, Lucien. Rev. hyg. et med. prevent. **57**, 81-112 (1935).
At 20° C, 0.2 mg nitrogen dioxide per liter gives a blue color in 15 seconds on starch-iodide paper (i.e., a concentration of 0.011% by volume). Alternatively, prepare a reagent by dissolving 1 to 2 grams of diphenylamine in 50 ml of water, and add dropwise 50 ml of concentrated sulfuric acid. Shake the air sample with water or sodium hydroxide, and add several drops of the sample solution to the reagent. Nitrogen dioxides produce a blue color in the solution. Add. Ref.: CA **29**, 3627 (1935).

10—THE USE OF INDICATORS FOR THE DETECTION OF POISONOUS GASES AND VAPORS

Heering, D. Gasmaske **8**, 88-89 (1936).
In 3 seconds, 0.2 mg per liter of oxides of nitrogen turns blue litmus paper red. The same concentration turns starch-iodide paper light blue in 5 to 15 seconds. Add. Ref.: CA **30**, 7059 (1936).

11—MODERN METHODS OF DETECTION AND DETERMINATION OF INDUSTRIAL GASES IN THE ATMOSPHERE

Leclerc, E. and R. Haux. Rev. universelle mines **12**, 293-298 (1936).
Starch iodide paper turns blue in 15 seconds with 0.2 mg per liter of air. Small quantities of nitrous acid may be detected with indigosol. Add. Ref.: CA **30**, 6672 (1936).

12—SOME METHODS FOR THE DETECTION AND ESTIMATION OF POISONOUS GASES AND VAPORS IN THE AIR (A Practical Manual for the Industrial Hygienist)

Zhitkova, A. S., translated by J. B. Ficklen. (Service to Industry, Box 133, West Hartford, Conn., 1936), pp. 66-72.
Detect oxides of nitrogen by moistening a filter paper strip with Griess reagent. The paper turns pink if nitrogen oxides are present.

13—COLORIMETRIC METHODS OF ANALYSIS

Snell, Foster D. and Cornelia T. Snell. (New York, D. Van Nostrand Co., Inc., 1936) 2nd Ed., p. 637.
Morgan's spot plate technique with diphenylamine (see above) may be used for rough quantitative estimation of nitrates in field work. The final concentration of sulfuric acid must be 70 to 90%. Prepare a series of standard solutions containing 1, 2, 3, 5, 7, 10, 15 and 20 ppm of nitrate nitrogen by diluting a solution containing 0.7216 g of potassium nitrate per liter (100 ppm of nitrate nitrogen).

The test method and colors are given in Morgan's article (above). Add. Ref.: CA **30**, 2883 (1936).

14—SIMPLE METHODS FOR THE DETECTION AND DE-TERMINATION OF POISONOUS GASES, VAPORS, SMOKES, AND DUSTS IN FACTORY AIR

Weber, Hans H. Zentr. Gewerbehyg. Unfallverhuet. **23**, 177-180 (1936).

Starch iodide paper turns light blue in 5 seconds with 0.21 mg nitrogen dioxide per liter; the color deepens in 15 seconds. Add. Ref.: CA **32**, 1609 (1938).

15—NEW REAGENT FOR CHLORINE AND OXIDIZING AGENTS

Noriega del Aguila, M. Prim. congr. peruano quim. (Actas y trab.) **1938**, 1001-1005; Chim. and ind. (Paris) **43**, 470 (1940); CA **34**, 4179 (1940).

Chlorine gas, bromine vapor, or nitrogen oxides can be detected in air by aspirating the sample through a 10% solution of pyramidone slightly acidified with acetic acid. Filter papers impregnated with the above solution are also adequate for the analysis. A violet to violet-red color is produced. The test is slightly less sensitive than that given by freshly-prepared starch-iodide paper.

16—DETECTION OF NITRITE IN PRESENCE OF NITRATE

Percs, Ernoe. Ber. ungar. pharm. Ges. **14**, 30-31 (1938); CA **32**, 3293 (1938).

The author describes a method of detection for nitrite in the presence of nitrate. The sample solution is neutralized and then 5 drops of 5.0 N sulfuric acid and 1 drop of a 0.1% aqueous solution of Trypan red are added. In presence of more than 0.005 mg nitrite ion the original orange-red color changes to violet within 10 minutes.

17— METHODS FOR THE DETECTION OF TOXIC GASES IN INDUSTRY. NITROUS FUMES

Anon. Dept. of Scientific and Industrial Research, London, England. Leaflet No. 5 (1939) 9 pp.; reprinted 1947.

Several test papers for the qualitative detection of nitrous fumes are unsuited to quantitative detection, because they lack either specificity or sensitivity, or because they involve a bleaching reaction in which the reagent quantity must be controlled carefully, difficult when the reagent is incorporated in a test paper. Starch iodide papers are fairly sensitive to low concentrations of nitrous fumes but are not specific and do not always absorb the gas completely. The Griess-Ilosvay reaction and the Bismarck brown test depend on a diazo reaction; both are specific and very sensitive to low concentrations. For the latter test, bubble the gas through a solution of m-phenylenediamine hydrochloride in acetic acid; an orange color, from the formation of Bismarck brown, indicates nitrous fumes. For the even more sensitive Griess-Ilosvay test, draw a measured volume

of the test atmosphere, by means of a hand pump in a portable apparatus, through a tube containing a mixed solution of a-naphthylamine and sulfanilic acid until the rose-pink color of the reagent matches that of a prepared standard. The article details the preparation of the reagent and the standard, and includes a table correlating number of pump strokes with concentration of nitrous fumes. Add. Ref.: CA **33**, 6470 (1939).

18—THE DETECTION OF TOXIC GASES AND VAPORS IN INDUSTRY

Vallender, R. B. Chem. and Ind. (London) **58**, 330-333 (1939).

Draw the test air through a side-arm bubbler into Griess-Ilosvay reagent (acetic acid solution of a-naphthylamine and sulfanilic acid). As little as 1 part in 100,000 readily colors the reagent pink. Add. Ref.: CA **33**, 4907 (1939).

19—A MODIFICATION OF THE GRIESS REAGENT FOR THE DETERMINATION OF NITRITES

Salei, P.I. Lab. Prakt. (U.S.S.R.) **15**, No. 12, 23 (1940); CA **35**, 4310 (1941).

Griess type dry reagents are convenient for determining nitrous acid. Succinic or oxalic acid may be substituted for the tartaric acid in the original Griess reagent. To prepare the reagent, grind in a mortar 0.1 g of a-naphthylamine, 1 g of sulfanilic acid, and either 5 g of succinic acid or 5 g of oxalic acid. If necessary, dissolve the mixture in 300 ml of water.

20—A COMPARISON OF DIFFERENT METHODS FOR TAKING AIR SAMPLES IN BOTTLES

Moskalev, P. and E. Yakuba. Lab. Prakt. (U.S.S.R.) **16**, No. 4, 24-25 (1941); CA **35**, 6891 (1941).

For the determination of nitrogen oxides the air samples were taken by the vacuum method and the oxides of nitrogen determined colorimetrically with phenoldisulfonic acid.

21—NITRITE FIELD METHOD FOR THE DETERMINATION OF OXIDES OF NITROGEN (EXCEPT N_2O AND N_2O_3)

Patty, F. A. and G. M. Petty. J. Ind. Hyg. Toxicol. **25**, 361-365 (1943).

The authors describe a field method for the determination of the oxides of nitrogen, using Griess-Ilosvay reagent and sodium nitrite standards. A 50 ml hypodermic syringe serves as a combined sampling medium, reaction chamber, and color comparison tube. The authors give directions for capping and filling the syringe and for drawing the air sample. The reagent consists of (1) 140 g of glacial acetic acid added to 1000 ml of nitrite-free distilled water; (2) 0.1 g of sulfanilic acid dissolved (with slight warming) in 300 ml of solution (1); and (3) 0.2 g of a-naphthylamine boiled for a few minutes in 40 ml of distilled water, then poured into 300 ml of solution (1). Just before use mix equal quantities of (2) and (3). Accurately measure 10 ml into the 50 ml syringe. Oxides of nitrogen turn the reagent red. Add. Ref.: CA **39,** 5205 (1945).

22—DETERMINATION OF THE OXIDES OF NITROGEN IN AIR

Cholak, Jacob and Robert R. McNary. J. Ind. Hyg. Toxicol. **25,** 354-360 (1943).

The authors discuss several methods, including the phenoldisulfonic acid method (Jacobs, CA **35,** 4314 (1941)); the diphenylamine spot test (Snell and Snell, see above); and the chloranil reaction (Deichmann and Schafer, CA **36,** 2877 (1942)). The standard phenoldisulfonic acid method requires very little and inexpensive equipment, while the accuracy in experienced hands is excellent. The diphenylamine method as a spot test for field work is sensitive and rapid; the color varies from a forget-me-not blue for 4.45 ppm to a deep blue for 65. ppm of nitrate. Other oxidizing products interfere with the test. The official British test with Griess-Ilosvay reagent (see above) depends on the diazotization of sulfanilic acid by nitrite and subsequent coupling with α-naphthylamine hydrochloride. The test, made by drawing a known amount of air through the reagents with a hand pump, is convenient for field use, but specific only for vapors of nitrous acid and its anhydride. Litmus or starch iodide test papers are neither specific nor quantitative, but in the absence of interference furnish a rapid, convenient, rough estimate of the concentrations of nitric oxides, especially the starch iodide paper. Add. Ref.: CA **39,** 5204 (1945).

23—COLORIMETRIC ESTIMATION OF NITRIC OXIDE

Kuz-minykh, I. N. Khimicheskaya Prom. **1944,** No. 8, 17-18; CA **40,** 2087 (1946).

The author describes a simplified method for transferring nitric oxide to tubes and sealing them. These tubes are used for comparing the color with similar tubes containing the sample.

24—DETERMINATION OF NITROGEN OXIDES IN AIR. PERMANENT COLOR STANDARDS FOR USE WITH METHOD OF PATTY AND PETTY

Averell, P. R., W. F. Hart, N. T. Woodberry, and W. R. Bradley. Anal. Chem. **19,** 1040-1041 (1947).

Patty and Petty's colorimetric field method for estimating nitrogen oxides in industrial air (see above) is based on the hydrolysis of nitrogen dioxide or tetroxide to nearly equimolecular amounts of nitric and nitrous acids in a reagent containing α-naphthylamine, sulfanilic acid, and acetic acid, which nitrite ion colors red. Permanent standards are desirable because the reagent color fades in a few hours. The authors found a suitable blend of red and blue dyes with which to dye cellophane strips to match 5, 10, 20, 30, 40, and 50 ppm of nitrogen dioxide in 50 ml of air at 25° C, using a G.E. recording spectrophotometer.·

They detail the preparation of the strips. Add. Refs.: CA **42,** 59 (1948); CA **42,** 840 (1948).

25—A RAPID METHOD FOR THE DETERMINATION OF NITROGEN OXIDES IN AIR

Flagg, John F. and Ralph Lobene. J. Ind. Hyg. Toxicol. **30,** 370-372 (1948).

The method assumes that in air, nitrogen oxide is converted to nitrogen dioxide. Absorb the nitrogen dioxide on silica gel, treat with diphenylamine, and compare the resulting blue color (proportional to the amount of nitrogen dioxide present) with standards. The method is applicable to air-gas mixtures containing 1 to 50 ppm of nitrogen dioxide. The sensitive and rapid method requires only simple apparatus and reagents, but has the disadvantage of limited accuracy. Ozone and other oxidizing gases probably interfere. Add. Ref. CA **43,** 1686 (1949).

26—DETERMINATION PROCEDURES

Magill, Paul L. Am. Ind. Hyg. Assoc. Quart. **11,** 55-63 (1950).

Collect nitrogen oxides by scrubbing 50 cubic feet of air in a scrubber containing 50 ml of 5% sodium hydroxide solution, and oxidize the nitrogen oxides in solution to nitric acid with hydrogen peroxide. Then estimate the nitric acid colorimetrically with phenoldisulfonic acid reagent. This method will measure 0.05 ppm with an accuracy of 10%. Add Ref.: CA **45,** 2612 (1951).

27—ULTRAVIOLET SPECTROPHOTOMETRIC DETERMINATION OF NITRITES WITH 4-AMINOBENZENESULFONIC ACID

Pappenhagen, J. M. with M. G. Mellon. Anal. Chem. **25,** 351-343 (1953).

Adjust to pH 1.4 a sample containing from 0.003 to 0.05 mg of nitrite nitrogen, and relatively free from organic matter. Add 1 ml of 4-aminobenzenesulfonic acid reagent, dilute to 50 ml and mix. After 3 minutes (but before 15 minutes) measure the absorbance of the diazo compound at 270 mu against a reagent blank. The method, rapid because the coupling reaction is eliminated, should be applicable to higher concentrations of nitrite than the standard Griess method. The authors give a table of the maximum permissible concentrations of interfering ions, and illustrate the ultraviolet spectra of 4-aminobenzenesulfonic acid and 4-sulfobenzenediazonium chloride. Add. Ref.: CA **47,** 5307 (1953). *This is included for possible application to detector techniques.*

28—NEW REAGENT FOR THE DETECTION OF THE NITRITE ION

Misra, A. L., R. C. Mehrotra, and J. D. Tewari. Z. anal. Chem. **139,** 89-92 (1953); CA **47,** 10408 (1953).

An aqueous solution of 2-amino-4-(chloromethyl)thiazolylhydrochloride produces a red coloration or a red precipitate in the presence of nitrite ion. The reagent is soluble in water and the reaction takes place instantaneously. The reagent is adequate for the detection of as little as 1 μg of nitrite ion.

29—ANALYTICAL PROCEDURE FOR THE DETECTION OF GASES

Guatelli, Manual A. Rev. asoc. bioquim. arg. **18**, 3-40 (1954).

To detect the nitrogen dioxide in an alkaline air sample by the Griess-Ilosvay reaction, mix equal volumes of solution I (1 g of sulfanilic acid made to 100 ml with water) and solution II (0.5 g a-naphthylamine made to 100 ml with water, boiled for 10 minutes, cooled, and diluted again to 100 ml). Add. Ref.: CA **48**, 8124 (1954).

30—COLORIMETRIC MICRODETERMINATION OF NITROGEN DIOXIDE IN THE ATMOSPHERE

Saltzman, Bernard E. Anal. Chem. **26**, 1949-1955 (1954).

The author eliminates the difficulties of sample absorption and lack of specificity in the determination of atmospheric nitrogen dioxide with a new, specific reagent which absorbs efficiently in a midget fritted bubbler at levels below 1 ppm. The reagent, a mixture of sulfanilic acid, N-(1-naphthyl)-ethylenediamine dihydrochloride, and acetic acid produces a stable, direct color with a sensitivity of a few parts per billion for a 10-minute sample at 0.4 liter per minute. The article details the preparation of reagents, standards, and known low concentrations of nitrogen dioxide. Ozone, chlorine, and hydrogen peroxide interfere; sulfur dioxide, hydrogen sulfide, and other nitrogen oxides, including nitric acid, do no. Add. Ref.: CA **49**, 6029 (1955).

31—RAPID METHOD FOR THE DETERMINATION OF LOW CONCENTRATIONS OF NITROGEN DIOXIDE IN LIQUID OXYGEN IN AIR SEPARATORS

Kobayashi, Yoshitaka and Tetsuzo Kitagawa. J. Chem. Soc. Japan, Ind. Chem. Sect. **58**, 651-654 (1955); CA **50**, 7664 (1956).

A detector tube for determining nitrogen dioxide in air is described. The tube consists of silica granules on which o-tolidine chloride has been adsorbed and dried. Nitrogen dioxide gas reacts with the o-tolidine chloride to produce a greenish-yellow color. The limit of detection is about 0.05 ppm.

32—DETERMINATION OF NITROGEN DIOXIDE AND NITRIC OXIDE IN AIR BY A LINEAR-COLORIMETRIC METHOD

Filyanskaya, E. D. Trudy Nauch. Sessii Vsesoyuz. Nauch.-Tekh. Inst. Okhrany Truda **1954** (**1955**), (No. 1) 205-209; Referat. Zhur., Khim. **1956**, 75319; Referat. Zhur., Met. **1957**, Abstr. No. 1649; AA **4**, 2941 (1957).

The linear-colorimetric method for the determination of gaseous impurities in air is based on the color change of a powder in an indicator tube when air is aspirated through it. The concentration of the impurity is calculated from the length of the indicator that has changed color. The reagent consists of silica gel, containing 38% water, saturated with an ethanolic solution of diphenylamine containing a small quantity of sodium chloride. The dependence of the length of the colored column on the concentration of nitrogen dioxide in the air has been established. With air containing 0.012 mg of nitrogen dioxide per liter, the length of the colored column is 10 mm in 5 minutes. To determine nitric oxide, the nitric oxide is oxidized to nitrogen dioxide and its concentration determined by difference. With a concentration of nitrogen dioxide or nitric oxide plus nitrogen dioxide of 0.005 to 0.2 mg per liter, the error of the determination is approximately 10%. Add. Ref.: CA **52**, 12663 (1958).

33—DETERMINATION OF NITROGEN DIOXIDIE IN AIR WITH THE AID OF 2-ETHOXY-6,9-DIAMINOACRIDINE LACTATE

Fedotov, V. P. Gigiena i Sanit. **21**, No. 9, 85-86 (1956); CA **51**, 3891 (1957).

Rivanol is recommended for determination of nitrogen dioxide in air. The sensitivity is sufficient for the accurate determination of between 0.004 to 0.1 mg per liter. Chlorine, iodine, hydrogen sulfide, sulfur dioxide, carbon dioxide, carbon monoxide, or ammonia do not interfere in low concentrations. Rivanol and potassium bisulfate are impregnated into silica gel which is introduced into suitable absorption tubes. The sample is aspirated through the tubes and in the presence of small quantities of nitrogen dioxide a pale pink coloration is produced. Higher concentrations will produce a red coloration.

34—AUTOMATIC APPARATUS FOR DETERMINATION OF NITRIC OXIDE AND NITROGEN DIOXIDE IN THE ATMOSPHERE

Thomas, M. D., J. A. MacLeod, R. C. Robbins, R. C. Goettelman, R. W. Eldridge, and L. H. Rogers. Anal. Chem. **28**, 1810-1816 (1956).

The authors use a modified Griess reagent (0.5% sulfanilic acid and 20 ppm of N-(1-naphthyl)ethylenediamine dihydrochloride in 14% acetic acid) as the color forming agent in an automatic system. Add. Ref.: CA **51**, 11771 (1957).

35—DETERMINATION OF VERY SMALL AMOUNTS OF NITRATE, NITRITE, AND HYDROXYLAMINE

Drozdov, N. S. and A. K. Iskandaryan. Zhur. Anal. Khim. **11**, 723-727 (1956) (English translation).

The authors' method is based on the Griess-Blom procedure, using 0.05 N sulfanilic acid in an acetic acid medium and 0.035 M 1-naphthylamine to produce red-colored azo compounds. The method is accurate for concentrations less than 10^{-6} mole of nitrite per liter. Add. Ref.: CA **51**, 8584 (1957).

36—DETECTION OF NITRITE AND NITRATE, PARTICULARLY TOGETHER, IN VERY DILUTE SOLUTIONS

Steensma, F. A. Chem. Weekblad **53**, 110-111 (1957) CA **51**, 8594 (1957).

Nitrite in acetic acid solution gives with benzidine a red to yellow color, detectable at 0.2 ppm, with no interference from nitrate. O-tolidine can be used instead of benzidine.

37—SPECTROPHOTOMETRIC DETERMINATION OF NITRITES

Leko, Alexander M. and Radomir P. Saper. Glasnik Chem. Drushtva, Beograd **22**, 161-165 (1957); CA **54**, 3050 (1960).

An improved method is proposed for the spectrophotometric determination of nitrites. The reaction is based on the formation of yellow p-nitrosodimethylaniline by the reaction of dimethylaniline with nitrites. *This reaction could be modified for application to a field method for the determination of nitrites.*

38—INDICATOR FOR NITROGEN OXIDE DETERMINATION IN AIR

Mokhov, L. A., Yu. F. Udalov, and V. S. Khalturin. U.S.S.R. (Pat. No.) 110,047, June 25, 1958; CA **52**, 13546 (1958).

The reagent is prepared by treating silica gel consecutively with alcoholic solutions of H acid, p-aminobenzoic acid, and nickelous chloride.

39—DETERMINATION OF NITROGEN DIOXIDE AND NITRIC OXIDE IN AIR

Gill, W. E. AEC Research and Development Report, HW 30331 REV (Hanford Atomic Products Operation, Richland, Wash.), 23 p. (1958).

The author investigated several methods for sampling and analyzing nitrogen dioxide, and developed a simple method for preparing known concentrations of nitrogen dioxide and nitric oxide. Color development is rapid for about 1 hour in 50 ml syringes containing Griess-Ilosvay type nirtogen dioxide absorbing reagents, and the author recommends waiting 1 hour before taking readings. The Griess-Ilosvay type reagents are not specific for nitrogen dioxide because they react significantly with nitric acid. The phenoldisulfonic acid method for determining nitrogen dioxide gives good recoveries in concentrations as low as 16 ppm in a 500 ml air sample. In mixtures of nitrogen dioxide and nitric oxide, approximately 40% is absorbed selectively on 4 g of 12 to 20 mesh silica gel when the nitrogen dioxide concentration is not more than 100 ppm. Prepare the Griess-Ilosvay reagents as follows: *Reagent A:*

Solution 1. Add 140 ml of glacial acetic acid to 1000 ml of water. *Solution 2.* Dissolve 0.1 g of sulfanilic acid in 300 ml of solution 1. *Solution 3.* Dissolve 0.2 g of 1-naphthylamine in 40 ml of water by boiling; add to 300 ml of solution 1. Just before use, mix equal parts of solutions 2 and 3. *Reagent B:* Grind the following reagents together into a mixed powder: 0.1 g of N-(1-naphthyl)-ethylenediamine dihydrochloride, 0.4 g of sulfanilamide, 9.5 g of tartaric acid. Dissolve all of the mixed powder in 1 liter of water, or add 100 mg to 10 ml of water for sampling. The dry mixture keeps for a year in the dark. *Reagent C:* Dissolve 5 g of sulfanilic acid in almost a liter of water containing 140 ml of glacial acetic acid. Add 20 ml of 0.1% N-(1-naphthyl)-ethylenediamine dihydrochloride, and dilute to 1 liter. *Phenoldisulfonic acid absorbing reagent:* N/10 sulfuric acid with 0.5 ml of 30% hydrogen peroxide per liter. Use phenoldisulfonic acid and reagent-grade ammonium hydroxide for color development. *Silica gel:* Boil 6 to 16 mesh silica gel with concentrated hydrochloric acid for 30 minutes, then wash 10 times with hot distilled water to remove the acid. Dry for 2 hours at 300° C. Sieve the silica gel to separate the 12 to 20 mesh particles. Place 4 g of the 12 to 20 mesh gel in glass tubes 6" long by 8 mm outside diameter and plug each end of the tube with wool. Add. Refs.: APCA **5**, 2795 (1959); Nucl. Sci. Abstr. **13**, 3569 (1959); CA **53**, 11099 (1959); IHD **24**, 595 (1960); Occ. Hyg. Abstr. **35**, 548 (1960).

40—DETECTION OF NITROGEN DIOXIDE IN AIR WITH DRY SENSITIZED PAPERS

Gelman, Charles, Robert Gamson, and Harold Klapper. Proc. 51st Annual Meeting, A.P.C.A., Philadelphia, Pa., pp. 19-1 through 19-12 (May 1958).

A dry detector paper for nitrogen dioxide, impregnated with 12% p-anisidine in methanol, changes from light yellow to red-brown when air containing nitrogen dioxide is drawn through the paper. The paper, which can be stored for several weeks before it gradually deteriorates, can detect 0.6 mg of nitrogen dioxide per cubic meter of air when a 50 ml air sample is drawn through. Ozone interferes but 0.4 mg of hydrogen chloride and 0.18 mg of sulfur dioxide do not. Ozone interference may be reduced by using a manganese dioxide prefilter, and a desiccant tube preceding the detector paper will help keep the sensitivity of the paper constant. *Subsequent investigation by the senior author indicates that the paper has too short a shelf life for routine use (personal communication). This laboratory failed in repeated attempts to stabilize the p-anisidine paper.* Add. Ref.: A.P.C.A. Abstracts **5**, 2461 (1959).

41—FIELD TYPE COLORIMETRIC TESTERS FOR GASES AND PARTICULATE MATTER

McConnaughey, P. W. Presented at the annual meeting of the American Industrial Hygiene Association, Atlantic City, N. J. (1958).

Nitrogen dioxide in air reacts with tetraphenylbenzidine and sulfuric acid, impregnated on silica gel in a detector tube, to form a greenish-blue stain. The length of the stain produced by a given gas concentration depends on the sample volume, sampling rate, diameter of the tube, and percent of impregnation used.

42—NITROGEN DIOXIDE INDICATOR

Kinosian, John R. and Byron R. Hubbard. Am. Ind. Hyg. Assoc. J. **19**, 453-460 (1958).

The absorbing reagent is prepared by wetting uniformly 100 g of 28 to 35 mesh silica gel with a fresh solution of 1% sulfanilic acid and 0.08% N-(1-naphthyl)-ethylenediamine dihydrochloride. Add the solution slowly with constant stirring until the silica gel is thoroughly moistened (40 to 80 ml of solution are required for 100 g of silica gel). Store the reagent in a calcium chloride desiccator for 24 to 48 hours (the gel then should be dry, granular, free-running, and white), then transfer to a tightly stoppered dark bottle and store in a refrigerator. The reagent gel is stable for at least 3 months. To use, plub 1 end of a glass tube 12 cm long by 3 mm inside diameter with a 1 cm square piece of glass cloth, add the silica gel to about 3 cm from the top of the tube (making a column approximately 6 cm long), hold the tube vertically and tap it to pack and level the gel, then hold the column in place by pushing a second plug of glass cloth on top of it. Even minute amounts of nitrogen dioxide in adsorbed air will stain the column intensely red, with the length of the stain being proportional to the concentration of the nitrogen dioxide. Nitric oxide does not interfere. Add. Refs.: IHD **23**, 328 (1959); Anal. Chem., Anal. Reviews **33**, 3R-13R (1961); CA **55**, 27723 (1961).

43—RAPID METHOD OF DETERMINATION OF NITROUS OXIDES IN THE AIR

Mokhov, L. A. and V. S. Khalturin. Lab. Delo **4**, No. 2, 26-27 (1958); CA **53**, 22644 (1959).

Prepare the improved silica gel used in the determination by adding 0.2 ml of saturated alcoholic benzidine hydrochloride solution to 0.5 g gel prepared according to the method of Mokhov and Demidov (CA **52**, 6057 (1958); see "Chemical Detectors," Vol. I, page 243) and mixing until the gel is dry. Add 0.1 ml of 5% alcoholic b-naphthol, mix until the mass becomes friable, then add 0.1 ml of 0.1% alcoholic nickelous chloride, and stir to complete dryness. Plug with cotton or glass wool a glass tube fused on 1 end, add a 3 mm layer of ignited quartz sand, then a 2 mm layer of the gel, then another 3 mm layer of sand. Evacuate the tube slightly and fuse it. To determine nitrous oxides in air open both ends of the tube, pass 100 ml of air through it for 30 seconds, and compare the color after 1 to 2 minutes with a standard scale ranging from 0.0005

to 0.1 mg per liter of nitrogen dioxide per 100 ml of air. The indicator sensibility is about 0.0005 mg per liter, with an accuracy of about ±3.5% The method correlates well with one using Griess-Ilosvay reagent. *The composition of the indicator is not given.* Add. Ref.: APCA Abstr. **6**, No. 8, 3454 (1961).

44—DETERMINATION OF SMALL CONCENTRATIONS OF NITROGEN OXIDES IN AIR

Plachenov, T. G. and E. E. Filyanskaya. Izvest. Vyssikh Ucheb. Zavedenii, Khim. i Khim. Tekhnol. **1958**, No. 1, 78-85; CA **52**, 14911 (1958).

The authors discuss some of the factors affecting the efficiency of the analysis of nitrogen dioxide. The properties of the indicator powder depend on the sensitivity of the reagent, the structure of the carrier, and the conditions of the reaction. A decrease of the specific surface of the indicator increases the length of the colored band and consequently decreases its intensity. As a reagent for nitrogen dioxide, m-phenylenediamine was used in silica gels and porcelain powder. The ratio of the volume of the solution in milliliters to the weight of powder (or silica gel) in grams should be 0.2:1; the quantities of the components in solution are 0.15% diphenylamine and 10% sodium chloride in 40% alcohol-water solution. The relation between the length of the colored band of the indicator powder and the concentration of nitrogen dioxide in the nitrogen dioxide and air mixture is linear, which permits the use of an indicator tube for the determination of nitrogen dioxide in that mixture. The variations of relative humidity within the limits 90 to 20% do not effect the length of the colored band or its intensity. Variations of the temperatures of the air from 0 to 30° have no influence either, except in the 0° region. Below 0° the effect is so appreciable that any reading is only an approximation. As nitric oxide does not affect the determination of nitrogen dioxide, it is thus possible to determine quantitatively both nitric oxide and nitrogen dioxide in the same mixture. The actual nitrogen dioxide is first determined, and, after oxidation of nitric oxide to nitrogen dioxide by the action of an acid solution of potassium permanganate, the total nitrogen dioxide is determined, and nitric oxide found by difference. Add. Ref.: IHD **22**, 1432 (1958).

45—SPECIAL INDICATOR TUBES FOR A RAPID DETERMINATION OF NITROGEN OXIDES IN THE AIR OF INDUSTRIAL ESTABLISHMENTS

Mokhov, L. A., Yu F. Udalov, and V. S. Khalturin. Zhur. Prikl. Khim. **32**, 452-453 (1959); AA **6**, 4980 (1959). (See article by same authors, above.)

The authors describe the construction of special indicator tubes, 80 to 100 mm in length and 3 to 5 mm in diameter. A saturated ethanolic solution of 20 ml of H-acid (8-amino-1-naphthol-3:6-disulfonic acid) is added to 1 g of silica gel. The mixture is stirred for 2 minutes and the ethanol is evaporated off. Added to this mixture are 20 ml of a 0.5% ethanolic solution of p-aminobenzoic acid. After drying the material is further mixed with a 0.1% ethanolic solution of nickel chloride. The indicator gel is introduced into the indicator tubes to a depth of 2 mm. Above this layer a 2 mm layer of silica gel is added followed by a glass- or cotton-wool plug and the open, broad end of the tube is sealed. Procedure for the determination of nitrogen oxides—the tube is broken open at both ends and 100 ml of the test air is aspirated through the broad end of the tube so that it emerges from the cone-shaped end. The color of the indicator is compared with a standard colorimetric scale. In the presence of nitrogen oxides the indicator changes from pale pink to a crimson-brown. The indicator is sensitive to 0.0005 mg per liter. Add. Ref.: CA **53**, 12540 (1959).

46—DETECTION OF OXIDES OF NITROGEN IN THE AIR

Zawadzki, S. Prace Central. Inst. Ochrony Pracy **9**, 211-216 (1959); CA **55**, 10763 (1961).

Oxides of nitrogen in air were detected on silica gel saturated with antipyrine, m-phenylenediamine, dimethylaniline, or Rivanol. The silica gel saturated with Rivanol was most suitable; it detected 0.005 mg oxides of nitrogen (expressed as N_2O_5) per liter of air.

47—REPORT ON THE DRAEGER GAS DETECTOR. NITROUS GASES

American Conference of Governmental Industrial Hygienists (A.C.G.I.H.). Transactions of the Twenty-first Annual Meeting, pp. 125-127 (1959).

The operating range of the indicator tube is 0.01 to 0.2 mg per liter (5 to 100 ppm). Calibration for this tube was made with nitrogen dioxide in the range of 5 to 10 ppm. The results indicated very limited accuracy of readings in this range with the tubes indicating abnormally high results.

48—NEW REAGENTS FOR THE COLORIMETRIC DETERMINATION OF MICROGRAM QUANTITIES OF NITRITE

Bark, L. S. and R. Catterall. Mikrochim. Acta, No. 4, 553-558 (1960).

Two new reagents for the determination of nitrite in acid solutions may be applicable to field detectors. One reagent is N-(2-aminophenyl) morpholine, the other is N-(2-aminophenyl) piperidine; in acid solutions either will detect up to 20 μg nitrite ion per ml. The reaction is sensitive to 0.05 μg nitrite ion per ml. Oxidizing agents interfere. Add. Refs.: Water Pollution Abstracts **34**, 634 (1931); Pub. Health Eng. Abstracts **41**, No. 8, S:48 (1961).

49—MODIFIED NITROGEN DIOXIDE REAGENT FOR RECORDING AIR ANALYZERS

Saltzman, Bernard E. Anal. Chem. **32**, 135-136 (1960).

Reagents of different compositions were tested for the Saltzman variation of the Griess-Ilosvay reaction, and the following modification was found best for use in recording air analyzers: dissolve 5 g of sulfanilic acid in almost a liter of nitrite-free water, add 50 ml of glacial acetic acid and 50 ml of 0.1% N-(1-naphthyl)-ethylenediamine dihydrochloride, and make to 1 liter. Keep tightly stoppered in a dark bottle. The reagent may be preserved for months in a refrigerator, as may also the 0.1% stock solution of the dye coupling reagent. This modified reagent yields about 5% less color than the original reagent, both with standard nitrite solution and in the midget fritted bubbler with air samples. Thus, the original relationship of 1 mole of nitrogen producing the same color as 0.72 mole of nitrite continues to hold. (This standardization factor should be checked for the absorbing column employed.) Add. Ref. CA **54**, 7416 (1960).

50—SIMPLE APARATUS FOR THE ANALYSIS OF TRACES OF IMPURITIES IN GASES. DETERMINATION OF OXYGEN IN INERT GASES AND HIGHER OXIDES OF NITROGEN IN NITROUS OXIDE

Seris, G., Ph. Vernotte, Mme. Klein, and A. M. Clave. Chim. anal. **42**, 200-202 (1960); CA **54**, 14817 (1960).

The authors describe an apparatus in which the gas sample reacts with a solution and the color developed by the reaction is measured photometrically. Griess reagent is used to determine less than 5 ppm nitric oxide or nitrogen dioxide in nitrous oxide.

51—DETERMINATION OF NITROUS OXIDE

Stanford, Evelyn C. and Charles A. Plantz (to Mine Safety Appliances Co.) U. S. (Pat. No.) 2,963,351, Dec. 6, 1960; CA **55**, 25604 (1961).

The authors describe a method for the determination of nitrogen dioxide. Nitrogen dioxide is determined by passing a gas in which it is contained through a transparent tube containing silica gel mixed with N,N,N',N'-tetraphenylbenzidine and acid. Nitrogen dioxide turns the tetraphenylbenzidine blue, and the length of color in the tube can be used as a measure of its concentration. The silica gel is prepared by mixing 0.3 mg reagent with 10 ml silica gel and heating the mixture for 45 minutes at 120°. The cooled mixture is added to 0.3-1 ml of 47% sulfuric acid to which has been added 0.6 ml water and stirred until it appears dry and free-flowing.

52—INFORMATION ON THE DRAEGER GAS DETECTOR

Draegerwerk Heinr. und Bernhard Draeger, Luebeck, Germany (distributed by New Jersey Safety Equipment Co., 299 Park Ave., East Orange, N. J.) The company manufactures 3 different nitrogen oxide detector tubes to use with its Wraeger Multi-Gas Detector:

a. NITROUS GAS DETECTOR TUBE. Information Sheet No. 44 (Nov. 1960). The NO + NO$_2$ 0.5/a Nitrous Gas Detector Tube contains a white indicating layer with calibrated ppm scale extending from 0.5 to 10. ppm. The scale figures are valid for 0.5 liter of test air, corresponding to 5 strokes of the bellows pump of the Multi-Gas-Detector. A preclensing or oxidizing layer precedes the indicating layer, to oxidize into nitrogen dioxide any nitrogen monoxide present in the air so that it, too, is measured; the indicating layer responds to nitrogen dioxide only. The indication is based on the reaction of nitrogen dioxide with a substituted aromatic amine, and the length of the blue-gray stain produced in the reagent layer by the nitrous gases indicates their concentration. The detector tube's shelf life is about 2 years.

b. NITROGEN DIOXIDE DETECTOR TUBE. Information Sheet No. 43 (Oct. 1960). The 0.5/b Nitrogen Dioxide Detector Tube is similar to the Nitrous Gas Detector Tube (above) except that the oxidizing layer is omitted, so that the tube responds only to nitrogen dioxide and not to nitrogen monoxide; the range, calibration scale, indicating reagent, and shelf life are the same. The gray-violet stain produced in the indicator by nitrogen dioxide is stable for several days if the tube is sealed with rubber caps and stored in the dark.

c. NITROGEN OXIDES DETECTOR TUBE. Information Sheet No. 22 (June 1959) The 100/a Nitrogen Oxides Detector Tube is designed to measure high concentrations of nitrogen oxides, in the range from 100 to 1200 ppm, corresponding to 0.2 and 2.5 mg per liter at 25° C and 760 mm. The calibration scale printed on the tube is correct for 0.5 liter of test air (representing 5 strokes of the aspirator bellows), and the scale numbers give parts of nitrogen dioxide in 10^4 parts of gas. If they are multiplied by 100 they give the concentration in ppm, again calculated as nitrogen dioxide. The indicator, an aromatic imide, is preceded by a preliminary filter and oxidizing layer which quantitatively converts any nitrogen monoxide present to nitrogen dioxide, which then is included in the estimation. The tube's storage life is at least 2 years.

53—U.S.S.R. LITERATURE ON AIR POLLUTION AND RELATED OCCUPATIONAL DISEASES. A SURVEY. VOL. 4

Levine, B. S. (U. S. Dept. of Commerce, OTS No. 60-21913, Washington 25, D. C., 1960).

Some of the pieces of apparatus mentioned, as well as several of the analytical methods, are applicable to field detection, especially those for nitrogen oxides in air.

54—NITROGEN DIOXIDE DETECTOR

Mine Safety Appliances Co., 201 N. Braddock Ave., Pittsburgh 8, Pa. Bull. 0805-4; Catalog 8B3621, Sect. 3, p. 13 (1961).

The Nitrogen Dioxide-in-Air (NO$_2$) Detector Kit includes a carrying case, a rubber bulb aspirator, a barrel with tube holder and rotating scale, and replaceable "break-tip" detector tubes containing silica gel impregnated with a chemical that changes color if the atmosphere contains nitrogen dioxide. The concentration of the gas in the range from 0.5 to 50. is determined by comparing the length of the colored stain produced in the detector tube by the nitrogen dioxide with the accompanying scale on the barrel.

NITROGEN DIOXIDE DETECTOR: Mix a solution consisting of 1 ml of Ninin, 1 g of sulfanilic acid, and 10 ml of ethyl alcohol with 100 ml of distilled water. Add 25 ml of the mixture to a beaker containing 25 g of silica gel. Allow the mixture to equilibrate for 1 hour, then spread it on a filter paper. Spread is consecutively on clean, dry filter papers to remove all excess reagent. Finally, dry the impregnated gel in nitrogen dioxide-free air and pack into appropriate glass detector tubes. The reaction of nitrogen dioxide with the reagent is vivid but not proportional to stain length. Humectants and acids in the reagent reduce its sensitivity. Papers treated with the reagent are extremely sensitive when freshly prepared but become less sensitive as they are dried. The gel is sensitive to about 0.5 ppm, and the first appearance of a colored front, plotted against air volumes, appears to be quantitative.

55—TEST TUBES FOR DETECTING NITROUS GASES

Draegerwerk Heinrich und Bernhard Draeger. Ger. (Pât. No.) 1,081,693, May 12, 1960 (Cl. 42 e); CA 55, 14177 (1961).

The preparation of test tubes for the determination of nitrous gases is described. Test tubes are prepared for measuring concentrations of nitrogen dioxide between 100 and 1200 ppm. One hundred parts of silica gel (particle size 6 to 7.5 mm and bulk d. 500 g per liter) were washed with acid and freed of organic imprities by roasting at 500°. The gel was then mixed with 0.2 part finely powdered carbazole until the reagent completely adsorbed on the surface of the gel. This colorless silica gel was turned lemon yellow by nitrogen dioxide, and the length of yellow zone was quantitatively calibrated for 100 to 1000 ppm of nitrogen dioxide. Nitrogen oxide can be oxidized to nitrogen dioxide by introducing a chromic oxide-impregnated calcium-aluminum silicate into the testing tube. Nitrogen oxides in diesel exhaust gases can be detected.

56—CONTINUOUS DETERMINATION OF NITROGEN OXIDES IN AIR AND EXHAUST GASES

Ripley, D. L., J. M. Clingenpeel, and R. W. Hurn. Abstr. 64, p. 25-W, Abstracts of the 145th meeting of the American Chemical Society, New York (1963).

The authors have developed, for atmospheric analyzers used in air pollution studies, and for determination of oxides of nitrogen in diluted automobile exhaust gases, a solid chemical oxidant that converts nitric oxide to the more readily determinable dioxide form. They prepare the oxidant by saturating glass fiber paper with a solution of sodium dichromate and sulfuric acid and then drying. A small amount of the oxidant in a glass tube through which the gas sample passes will oxidize the nitric oxide to nitrogen dioxide and give complete recovery of the mono- and dioxide present. Add. Ref.: Ind. Hyg. News. Rept. **6**, No. 9 (1963).

See Section One

For references 33, 69, 85, 96, 104, 106, 119, 125, 129.

Nitroglycerine

See Section One
For reference 60.

Oxidizing Agents

1—OXIDATION-REDUCTION PAPERS

Sansoni, Bruno. Naturwissenschaften **41**, 213 (1954); CA **49**, 3633 (1955).

The author presents a method for the preparation of oxidation reduction papers. The impregnation of filter paper with the alcohol-solution intermediate stages of the leucomethylene blue-methylene blue redoxites (Cf. CA **49**, 3632 (1955)), followed by hardening in a drying oven yields "redox" paper. The oxidized form is dark blue, the reduced form pure white. The capacity is from 0.009 to 0.013 meq of trivalent iron per square centimeter. The paper is useful as a test for free oxygen.

2—SODIUM METAVANADATE AS A VOLUMETRIC RE-AGENT. III. DIPHENYLAMINE INDICATOR METHOD

Singh, Balwant and Ranjit Singh. Research Bull. Panjab Univ. **71**, 63-66 (1955); CA **49**, 15606 (1955).

A method is described whereby several materials can be determined with sodium metavanadate. Sodium metavanadate can be used as an oxidizing agent in sulfuric acid solutions for the determination of potassium permanganate, potassium dichromate, potassium bromate, potassium iodate, potassium peroxydisulfate, and hydrogen peroxide, with diphenylamine as an internal indicator. *This procedure might be applied to the analysis of the above substances in air.*

3—MODIFICATION OF FERROUS THIOCYANATE COLORIMETRIC METHOD FOR DETERMINATION OF SOME ATMOSPHERIC OXIDANTS

Todd, Glenn W. Anal. Chem. **27**, 1490-1492 (1955). This method for the determination of gaseous oxidants is a modification of the ferrous thiocyanate method for peroxides. Prepare the reagent by adding 0.5 g of ammonium thiocyanate and 1 ml of 6 N sulfuric acid to 100 ml of water. Add 0.1 g of ferrous ammonium sulfate, shake, and dilute with 100 ml of water. The reagent should be prepared fresh daily, although the pigment formed on standing can be removed with decolorizing carbon. The reagent is somewhat sensitive to nitrogen dioxide but not to nitrous oxide, formic acid, formaldehyde, valeric acid, or isovaleraldehyde. Prepare a standard curve by adding known amounts of ferric iron to the reagent. Add. Refs.: CA **49**, 15606 (1955); AA **3**, 576 (1956).

4—THE USE OF REACTIONS OF THE SYNTHESIS OF SOME ORGANIC DYES FOR THE DETECTION OF THE OXIDIZING ANIONS

Vil'borg, S. S. and V. A. Drozdov. Trudy Moskov. Khim.-Tekhnol. Inst. im. D. I. Mendeleeva **1956**, No. 23, 130-134; CA **53**, 6876 (1959).

The authors describe new reagents for detecting small quantities of oxidizing agents. *Possibly they might be applied to field detectors.*

5—APPLICATION OF THE CUPROUS REBEANATE RE-ACTION TO THE DETECTION OF OXIDANTS, OF PER-OXIDES, OF QUINONES AND OF HEMATINIC DERIVA-TIVES (LABORATORY NOTE)

Dubouloz, Pierre, Joseph Fonderai and Rosy Marville. Bull. soc. chim. France **1957**, 564-565; CA **51**, 10298 (1957).

The authors describe a sensitive technique for the detection of oxidants. The limit of sensitivity is 5×10^{-6} mole per square centimeter.

6—THE APPLICATION OF PHENOLPHTHALIN REAGENT TO ATMOSPHERIC OXIDANT ANALYSIS

Haagen-Smit, A. J. and Margaret F. Brunelle. Intern. J. Air Pollution **1**, 51-59 (1958/9).

The authors present a colorimetric method, based on the oxidation of phenolphthalin to phenolphthalein, for measuring a form of air pollution characterized by a strong oxidizing effect. Pass air for 10 minutes, at a rate of 900 ml per minute, through 10 ml of diluted phenolphthalin-copper sulfate reagent in a bubbler; compare the color developed with those of a standard curve in a Klett-Summerson colorimeter. The amount of oxidant determined by this method correlates well both with subjective observation and with comparative data obtained by several other methods. Add. Ref.: CA **53**, 4620 (1959).

7—DETECTION OF ORGANIC OXIDANTS IN SPOT ANALYSIS. DIFFERENTIATION OF CHLORAMINE-T AND ALKALI HYPOCHLORITES

Feigl, F. and R. A. Rosell. Z. anal. Chem. **159**, 335-339 (1958); CA 52, 7927 (1958).

The authors describe detection methods for organic oxidants. The thio analog of Michler's ketone on filter paper yields a blue spot with aqueous solutions of chloramine-T and-B, N-bromosuccinimide and N-chlorosuccinimide, chloranil, bromanil, and benzoyl peroxide. All except chloramine-T and-B yield a blue spot with tetramethyldiaminodiphenylmethane on filter paper. The bromo- and chlorosuccinimides only yield brown hydrated thallic oxide on addition of alkaline thallous iodide at room temperature. N-bromosuccinimide yields a red spot on filter paper containing fluorescein. To test for chloramine-T in the presence of hypochlorite add hydrogen peroxide and divalent zinc to decompose the hypochlorite and do the previous test. To detect hypochlorite in the presence of chloramine-T add alkaline thallous iodide at room temperature and look for a brown precipitate. Both oxidize thallous iodide at higher temperature.

Oxygen

1—A NEW ABSORBENT FOR OXYGEN IN GAS ANALYSIS

Feiser, Louis F. J. Am. Chem. Soc. **46**, 2639-2647 (1924).

Dissolve in dilute alkali a mixture of sodium anthrahydroquinone-B-sulfonate and sodium hyposulfite in large molar excess to obtain a deep red solution which will absorb oxygen rapidly and efficiently. Add. Ref.: J. 291.

2—COLORIMETRIC METHOD FOR THE DETERMINATION OF DISSOLVED OXYGEN

Gilcreas, F. Wellington. J. Am. Water Works Assoc. **27**, 1166-1177 (1935); J. 291.

Oxygen dissolved in water may be determined colorimetrically utilizing 2,4-diaminophenol dihydrochloride as the colorimetric reagent. The reagent yields a red color which is proportional to the oxygen content, and a yellow color which is not proportional to the oxygen content. Add. Ref.: CA 30, 197 (1936).

3—DETERMINATION OF TRACES OF IMPURITIES IN COMMERCIAL GASES, PARTICULARLY OXYGEN

Grant, J. Ind. Gases **16**, 138-141 (1935); Chim. and ind. **37**, 655; CA **31**, 6133 (1937).

A method for the determination of oxygen is presented. One of the best tests for the detection of oxygen is to pass the gas through an air-free alkaline aqueous solution of manganous hydroxide and potassium iodide containing starch; the sensitivity of the reaction is 0.05% oxygen.

4—RAPID DETERMINATION OF OXYGEN IN ATMOSPHERIC GASES

Kling, Andre and Maurice Claraz. Compt. rend. **203**, 319-321 (1936); CA **30**, 6671 (1936).

The method described depends on the fact that an alkaline solution of a ferrous salt absorbs oxygen and that upon addition of a small quantity of methylene blue which is first colorless, becomes blue when the oxidation reduction potential reaches 14.2. From the volume of a given mixture required to cause such a change of color the percentage of oxygen present is calculated.

5—DETERMINATION OF SMALL AMOUNTS OF OXYGEN IN GASES

Brady, L. J. Anal. Chem. **20**, 1033-1037 (1948).

The author describes a rapid procedure for determining the oxygen content of such gases as nitrogen, argon, acetylene, and mixtures of carbon monoxide, carbon dioxide, and nitrogen. From 0.1% to less than 0.001% of oxygen can be determined conveniently. When a colorless alkaline solution of sodium anthraquinone-B-sulfonate is reduced with a suitable reducing agent (e.g., amalgamated zinc), the sulfonate turns red and in that form reacts with oxygen quantitatively. The change in optical density caused by the oxidation of the reagent can be measured with a photoelectric colorimeter and it is a function of the oxygen present. The analysis is unaffected by small quantities of hydrocarbons, phosphine, carbon monoxide, carbon dioxide, or sulfur compounds. The reaction is adaptable to spot tests by bringing a measured volume of the gas into contact with a fixed volume of reagent. The author describes a suitable apparatus and gives directions for making the test and for calibrating the apparatus. Add. Ref.: CA **43**, 1286 (1949).

6— DETERMINATION OF SMALL AMOUNTS OF OXYGEN IN GASES AND LIQUIDS

Hirano, Shizo and Mitsuko Kitahara. J. Chem. Soc. Japan, Ind. Chem. Sect. **56**, 325-327 (1953); CA **48**, 10487 (1954).

The addition of 1 cc of oxygen dissolves 11.35 mg of metallic copper in ammonium hydroxide solution. This property was utilized to determine the amount of oxygen in air (0.36 to 0.94 cc oxygen in 1.7 to 4.5 cc air, error: 2 to 3%). The free oxygen in water as well as in aqueous solutions of sodium nitrite, sodium hydroxide, and manganese chloride was also determined and compared with the Winkler method. *This reaction might be applied to field detection of oxygen.*

7—A CHROMOMETRIC METHOD FOR DETERMINING THE OXYGEN CONTENT OF AIR

Mueller, Eugen and Horst Metzger. Chem.-Ztg. **78**, 317-322 (1954); CA **48**, 10487 (1954).

The authors describe a colorimetric method for determining the oxygen content of air. The method depends on the change in color of a dye solution when shaken with air. By using the carbohydrate of Tschitschibabin a process has been developed by which unskilled labor can determine on the spot whether or not air is breathable. The principles involved are discussed, with many organic formula equations. 38 references.

8—PHOTOELECTRIC ABSORPTIOMETER FOR DETERMINATION OF SMALL AMOUNTS OF GASES IN AIR

Barley, Thomas, Joseph H. Elliott, and Richard P. Kinsey. U. S. (Pat. No.) 2,829,032, Apr. 1, 1958; CA **52**, 11490 (1958).

An apparatus is described which can determine the concentration of one gas in the presence of another with an accuracy of 0.5 ppm. It records continuously the color changes in a specific solution, such as alkaline pyrogallol or ammoniacal cuprous chloride for oxygen.

9—OXYGEN INDICATOR

Strange, John P. (to Mine Safety Appliances Co.). U. S. (Pat. No.) 2,823,985, Feb. 18, 1958; CA **52**, 7036 (1958).

An apparatus for indicating the presence of oxygen in a gas stream is described. The indicator used is an ammoniacal solution of cuprous chloride. The passage of gas pushes slugs of the solution through an inclined cross arm. When these slugs turn blue, the presence of oxygen is indicated. A copper screen or turnings placed further along the path of the liquid changes the color back to clear unless oxygen is present in more than a trace.

10—A SELF-SAMPLING INDICATOR TUBE FOR OXYGEN

Dixon, B. E. and Kiff, P. R. Talanta **4**, 203-205 (1960). Manganous oxide on a silica gel base in an evacuated glass tube absorbs oxygen. The evacuated silica gel acts as its own pump and no other sampling apparatus is required. Admit the test air to the reagent by breaking the end of the tube; oxygen changes the color of the absorbent from green to brown, indicating the percentage of oxygen in less than 1 minute. The tubes are stable for at least 2 years. Add. Ref.: CA **58**, 7364 (1963).

11—SIMPLE APPARATUS FOR THE ANALYSIS OF TRACES OF IMPURITIES IN GASES. DETERMINATION OF OXYGEN IN INERT GASES AND HIGHER OXIDES OF NITROGEN IN NITROUS OXIDE

Seris, G., Ph.Vernotte, Mme. Klein, and A. M. Clave. Chim. anal. **42**, 200-202 (1960); CA **54**, 14817 (1960).

An apparatus for the determination of oxygen is described by the authors. The apparatus allows the gas sample to react with a solution and the color developed is measured photometrically. Oxygen is determined at less than 5 ppm level by oxidation of reduced ammonium anthraquinone-2-sulfonate in sodium carbonate solution.

See Section One
For references 69, 72.

Ozone

1—DISTINCTION BETWEEN OZONE AND NITROUS ACID OR HYDROGEN PEROXIDE

Erlwein, G. and T. Weyl. Ber. **31**, 3158-3159 (1898); BOT 13, p. 42.

Ozone produces a wine-red coloration with a solution of m-phenylenediamine, both in the presence of acids and alkalies. Neither nitrous acid nor hydrogen peroxide produces any coloration of the diamine. A freshly-prepared solution of 0.1 to 0.2 g of m-phenylenediamine hydrochloride and 10 cc of 5% aqueous soda, made up to 100 cc (use 25 cc of this) gives a yellowish brown coloration with 0.08 mg of ozone. Add. Ref.: W., Vol. II, p. 430.

2—MICROCHEMICAL TEST FOR ALKALIES AND ACIDS; DETECTION OF SMALL QUANTITIES OF OZONE AND WATER

Emich, E. Monatsh. **22**, 670-678 (1901); BOT 12, p. 41.

Silk which has been colored with litmus, can be used for the detection of ozone in the presence of potassium iodide or postassium ferrocyanide when red litmus is used. When sulfur or potassium thiocyanate is used the reaction requires that blue litmus be substituted for the red.

3—NEW REAGENT FOR THE DETECTION OF OZONE

Chlopin, G. V. Z. Uahr.-Genussm. **5**, 504-505 (1902); BOT 9, p. 41.

Strips of ordinary filter paper are dipped in a moderately concentrated alcoholic solution of a dye, sold under the name of "Ursol D," and dried. When moistened with water and exposed to the action of ozone, the strips are colored blue. Hydrogen peroxide and carbon dioxide have no action on the papers. Nitrous fumes, chlorine and bromine give a bluish-green coloration, soon changing to yellow. Add. Ref.: W., Vol. II, p. 438.

4—OLD AND NEW REACTIONS OF OZONE

Arnold, C. and C. Mentzel. Ber. **35**, 1324-1330 (1902); BOT 7, p. 40.

The many well known tests for ozone, such as zinc or potassium iodide and starch, guaiacum tincture, potassium iodide and an indicator for alkalinity, thallium hydroxide, tetramethyl-p-phenylenediamine, the phenylenediamines, and silver foil, are criticized, because they are not sufficiently characteristic and all are disturbed by the presence of chlorine, bromine, nitrous acid, or hydrogen peroxide. The best of these tests consists of a paper impregnated with potassium iodide and phenolphthalein or rosolic acid. The authors recommend test papers impregnated with a saturated alcoholic solution of benzidine or tetramethyldi-p-aminophenylmethane. The benzidine papers assume a brown color in the presence of ozone, blue with nitrous fumes, blue and then red-brown with chlorine, and do not react with hydrogen peroxide, hydrogen cyanide, ammonia, hydrogen sulfide, or ammonium sulfide. Test papers of tetramethyldi-p-aminophenylmethane are even more sensitive than the benzidine papers; with ozone they give a violet coloration, with nitrous fumes a straw-yellow, and with chlorine or bromine a dep blue; they do not react with hydrogen peroxide and the sensitivity of the ozone reaction is considerably increased by the presence of free acetic acid. Add. Refs.: Analyst **27**, 291 (1902); W., Vol. II, p. 438.

5—IMPROVED REACTIONS AND METHODS OF PREPARATION OF OZONE; URSOL D AS A REAGENT FOR OZONE

Arnold, C. and C. Mentzel. Ber. **35**, 2902-2907 (1902); BOT 8, p. 41.

Test papers impregnated with tetramethyldi-p-aminophenylmethane yield a violet color with ozone only when it is completely acid free. Ozone is most easily determined in an aqueous solution by adding 1 or 2 drops of a methyl alcoholic solution of tetramthyldi-p-aminophenylmethane and 1 to 2 cc of an aqueous solution of silver nitrate or manganous sulfate. Add. Ref.: W., Vol. II, p. 322 (see below).

6—DETECTION OF OZONE BY MEANS OF SILVER

Thiele, H. Z. Offentl. Chem. **12**, 11-12 (1906); BOT 264, p. 101

The author has observed that silver foil or coins are no longer blackened when exposed to an atmosphere containing ozone. When, however, the silver has been momentarily heated in a flame or has been polished with emery paper, it is at once blackened by the presence of ozone. If the trace of oil derived from the fingers is the cause of the non-appearance of the black color, it is curious that so extremely minute a trace of fat as must be present should prohibit the reaction.

7—THE DETECTION OF OZONE

Fischer, F. and H. Marx. Ber. **39**, 2555-2557 (1906); Analyst 31, 417-418 (1906).

Paper moistened with alcoholic tetramethyl-p-diamido-di-phenylamine turns violet in contact with ozone. The test paper must be used moist because ozone colors the dry paper yellow. Oxides of nitrogen color the moist paper straw yellow, while mixtures of ozone and nitrous oxides give dirty-brown intermediate shades. If either the ozone or the nitrous oxide predominates in the gas mixture, the paper gives the color of the gas that is in excess. Add. Ref.: Analyst **64**, 492-499 (1939).

8—A REAGENT AND METHOD FOR THE ESTIMATION OF OZONE

Benoist, L. Compt. rend. **168**, 612-615 (1919); BOT 18, p. 43.

Ozone can be determined at the 1 μg level by means of a fluorescein reagent. The fluorescent color is quantitatively bleached by ozone according to the reaction of 2 molecules of ozone with 1 of fluorescein. Add. Ref.: Analyst **44**, 183 (1919).

9—CRITIC OF OZONE DETERMINATIONS (A CONTRIBUTION TO THE PROBLEM OF GAS INTOXICATIONS IN RONTGEN ROOMS)

Loenne, F. Munch. med. Wochschr. **68**, 1519-1520 (1921); BOT 14, p. 42.

Guthmann used the method of Erlwein and Weyl (previously abstracted), for the detection of ozone. Ozone is detected with m-penylenediamine hydrochloride in alkaline solution. The m-phenylenediamine hydrochloride is used in sodium hydroxide solution in which nitrous acid and hydrogen peroxide do not react. This solution does react with air as well as with nitroso compounds in much shorter time than had been previously thought. Ozone has not been determined satisfactorily by this method.

10—A NEW METHOD FOR THE ESTIMATION OF OZONE IN AIR

Egorov, M. S. Z. Untersuch. Lebensm. **56**, 355-364 (1928); BOT 19, p. 43.

A new method is presented for the determination of ozone in air. The method is based on the formation of fluorescein from the leuco compound by the action of ozone. One mg of fluorescein is dissolved in a few drops of 10% sodium hydroxide and 10 cc of saturated sodium hydroxide solution are added to this solution. The resulting solution is shaken with zinc dust until the fluorescence disappears. After filtration 1 drop of this solution is added to 10 cc of 0.5% sodium hydroxide in a test tube. Air is aspirated through this solution at a maximum rate of 12 to 15 liters per hour. The fluorescence is stable in alkaline solution and is unaffected by hydrogen peroxide or oxides of nitrogen. The method is sensitive, rapid, and specific. One part by weight of fluorescein is produced by 0.96 parts of ozone. One laboratory has reported that the reaction of leuco-fluorescein with ozone depends on the amount of the zinc remaining in the solution after reduction. The sensitivity of each batch of leuco-fluorescein varied.

11—DETERMINATION OF ATMOSPHERIC OZONE BY FULORESCEIN

Heller, W. Compt. rend. **200,** 1936-1938 (1935); BOT 21, p. 43.

A modification of Benoist's fluorescein method (see earlier abstract) is described, but it is not completely satisfactory. Errors occur due to the fact that the ratio of ozone to the fluorescein destroyed depends on the pH, varies with the amount of the fluorescein, and increases as the partial pressure of ozone decreases. These factors make the results obtained unreliable. On the other hand, the method is more reliable than an iodimetric one in that it is inappreciably affected by other constituents of the atmosphere, such as nitric oxide, nitrogen dioxide, carbon dioxide, etc.

12—THE DETECTION OF TOXIC GASES AND VAPORS

Leroux, Lucien. Rev. hyg. et med. prevent. **57,** 81-112 (1935).

Strips of filter paper moistened successively in 1% potassium iodide and 10% starch paste, then dried, turn blue in the presence of ozone because iodine is liberated. If the ozone concentration is high iodate forms and the blue color disappears. Chlorine and heavy concentrations of other gases react similarly. To check whether the blue color was caused by these compounds, test with a piece of red litmus paper impregnated with potassium iodide, which will not be changed by chlorine or nitrogen gases, but will be turned blue by ozone because the ozone liberated potassium hydroxide. Make a different detector by impregnating filter paper strips with thallium hydroxide, then drying them. Ozone turns the strips brown through the formation of thallium peroxide. Add. Ref.: CA **29,** 3627 (1935).

13—DETERMINATION OF TRACES OF IMPURITIES IN COMMERCIAL GASES, PARTICULARLY OXYGEN

Grant, J. Ind. Gases **16,** 138-141 (1935); Chimie et industrie **37,** 655; CA **31,** 6133 (1937).

An ozone determination utilizing the bleaching effect of ozone on fluorescein is described. Add. Ref.: BOT 20, p 43.

14—COLOUR TESTS FOR CHLORINE, OZONE AND HYPOCHLORITES WITH METHANE BASE

Masterman, A. T. Analyst **64,** 492-499 (1939).

The addition of ozone gas to a solution of methane base in the presence of an acid (acetic, hydrochloric, or phosphoric) gives a sequence of characteristic colors, violet to amethyst to rose to ruby red. Test paper soaked in the methane base solution gives a violet color with ozone. (Methane base, or tetramethyl base, is 4,4'-tetramethyl-diaminodiphenylmethane, and is readily soluble in carbon tetrachloride, less soluble in alcohol or acetone.) Add. Refs.: BOT 16, p. 42 CA **33,** 6750 (1939).

15—OZONE DETECTION AND DETERMINATION

Ozone will liberate iodine from starch-iodide paper; other oxidizing agents, such as chlorine, hydrogen peroxide, etc., give the same reaction. Ozone in contact with potassium iodide impregnated litmus paper reacts with the potassium iodide to form potassium hydroxide, which changes the litmus paper from pink to blue. J. 292.

16—DETECTION OF OZONE. W., Vol. II, p. 183.

According to P. N. van Eck (Pharm. Weekblad **62,** 365-376 (1925)) ozone gives a violet color with a solution prepared by dissolving 0.5 g of a-naphthylamine and 50 g of tartaric acid in 100 ml of water.

17—IBID. p. 322.

C. Arnold and C. Mentzel (Ber. **35,** 2902 (1902); Z. angew. Chem. **15,** 1093 (1902)) used filter paper impregnated with a saturated alcoholic solution of benzidine to detect ozone. Ozone reacted with the benzidine to color the filter paper brown. *(See article by same authors above.)*

18—IBID. p. 435

Ozone turns a colorless solution of m-phenylenediamine hydrochloride wine-red. Nitrite and hydrogen peroxide do not interfere if the reagent is used in alkaline solution. Pass the air suspected of containing ozone through 25 ml of a freshly-prepared solution containing 0.1 to 0.2 g of m-phenylenediamine hydrochloride in 90 ml of water and 10 ml of 5% sodium hydroxide. As little as 0.08 mg of ozone produces a yellowish-brown color within 5 seconds. With a greater ozone concentration the color finally is wine-red.

19—DETECTION OF NITRITE, OZONE, AND HYDROGEN PEROXIDE. W., Vol. IV, p. 510.

According to Schoenbein (J. prakt. Chem. **92,** 150; Z. anal. Chem. **4,** 116 (1865)) an aqueous solution of indigo carmine, which has been acidified with hydrochloric acid and just decolorized with an alkali sulfide, is colored blue by treatment with nitrite, ozone, and hydrogen peroxide.

20—DESCRIPTION OF A SIMPLE APPARATUS FOR THE MEASUREMENT OF THE OXIDATION POWER OR ITS FACTORS AND OF THE DUST CONTENT OF THE AIR

Effenberger, E. Meteorol. Rundschau **2,** 280-283 (1949); BOT 11, p. 41.

A slightly wetted filter paper impregnated with a material which darkens or becomes colored on oxidation is evaluated photometrically or by comparison with a color scale after a known volume of air has been aispirated through it. Nitrogen dioxide interferes with the ozone determination.

21—COLORIMETRIC DETERMINATION OF HIGHLY DILUTED OZONE IN OXYGEN

Dorta-Schaeppi, Y. and W. D. Treadwell. Helv. Chim. Acta **32**, 356 (1949); BOT 10, p. 41.

Ozone can be determined colorimetrically by passing the sample through indigodisulfonic acid. The reagent is prepared by heating 0.131 g of indigo with 2 ml of concentrated sulfuric acid for one hour. The reaction product obtained after cooling is diluted to 500 ml in a volumetric flask. Each ml of the 0.5×10^{-4} M indigo solution is buffered to pH 6.85 with a solution obtained by mixing 0.1 M dibasic sodium phosphate with an equal volume of 0.1 M monobasic potassium phosphate. At this pH, nitrite does not bleach the indigo. After the absorption the color is measured with light passing through a yellow mercury 578 filter.

22—GAS ANALYSIS

Nash, Leonard K. Anal. Chem. **22**, 108-121 (1950).

The bleaching action exercised on indigodisulfonic acid by ozone serves to determine a few parts per million of this componet.

23—DETERMINATION OF OZONE IN THE PRESENCE OF NITROGEN DIOXIDE AND HYDROGEN PEROXIDE

Shchirskaya, V. A. Gigiena i Sanit. **1954**, No. 8, 41-53; CA **48**, 13536 (1954).

A method is described for the determination of ozone in the presence of hydrogen peroxide and nitrogen dioxide. Chromic trioxide can be used satisfactorily as an absorbent for vapors of hydrogen peroxide at concentrations of 0.005 to 1.1 mg per liter in air during the estimation of ozone in the presence of hydrogen peroxide. Silica gel saturated with 0.02 M potassium dichromate absorbs nitrogen dioxide at concentrations of 0.001 to 0.02 mg per liter for the determination of ozone in the presence of nitrogen dioxide. Add. Refs.: CA **47**, 9861 (1953); IHD **19**, 114 (1955).

24—DETERMINATION OF TOXIC GAS COMPONENTS IN AIR BY THE REICH STOP-METHOD

Kraus, E. Chem. Tech. (Berlin) **7**, 552-555 (1955); CA **50**, 12750 (1956).

The author proposes a procedure, based on the Reich method, for determining traces of various gases. He determines ozone by absorption in a 0.01 N solution of arsenous oxide containing dilute potassium iodide and starch. Add. Ref.: AA **3**, 1893 (1956).

25—MODIFICATION OF FERROUS THIOCYANATE COLORIMETRIC METHOD FOR DETERMINATION OF SOME ATMOSPHERIC OXDIANTS

Todd, Glenn W. Anal. Chem. **27**, 1490-1492 (1955).

Phenolphthalein is a useful reagent for the determination of oxidants. Some atmospheric peroxides interfere with the analyses but the reagent has a greater sensitivity to ozone than to these peroxides.

26—A METHOD FOR THE DETERMINATION OF TRACES OF OZONE

Deckert, W. Z. anal. Chem. **153**, 189-193 (1956); AA **4**, 882 (1957).

The method depends on the reddening of ferric oxide-potassium thiocyanate impregnated paper in the presence of ozone. (cf. AA **3**, 3206 (1956)). The lower limit of detection is 10 μg of ozone in 10 liters of air; ozone concentration in the range of 0.01 to 10 mg per liter can be determined with an accuracy of plus or minus 10% by measuring the area of paper reddened by the stream of sample gases. Hydrogen peroxide and acids interfere and must be removed prior to the determination.

27—COLORIMETRIC PROCEDURE FOR QUANTITATIVE DETERMINATION OF ATMOSPHERIC OZONE

Allison, Albert R., Alvin D. Delman, Alban E. Ruff, and Bernard B. Simms. U. S. (Pat. No.) 2,849,291, Aug. 26, 1958; CA **52**, 19726 (1958).

Ozone in air is determined by aspirating the air sample through a dilute solution of N-phenyl-2-naphthylamine in o-dichlorobenzene until a color change occurs. The depth of color produced is compared to the color obtained by passing a known concentration of ozone through the same solution. The method is accurate for concentrations of 6 to 600 ppm.

28—MICRODETERMINATION OF OZONE IN SMOG MIXTURES: NITROGEN DIOXIDE EQUIVALENT METHOD

Saltzman, Bernard E. and Nathan Gilbert. Am. Ind. Hyg. Assoc. J. **20**, 379-386 (1959).

The authors describe a new method for conveniently and specifically determining low concentrations of ozone in air, even in the presence of large amounts of other commonly occuring oxidizing or reducing gases. Ozone was stoichiometrically converted to, and determined as, nitrogen dioxide, by the addition of known amounts of gaseous nitric oxide to the sample air stream and allowing a short reaction flow time. Better than 95% conversion was obtained when 1 ppm excess nitric oxide and 40 seconds reaction time were used. In the short time allowed, oxidation of nitric oxide by air and organic oxidants was negligible. Results for pure ozone were in good agreement with those of an iodide reagent. For synthetic smog oxidant mixtures (generated by the ozone reaction with 1-hexene) the method appeared specific for ozone, whereas the iodide reagent also responded to organic oxidants. Thus the mixture could be differentiated into two oxidant components by simultaneous application of the two methods. Reducing gases such as sulfur dioxide and hydrogen sulfide did not appreciably interfere even in 100 to 1 ratio to ozone. The method appears to be readily adaptable to automatic recording of ozone in smog without interference from associated pollutants. Add. Ref. APCA Abstracts 5, No. 7, 2804 (1959).

29—A RAPID METHOD FOR DETERMINING OZONE IN AIR

Mokhov, L. A. and V. P. Dzedzichek. Industrial Laboratory (Engl. transl. of Soviet Journal, Zavodskaya Laboratoriya) 25, No. 11, 1362-1363 (1959). One end of a glass tube 60 mm long and 3 mm i.d. was drawn out, and a glass wool plug pushed in from the wide end of the tube. This was followed by a 3 mm length of ozone-indicating gel, a 2 mm glass wool layer, a 9 mm layer of absorbent gel to remove interfering nitrogen oxides, and, finally, a 2 mm glass wool plug. For the indicator gel, 1 g of silica gel (particle size, 1 mm diameter) was impregnated with 2 ml of 0.01% indigo carmine solution and 1 ml of 10% magnesium sulfate septahydrate (water is necessary for the reaction), and the silica gel then dried until it was free-flowing. For the absorbent to prevent contact of atmospheric nitrogen dioxide with the indicator, silica gel was impregnated with a solution of chromic anhydride and concentrated sulfuric acid. Three liters of air had to pass through the indicator tube to determine ozone concentrations down to 0.0001 mg per liter, while 1 liter was sufficient for 0.0007 mg ozone per liter. As soon as the gel changed color, the air flow was stopped and the pale blue to blue gel color was compared with standards produced from water colors on paper. The glass tubes are described in detail by L. A. Mokhov in Laboratornoe Delo, No. 1, 48 (1956), and the reference for the absorbent gel is Mokhov, L. A. and I. P. Shinkarenko, Sovetskaya Meditsina, No. 11, 67 (1955). The calibration of the standards is described by Alekseeva, M. V., B. E. Andronov, S. S. Gurvits, and A. S. Zhitkova in "The Determination of Noxious Substances in the Air of Industrial Establishments" (Goskhimizdat 109-113, 1954) (in Russian). Add. Ref.: CA 54, 9172 (1960).

30—RAPID METHOD OF DETERMINING OZONE IN THE ATMOSPHERE

Mokhov, L. A. and Dzedzichek, V. P. Zavodskaya Lab. 25, 1304-1305 (1959); CA 54, 9172 (1960). The authors present a method of analysis for ozone in the presence of nitrogen dioxide. Silica gel impregnated with indigo carmine solution and magnesium sulfate septahydrate is dried and used for determining the ozone content of the air. In presence of ozone and water, the blue indicator gel is decolorized. A known volume of air is passed through a tube containing the indicator gel, and the resulting color is compared with standards produced with water colors on paper and calibrated titrimetrically. To prevent contact of atmospheric nitrogen dioxide with the indicator, the air is first passed through an absorbent consisting of silica gel impregnated with a solution of cromium trioxide in concentrated sulfuric acid.

31—NEW METHODS FOR THE DETERMINATION OF VERY SMALL AMOUNTS OF OZONE

Peregud, E. A. and E. M. Stepanenko. J. Anal. Chem. U.S.S.R. 15, No. 1, 101-103 (1960) (in English). Sensitive methods for the determination of ozone include those based on extinction of the luminescence of luminol and fluorescein, and a change in the color of silica gel impregnated with fuchsin solution. Prepare indicator powder containing luminol by dissolving 0.025 g of luminol (3-aminopthtalhydrazide) in 25 ml of 0.1 N sodium hydroxide, diluting to 100 ml with distilled water, then diluting this stock solution 1 to 100 with water. Impregnate 1 g of silica gel with 2 ml of the dilute solution, mix well, and dry for 1 hour at 100°. For the fluorescein indicator powder, dissolve 0.04 g of the dye in 1 ml of 10% potassium hydroxide, dilute to 100 ml with distilled water, then dilute the stock solution 1 to 20. Impregnate 1 g of silica gel with 1.6 ml of the dilute solution, and dry the silica gel in an oven at 100° for 1 hour. To make the stock solution of fuchsin indicator powder, dissolve 0.01 g of fuchsin base in 20 ml of alcohol and dilute to 100 ml with water. For the working solution, mix 6 ml of the stock solution with 5 ml of water and 1 ml of 0.01 N hydrochloric acid. Impregnate 1 g of silica gel with 1.6 ml of the mixture and dry at 100° for 1 hour. Pack each indicator powder in glass tubes (45 mm long and 2.5 mm diameter) as tightly as possible. To determine ozone, remove the cap from an indicator tube, connect one end to an aspirator, and draw 1 liter of air at a uniform rate through the tube in the course of 40 minutes. Examine the tube under ultraviolet light, mark the boundaries of the extinguished zone, then measure the length in mm under ordinary light. Ozone will cause extinction of the bright blue fluorescence of luminol, with the formation of a dull, greenish color. Ozone also will decolorize the fluorescein indicators, with the decolorized part deprived of its characteristic greenish-yellow fluorescence in ultraviolet light. Ozone reacts with the fuchsin indicator to form a blue-violet color. With all three indicators, the length of the section which reacts is proportional to the ozone concentration. The luminol is the most sensitive of the three to ozone, and also the least sensitive to nitrogen oxides; 1 mm of is extinguished zone corresponds to 0.15 μ of ozone. Should the extinction of fluorescence or the change in color extend the length of the whole tube, repeat the determination with a smaller volume of test air.

32—DETERMINATION OF TRACE CONCENTRATIONS OF OZONE

Bovee, Harley H. Ind. Hyg. News Rept. 3, No. 7 (July, 1960). Place 10 ml of reagent (1% sodium diphenylamine sulfonate in 0.02% perchloric acid) in a midget impinger and sample at a rate of 0.1 cfm for 10 minutes, or until a satisfactory color develops. Replace any evaporation loss by diluting to 10 ml with distilled water. Measure the density at 593 mu in a colorimeter, and compare with a standard curve prepared from known concentrations of ozone. *A simple modification would make this method applicable to field use.* Add. Ref.: CA **54**, 1161 (1960). *We have not included in this section references to the cracking of rubber by ozone, observations commonly used in air pollution studies.*

See Section One
For references 90, 129.

Pentaerythritol Tetanitrate
PETN

See Section One
For reference 60.

Phenarsazine Chloride

See Section One
For reference 52.

Phenols

1—THE DETECTION OF PHENOLS BY THE GERNGROSS COLOR REACTION WITH TYROSINE.

Anger, V., S. Ofri, Z. anal. Chem. 203 (5), 350-4 (1964) CA **61**, 8879 (1966).
A colorimetric reaction using 1-nitroso-2-naphthol is described for the detection of p-substituted phenols. A red coloration indicates a positive reaction. Positive tests were found with the following: p-aresol, p-phenylphenol, phenolphthalein, resorcinol, phloroglucinol and 2-naphthol.

Phenylcarbylamine Chloride

1—TESTS AVAILABLE FOR THE IDENTIFICATION OF SMALL QUANTITIES OF THE WAR GASES

Cox, H. E. Analyst **64**, 807-813 (1939).
Small quantities of war gases can be determined with a solution of Sudan red and ferric chloride diluted with chalk. Add. Refs.: Ligtenberg. H. L. Chem. Weekblad **34**, 321 (1937); Analyst **62**, 572 (1937); CA **34**, 541 (1940).

P-Phenylenediamine

1—THE CHEMICAL EXAMINATION OF FURS IN RELATION TO DERMATITIS

Cox, H. E. Analyst **54**, 694-703 (1929).
A method for the determination of p-phenylenediamine is described. A violet color produced by the addition of 2 drops of ferric chloride to the neutral or slightly acid sample indicates the presence of the diamine. If hydrogen sulfide solution is added 1 ml at a time the violet color becomes much more pronounced. M-phenylenediamine and 1:2:4-m-toluylenediamine do not interfere; 1:3:4-m-toluylenediamine and p-aminophenol give similar colors. An alcoholic solution of p-dimethylaminobenzaldehyde added to an acidified solution of p-phenylenediamine turns red; all of the other compounds mentioned above give a yellow color.

2—THE CHEMICAL EXAMINATION OF FURS IN RELATION TO DERMATITIS

Cox, H. E. Analyst **58**, 738-748 (1933).
Add to 10 ml of the test solution (containing approximately 2 parts p-phenylenediamine per 100,000) indamine reagent (3 drops of 1% aniline hydrochloride and 3 drops of 1% ferric chloride). The maximum intense blue-green color with p-phenylenediamine develops, at pH 4.5, within a minute, and lasts for several minutes. The indamine reagent is convenient, but is not specific for this diamine. Alternatively, add to 10 ml of the test solution indophenol reagent (3 drops of 1% phenol solution and 3 drops of sodium hypochlorite solution), which produces an intense violet color with p-phenylenediamine. Add. Ref.: J. 562.

3—SPOT TESTS. VOL. II. ORGANIC APPLICATIONS

Feigl, Fritz, transl. by Ralph E. Oesper. (Elsevier Publ. Co., New York, 1954). p. 296.
P-phenylenediamine in slightly acid solution is converted to the indamine dye, phenylene blue, when mixed with an oxidant in the presence of aniline. Mix a drop of the acetic acid test solution with a drop of aniline water (1 drop aniline in 50 ml of water) and add several crystals of potassium persulfate. A blue color, light to dark in proportion to the amount of p-phenylenediamine present, appears immediately. The dilution limit is 1 part in 100,000 and the limit of identification is 0.5 μg.

Phosgene

1—A DELICATE COLOR TEST FOR MICHLER'S KETONE AND A LESS SENSITIVE TEST FOR PHOSGENE AND DIALKYLANILINES

Gilman, Henry, O. R. Sweeney, and L. L. Heck. J. Am. Chem. Soc. **52**, 1604-1607 (1930).

The delicate color test of Gilman, Schulze, and Heck for reactive organo-metallic compounds is applied as a test for Michler's ketone and for phosgene. To test, add a small quantity of the reactive organo-metallic compound to Michler's ketone in benzene; hydrolyze, then develop the color with glacial acetic acid solution of iodine. A 2.25 M solution of phenylmagnesium bromide gives a positive test with 1 ml of 0.00001 M Michler's ketone in a benzene solution. If phosgene would react quantitatively with dimethylaniline to give Michler's ketone, the test would be positive for as little as 0.000001 g of phosgene.

2—THE INFLUENCE OF ACID CHLORIDES AND OF PYRROLE ON THE COLOR TEST FOR REACTIVE ORGANOMETALLIC COMPOUNDS. THE CONSTITUTION OF PYRRYLMAGNESIUM HALIDES

Gilman, Henry and Lloyd L. Heck. J. Am. Chem. Soc. **52**, 4949-4954 (1930).

A very small volume of the organometallic mixture to be tested is added to Michler's ketone in benzene, hydrolyzed with water, and the color developed with a glacial acetic acid solution of iodine. (See previous article by same authores, above.)

3—DETERMINATION AND COLLECTION OF GASES

Kolobaev, N. Khim. Oborona **10**, No. 11, 12-13 (1934); Chem. Zentr. **1935**, I, 2631; CA **30**, 5463 (1936).

The article describes various types of apparatus for the detection of war gases. The prokofjew apparatus makes possible the detection of chlorine and phosgene in the presence of each other. The air is forced first over fluorescein paper, then through a chemical absorbent and activated carbon, and finally over paper previously treated with gaseous dimethylaminobenzaldehyde and diphenylamine for the detection of phosgene. The author recommends a Boguzkij gas collecting apparatus (an 8 liter cylinder with oval bottom). A larger portable combined apparatus for gas determinations in the field ("G-3") contains reagents for chlorine, carbon monoxide, hydrogen cyanide, phosgene, yperite, and arsine, and can be used for detecting the gases in soil and in water.

4—THE DETECTION OF TOXIC GASES AND VAPORS

Leroux, Lucien. Rev. hyg. et med. prevent. **57**, 81-112 (1935).

Paper impregnated with dimethylaminobenzaldehyde turns pale yellow with 1 ppm of phosgene by volume, citron yellow with 5 ppm, and brownish orange with 1000 ppm. The color appears in from 12 to 15 seconds. Prepare the dimethylaminobenzaldehyde paper by dissolving separately 1 g of p-dimethylaminobenzaldehyde and 1 g of diphenylamine, each in 5 ml of absolute ethyl alcohol, at room temperature. Filter the aldehyde solution into the diphenylamine solution, and protect the mixture from air and light. Impregnate filter paper strips with the solution in an atmosphere of carbon dioxide, and dry them in the same atmosphere. The papers remain sensitive for 3 months. Add. Ref.: CA **29**, 3627 (1935).

5—THE USE OF INDICATORS FOR THE DETECTION OF POISONOUS GASES AND VAPORS

Heering, D. Gasmaske **8**, 88-89 (1936).

Reagent paper impregnated with p-methylaminobenzaldehyde and diphenylamine turns brown in the presence of phosgene. Two mg per liter of phosgene colors filter paper strips, impregnated with nitrosodiethylaminophenol in xylene, blue-green in from 2 to 4 seconds. Add. Ref.: CA **30**, 7059 (1936).

6—SHORT SCHEME OF ANALYSIS FOR THE DETECTION OF POISON GASES

Studinger, J. (With Notes on Their Odour and Irritant Action by R. Mueller). Chem. and Ind. (London) **15**, 225-231 (1937). Translated by F. G. Crosse from the original article in Mitteilungen aus dem Gabiete der Lebensmitteluntersuchung und Hygiene **27**, 8-23 (1936) (see CA **31**, 6367 (1937)).

A test paper can be used for the detection of phosgene. The paper is prepared by moistening with a solution made by dissolving a mixture of dimethylaminobenzaldehyde (5 g) and diphenylamine (5 g) in 100 cc of 95% alcohol. In presence of phosgene a yellow to orange tint is obtained. (Chlorine gives a green color. Also fuming gases, such as chlorosulfonic acid and titanium tetrachloride, yield positive reactions.) Another method for detecting phosgene requires the following reagents: "1:3:6-nitrosodimethylaminophenol (0.05 to 0.1 g) dissolved in 50 cc of hot xylene, m-diethylaminophenol (0.25 g) dissolved in 50 cc of xylene. Before use 5 cc of the solution of the nitroso-compound are mixed with 1 to 2 cc of the diethylaminophenol solution and the mixture is soaked up by filter paper. This test paper is held in the air above the sample. Phosgene gives a green coloration which is specific for this gas. The chlorine interference can be eliminated by passing the sample through cotton wool soaked in potassium iodide. Phosgene is not affected by this treatment. Add. Ref.: CA **31**, 3588 (1937).

7—IDENTIFICATION OF WAR GASES

Liberalli, Marcelo Robertson. Rev. quim. farm. (Rio de Janeiro) **4**, 49-53 (1939).

Paper impregnated with a 95% alcoholic solution of p-dimethylaminobenzaldehyde and diphenylamine changes from white to yellow in the presence of phosgene, and is sensitive to 1 part in 100,000. The paper also reacts with an equal concentration of chlorine, but may be made specific by substituting aniline for the diphenylamine. Two percent solution of aniline is another reagent for identifying phosgene. Add. Ref.: CA **33**, 7921 (1939).

8—THE DETECTION OF TOXIC GASES AND VAPORS IN INDUSTRY

Vallender, R. B. Chem. and Ind. (London) **17**, 330-333 (1939).

As little as 1 ppm of phosgene will cause poisoning. This amount will produce a yellow stain on paper impregnated with diphenylamine-p-dimethylaminobenzaldehyde.

9—TESTS AVAILABLE FOR THE IDENTIFICATION OF SMALL QUANTITIES OF THE WAR GASES

Cox, H. E. Analyst **64**, 807-813 (1939).

Soak filter paper in 5 ml of 0.5% 1,3,6-nitrosodimethyl-aminophenol and 2 ml of 0.5% solution of m-diethylaminophenol, both in xylene. The paper turns green with traces of phosgene. Moisten the paper before use with alcohol if it has dried. The reaction is specific. Another test uses filter paper impregnated with copper sulfate, dried, and dusted with phenylhydrazine cinnamate. In the presence of a drop of water as little phosgene as 1 in 50,000 produces a violet color. Add. Ref.: CA **34**, 541 (1940). References cited in the above article: Kling, A. and E. Schmutz. Compt. rend. **168**, 773 (1919). Delepine, M., R. Bouris, and L. Ville. Bull. Soc. Chim **27**, 286 (1925). Kretov. J. prikt. khim. **2**, 483 (1929). Anger, V. and S. Wang. Mikrochim. Acta **8**, 24 (1938).

10—METHODS FOR THE DETECTION OF TOXIC GASES IN INDUSTRY. PHOSGENE

Anon. Dept. of Scientific and Industrial Research, London, England. Leaflet No. 8 (1939) 7 pp.

A test paper impregnated with diphenylamine and p-dimethylaminobenzaldehyde will detect low concentrations of phosgene, as little as 1 part in 1,000,000 (4 μg per liter) producing a yellow to orange stain on the exposed paper in a few minutes. The test can be made quantitative by drawing a known volume of the test atmosphere through a definite area of test paper with a hand pump of specified capacity. A color chart correlates the number of strokes of the pump required to produce a stain of a certain intensity with the concentration of the gas. Concentrations of as little as 4 μg per liter take not more than 85 strokes of the pump. The stains are transient, therefore sampling and comparison must be rapid. The test papers

also are sensitive to hydrogen chloride and chlorine, but traces of these gases may be removed by first drawing the air sample through a guard tube containing pumice granules impregnated with sodium thiosulfate and sodium iodide. Add. Ref.: CA **34**, 1935 (1940).

11—DETECTION METHODS OF WAR MATERIALS PROPOSED IN LITERATURE

Dultz, George. Wien. Pharm. Wochschr. **72**, 548-552 (1939); CA **34**, 542 (1940).

A review dealing with phosgene detection methods is presented.

12—TUBE FOR THE DETECTION OF POISONOUS SUBSTANCES

Chema, Ltd. and Jan Sigmund. Brit. (Pat. No.) 519,-957, April 10, 1940; CA **36**, 589 (1942).

A method for the determination of phosgene is presented. The detector consists of wool impregnated with dimethyl-aminobenzaldehyde.

13—RAPID METHOD FOR THE DETERMINATION OF GASES IN THE AIR

Patty, F. A. Am. J. Public Health **30**, 1191 (1940); J. 305.

A phosgene test paper impregnated with an alcoholic solution of p-dimethylaminobenzaldehyde and diphenyl-amine is more reliable and satisfactory than conventional methods with concentrations of 0.5 to 2 ppm of phosgene. When the paper is suspended in the atmosphere 0.5 ppm of phosgene produces a light lemon-yellow color in 4 to 5 minutes and a dark yellow in 10 to 15 minutes. Higher concentrations produce proportionately greater color changes up to a dark orange, which occurs in about 8 minutes with 2 ppm and in 15 minutes with 1 ppm. Chlorine and hydrochloric acid react similarly.

14—DETECTION OF WAR GASES. I. DYESTUFFS AS REAGENTS FOR DETECTING PHOSGENE

Pu, Tung-Lieh and Chien-Tao Lo. J. Chinese Chem. Soc. **8**, 140-142 (1941); CA **37**, 6053 (1943).

Several reagents applicable to phosgene are described by the authors. Methyl violet, methyl violet B, gentian violet B, and rosaniline were found to be specific for the detection of phosgene in air. Distinct color changes were obtained at gas concentrations of 0.7 mg per liter of air within one second.

15—VAPOR DETECTOR TUBES AND DETECTOR KIT FOR SOME CHEMICAL AGENTS USED IN GAS WARFARE

Fenton, Paul F. J. Chem. Education **20**, 564-565 (1943).

A drop of diphenylamine and a drop of dimethylamino-benzaldehyde added successively to pure silica gel contaminated with phosgene (in a type A tube) forms an orange color. This reaction may be adapted to a special detector tube containing silica gel and the 2 reagents, separated from one another by cotton plugs. After aspirating contaminated air through the tube, drain several drops of alcohol through the entire length of the tube to develop an orange color. Filter paper strips impregnated with dimethylaminobenzaldehyde turn pale green when exposed to phosgene, then bright orange upon the addition of diphenylamine. Add. Ref.: CA **38**, 898 (1944).

16—DETECTION OF WAR GASES

Fenton, Paul F. J. Chem. Education **21**, 488-489 (1944).

To a small portion of the contaminated silica gel add 1 drop of diphenylamine (10% solution in alcohol) and 1 drop of dimethylaminobenzaldehyde (10% solution in alcohol). A yellow color indicates phosgene. The reaction is not specific. Add. Ref.: CA **39**, 135 (1945).

17—IDENTIFICATION OF GAS WARFARE AGENTS

Zais, Arnold M. J. Chem. Education **21**, 489-490 (1944).

The author presents a systematic procedure for detecting various war gases. A paper impregnated with a solution containing equal parts of 1,2,4-nitrosodiethylaminophenol and m-diethylaminophenol turns green when phosgene is present. Add. Ref.: CA **39**, 135 (1945).

18—PHOTOCHEMICAL TRANSFORMATION OF CHLOROPICRIN TO PHOSGENE. I. NEW REAGENTS SENSITIVE AND SPECIFIC FOR THESE TWO SUBSTANCES

Moureu, Henri, Paul Chovin, and Louis Truffert. Arch. maladies profess. med. travail et securite sociale **11**, 445-452 (1950); CA **45**, 6495 (1951).

To test for phosgene impregnate filter paper with equal parts of an 8% solution of p-dimethylaminobenzaldehyde in 95% ethanol and an alcoholic solution of an aromatic amine. Dimethylaniline (25% in 95% ethanol) gives a blue color and is very sensitive. An even more sensitive paper contains a mixture of equal parts of a saturated solution of p-dimethylaminobenzaldehyde in 95% ethanol and a 25% solution of dimethylaniline in 95% ethanol, which can detect 10 mg of phosgene per cubic meter of air even in the presence of 10 to 12 times that concentration of chlorine or chloropicrin.

19—REAGENTS FOR THE DETECTION OF PHOSGENE GAS

Hayashi, Mosuke, Mitsuo Okazaki, and Zenichi Shinohara. J. Soc. Org. Synthet. Chem., Japan **12**, 273-280 (1954); CA **51**, 949 (1957).

The authors investigate a test paper which allows the determination of phosgene in the presence of chlorine or hydrogen chloride. Enough p-dimethylaminobenzaldehyde 0.001 mole in 5 ml alcohol + dimethylaniline 0.001 mole

in 5 ml alcohol or p-dimethylaminobenzaldehyde 0.001 mole in 5 ml alcohol + dimethyl-2-naphthylamine 0.001 mole in 5 ml alcohol is applied to filter paper to make a circle about 10 mm in diameter, and the test is made at once. These test papers turned green to blue in the presence of phosgene with high sensitivity. Filter paper soaked in p-dimethylaminobenzaldehyde 0.002 mole in 5 ml alcohol + dimethyl-2-naphthylamine 0.002 mole in 5 ml alcohol and dried in a dark chamber was as sensitive as the first tests.

20—SAMPLING AND ANALYZING AIR FOR CONTAMINANTS IN WORK PLACES

Silverman, Leslie. Encyclopedia of Instrumentation for Industrial Hygiene, edited by Yaffe, Charles D., Dohrman H. Byers, and Andrew D. Hosey. (Univ. of Michigan, Inst. of Industrial Health, Ann Arbor, Mich., 1956) pp. 7-25.

Whatmon No. 1 filter paper impregnated with diphenylamine and p-dimethylamine benzaldehyde turns from light yellow to orange with from 1 to 100 ppm of phosgene. Chlorine and hydrogen chloride interfere, but may be removed by first drawing the air sample through pumice soaked with sodium thiosulfate and sodium iodide.

21—A NEW SPECIFIC COLOR REACTION OF PHOSGENE

Lamouroux, Andre. Mem. poudres **38**, 383-386 (1956); CA **51**, 11174 (1957).

When an ethyl ether solution of 4-(4-nitrobenzyl)pyridine is added to an ethyl ether solution of phosgene, an addition product precipitates which gives a violet color with alkali. *This reaction might be applied to the detection of phosgene* by passing the contaminated air sample through dimethylformamide or diethyl phthlate containing 4-(4-nitrobenzyl)pyridine. If phosgene is present, the quantity could be determined by comparing the solution with known concentrations at 415 mu. The optical density curve is rectilinear up to 5 μg of phosgene per ml.

22—A DETECTOR-PAPER FOR PHOSGENE

Liddell, H. F. Analyst **82**, 375 (1957).

A mixture of diphenylamine and p-dimethylaminobenzaldehyde, widely used to detect phosgene, has the disadvantages that the color change from white to yellow is difficult to see, and the reagent is very sensitive to mineral avid vapors, which give it the same color as phosgene. A better reagent is a solution of 1.68 g of N-ethyl-N-2-hydroxyethylaniline, 0.75 g of p-dimethylaminobenzaldehyde, and 2.5 ml of diethyl phthalate in 25 ml of ethanol, acetone, or chloroform. Impregnate Whatman No. 1 filter paper with the reagent just before use and let dry (the reagent itself keeps well in the dark). Phosgene changes the white paper to bright blue; mineral acid vapors do not interfere. The reagent is sensitive to 0.5 μg phosgene (1 μg phosgene per liter of air). Add. Ref.: CA **51**, 11930 (1957).

23—SENSITIVE DETECTOR CRAYONS FOR PHOSGENE, HYDROGEN CYANIDE, CYANOGEN CHLORIDE, AND LEWISITE

Witten, Benjamin and Arnold Prostak. Anal. Chem. **29**, 885-887 (1957).

The detector crayon's ingredients are: 4-(p-nitrobenzyl)-pyridine 2%, N-phenylbenzylamine 5%, sodium carbonate 5% and blanc fixe, neutral, amorphous, dry 88%. Prepare a sufficient quantity of a benzene solution of the nitrobenzylpyridine and phenylbenzylamine so that the blanc fixe completely absorbs the solution and yet is completely wetted. Allow the benzene to evaporate overnight, then impregnate the mixture with aqueous sodium carbonate, again using enough water so that the solution is completely absorbed by the solid, and the entire mass is completely wetted. Dry the mass, powder, and press into crayons in a ⅝" diameter cylinder. The light yellow marks from this crayon turn red in the presence of phosgene; high concentrations of hydrogen chloride interfere. The crayons remain stable at room temperature for more than a year. The concentration-time equivalent of 0.03 mg minute per cubic meter is equivalent to detecting 8 parts per billion in 1 minute. Extremely high concentrations of phosgene tend to fade the red color of the crayon mark. Another phosgene detector, reported by Witten et al., uses a mixture of 2-amino-Michler's ketone and N-phenyl-1-naphthylamine. Add. Refs.: IHD **21**, 904 (1957); CA **51**, 11915 (1957).

24—A FIELD METHOD FOR THE DETERMINATION OF PHOSGENE

Dixon, B. E. and G. C. Hands. Analyst **84**, 463-464 (1959).

Soak Whatman No. 1 filter paper strips in a solution of 2% w/v 4-p-nitrobenzylpyridine and 4 % w/v N-benzyl-aniline in benzene, drain, and dry. Use a sampling head which exposes a 1 cm diameter circle of the paper at a flow rate of 3 ml per second, with a rubber bulb as the pump. Compare the color formed by the phosgene with similarly prepared standards or with Lovibond colored glass standards. Remove chlorine from the air sample with a dry filter paper previously impregnated with aqueous 4% sodium iodide and 10% sodium thiosulfate, on the inlet side of the test paper. Acetyl chloride in the air will reduce markedly or even suppress stain color. Benzyl chloride, trichloroethylene, and chloroform up to 300 ppm do not interfere; benzoyl chloride gives a transient orange stain. The sensitivity of the method is 0.25 ppm, and the method is accurate for up to 10 ppm of phosgene. Add. Ref.: CA **54**, 163 (1960).

25—QUALITATIVE DETECTION OF PHOSGENE (IN AIR)

Forostynan, Yu. N. and G. V. Lazur'evskii. U.S.S.R. (Pat. No.) 122,634 (18.9.59); A. A. **7**, 5040 (1960).

The analysis depends upon utilization of a filter paper soaked in anabasine or in a mixture with related alkaloids which produce a purple to intense red color on contact with an atmosphere containing phosgene. The limit of detection is 0.003 mg per liter. Other halogen compounds do not interfere.

26—INFORMATION ON THE DRAEGER GAS DETECTOR. 0.25/b PHOSGENE DETECTOR TUBE

Draegerwerk Heinr. und Bernhard Draeger, Luebeck, Germany (distributed by New Jersey Safety Equipment Co., 299 Park Ave., East Orange, N. J.). Information Sheet No. 38 (May 1960).

The 0.25/b Phosgene Detector Tube, for use with the Draeger Multigas-Detector, includes a white precleansing layer for eliminating interfering gases, and a yellow indicating layer with scale calibrated in ppm. The indicator (aromatic amino aldehydes) turns blue-green with phosgene in the range of 0.25 to 15 ppm. The range is valid for 5 strokes of the bellows pump, equivalent to 0.5 liter of air sample. The indicator is specific for phosgene; ammonia, chlorine, nitrous gases, and hydrochloric acid do not interfere except minimally at high concentrations. Chlorine and nitrous gases alone turn the indicator orange; in combination with phosgene a high excess of nitrous gases may pale sightly the green color caused by the phosgene. The tubes may be stored for at least 2 years.

27—JEFFERSON PHOSGENE DETECTOR TUBE #300

Jefferson Equipment Co., Jefferson Ave., Orange, N. J. (1963).

The color code green-white-white identifies Brothers Phosgene Detector Tube #300. To use, insert the tube into the calibrated, hand operated volumetric pump of the Brothers Model 60 Gas Detector and note the volume of air drawn to produce the first color change. A change from yellow to green indicates phosgene. The kit includes a chart correlating ppm indicated by first color change with volume of air sample drawn, e.g.:

Air Sample Drawn	Indicates at 1st Color Change
100 ml air	1 ppm
50 ml air	5 ppm
25 ml air	50 ppm

28—PHOSGENE IN AIR—DEVELOPMENT OF IMPROVED DETECTION PROCEDURES.

Linch, A. L., S. S. Lord, Jr. PhD., K. A. Kubetz, PhD., M. R. De Brunner, PhD. AIHAJ, 26(5) 465-474 (1965).

The authors describe several methods for the rapid detection and determination of phosgene. One method involves using Whatman No. 1 filter paper saturated with 5% aqueous sodium carbonate, a 4% solution of N benzyl-aniline and 2% 4-(4'-nitrobenzyl) pyridine in benzene. The prepared paper has a shelf life of five months. The optimum air flow rate is 190 ml/minute for each cm² of exposed paper area for a duration of 5 min. The color produced is proportional to the phosgene concentration in the range of 0.002 to 2 ppm.

See Section One

References 25, 29, 35, 36, 37, 39, 41, 48, 52, 53, 54, 64, 86, 90, 109, 119, 120, 125.

Phosphates

1—DETECTION OF ORTHOPHOSPHATES BY MEANS OF DROP REACTIONS

West, Philip W. and Thomas Houtman. Ind. Eng. Chem., Anal. Ed **14,** 597-599 (1942); CA **36,** 4776 (1942).

The authors describe the preparation of solutions of (1) strychnine molybdate and (2) benzidine. To .1 drop of a neutral or weakly acid solution containing 1% phosphate add, on a spot plate (black preferred) 1 drop of the strychnine molybdate reagent. If a precipitate appears against the black background add 1 drop of the benzidine reagent and sufficient saturated solution of sodium acetate to neutralize the excess acid. A blue-green color, seen against the white background of a white spot plate, is positive for phosphate.

2—DETECTION OF TRACE AMOUNTS OF PHOSPHATES BY IMPREGNATION TECHNIQUE

Antoszewski, Roman and Stanislaw Knypl. Chem. Anal. (Warsaw) **5,** 11-15 (1960) (English summary); CA **54,** 15074 (1960).

The authors describe a procedure for the detection of phosphate. A strip of Whatman No. 1 paper is saturated with 1.5% ammonium molybdate and dried in a stream of hot air. The paper is then immersed in 4% quinoline (in 6 N hydrochloric acid), and washed with water. A drop of the sample, acidified with 1.25% sulfuric acid, is placed on the strip, dried at 98 to 100° for 1 minute, and developed in a mixture containing methyl alcohol 0.7, anhydrous sodium sulfite 25.0, hydroquinone 2.7, and anhydrous sodium carbonate 12.5 g per liter. Good results were also obtained by immersing the paper in benzidine solution (prepared by dissolving 50 g of benzidine in 10 ml of glacial acetic acid and diluting with water to 100 ml) for 2 minutes and then in saturated aqueous sodium acetate. Nitric acid, potassium chloride, sodium chloride, calcium chloride, ammonium sulfate, ferrous sulfate, magnesium sulfate, and ammonium nitrate in amounts 100 times those of phosphorus did not affect results. The highest phosphorus-silicon dioxide ratio at which trivalent phosphate ion can be detected is 1:20.

Phosphine

1—SENSITIVE TEST FOR THE HYDRIDES OF ARSENIC, ANTIMONY AND PHOSPHORUS BY MEANS OF GOLD CHLORIDE.

Zimmerman, W. Apoth. Ztg. **36,** 26 (1921); J. Chem. Soc. **120,** II, 276 (1921); CA **15,** 2691 (1921).

Filter paper containing 1 drop of sodium chloroaurate takes on a violet coloration in the presence of small quantities of the hydrides of arsenic, antimony, or phosphorus. Organic matter must be destroyed prior to analysis and hydrogen sulfide interferes by producing a brown stain.

2—THE DETECTION OF TOXIC GASES AND VAPORS

Leroux, Lucien. Rev. hyg. et med. prevent. **57,** 81-112 (1935).

Impregnate Schleicher and Schuell No. 597 filter paper with 5% aqueous mercuric cadmium iodide solution and dry for 30 minutes at 80° C. Cut into strips and store protected from air and dampness in a bottle containing calcium chloride. Before use moisten the paper with 1 drop of acetic anhydride. A yellow-orange color develops in 10 minutes with from 0.01 to 0.1 mg phosphine per liter. Hydrogen sulfide interferes by producing a similar yellow color; arsine interferes by turning the reagent brown. Add. Ref.: CA **29,** 3627 (1935).

3—SIMPLE METHODS FOR THE DETECTION AND DETERMINATION OF POISONOUS GASES, VAPORS, SMOKES, AND DUSTS IN FACTORY AIR

Weber, Hans H. Zentr. Gewerbehyg. Unfallverhuet. **23,** 177-180 (1936).

Impregnate S and S No. 597 filter paper with 5% aqueous mercuric cadmium iodide solution and dry for 30 minutes at 80° C in a drying oven. Store in a rubber-stoppered glass container which contains a layer of calcium chloride covered with a layer of cotton. (Damp reagent paper will react with hydrogen sulfide.) Before use moisten the paper with a drop of acetic anhydride. The paper turns orange-yellow with 0.1 mg per liter of phosphine, and yellow with only 0.01 mg per liter. Arsine interferes. Add. Ref.: CA **32,** 1609 (1938).

4—THE USE OF INDICATORS FOR THE DETECTION OF POISONOUS GASES AND VAPORS

Heering, D. Gasmaske **8,** 88-89 (1936).

Mercuric cadmium iodide paper turns yellow-orange at 0.1 mg per liter in 600 seconds, and a very distinct yellow at 0.01 mg per liter in 600 seconds. Silver nitrate paper turns brown to black with phosphine; hydrogen sulfide must be removed before testing for the phosphine. Add. Ref.: CA **30**, 7059 (1936).

5—MODERN METHODS OF DETECTION AND DETERMINATION OF INDUSTRIAL GASES IN THE ATMOSPHERE

Leclerc, E. and R. Haux. Rev. universelle mines **12**, 293-298 (1936).

Paper impregnated with mercuric cadmium iodide turns yellow-orange in 10 minutes with from 0.01 to 0.1 mg phosphine per liter. Add. Ref.: CA **30**, 6672 (1936).

6—ANALYTICAL CHEMISTRY OF INDUSTRIAL POISONS, HAZARDS, AND SOLVENTS

Jacobs, Morris B. Interscience Publishers, Inc., New York (1941) p. 278.

Phosphine may be detected by the brown to black color it gives to filter paper treated (wet) with silver nitrate solution.

7—DETECTION OF PHOSPHINE AND HYDROGEN SULFIDE IN ACETYLENE

Kitagawa, Tetsuzo and Tadahiko Ogawa. J. Electrochem. Soc. Japan **19**, 258-261 (1951); CA **46**, 1920 (1952).

Silica gel containing small quantities of a mercury complex in a copper salt can be used for the determination of phosphine. As little as 0.002 to 0.08% of phosphine can be detected quantitatively in 5 minutes.

8—SIMPLE DETERMINATION OF PHOSPHINE IN AIR IN THE MANUFACTURE OF ZINC PHOSPHIDE BAIT

Filz, Wilhelm. Mitt. chem. Forsch.-Insts. Wirtsch. Oesterr. **8**, 61-62 (1954); CA **48**, 14095 (1954).

A rapid determination of phosphine in air is described. The sample is aspirated through a solution of silver nitrate and the presence of phosphine is determined by the discoloration produced in the silver nitrate solution.

9—SAMPLING AND ANLYZING AIR FOR CONTAMINANTS IN WORK PLACES

Silverman, Leslie. Encyclopedia of Instrumentation for Industrial Hygiene, edited by Yaffe, Charles D., Dohrman H. Byers, and Andrew D. Hosey. (Univ. of Michigan, Inst. of Industrial Health, Ann Arbor, Mich., 1956) pp. 7-25.

Whatman No. 1 filter paper impregnated with 1% silver nitrate turns from brown to black with from 1 to 100 ppm of phosphine. Arsine and stibine interfere.

10—NEW COLOR REACTION FOR THE DETERMINATION OF PHOSPHINE

Vasak, V. Chem. Listy **50**, 1116-1119 (1956); AA **4**, 1508 (1957).

The pyridine solution of silver diethyldithiocarbamate, commonly used for the detection and determination of arsine and detection of stibine will also produce a color reaction with phosphine. This reaction can be used for the detection of phosphine. The silver salt of 2-mercaptobenziminazole has been proposed for the same purpose, and a procedure suitable for the use of this reagent for the detection of phosphine, white phosphorus and its lower oxidation products has been developed.

11—DETERMINATION OF PHOSPHINE IN ACETYLENE

Strizhevskii, I. I. and V. P. Zaitseva. Zavodskaya Lab. **22**, 546-547 (1956); CA **50**, 12749 (1956).

The determination of phosphine with mercuric sulfate produces results which are in agreement with those of photometric methods. The acetylene-phosphine sample is aspirated into a test tube containing 10 ml reagent solution (prepared from 15 g potassium chloride in 200 ml water and 10.9264 g mercuric sulfate) until phosphine begins to escape from the exit tube (test with silver nitrate yielding a silver precipitate). The content of phosphine is given by % Phosphine = 0.254/V, where V is the gas sample volume in liters under standard conditions.

12—RAPID DETERMINATION OF PHOSPHINE IN AIR

Nelson, J. P. and A. J. Milun. Anal. Chem. **29**, 1665-1666 (1957).

Impregnate silica gel tubes with silver nitrate: to a solution containing 1.5 g silver nitrate in 100 ml of distilled water, add 76 g of 16 to 28 mesh silica gel and stir the mixture for 15 minutes. Decant the excess silver nitrate solution, dry the silica gel at 90° C for 3 hours, and sieve to a 30 to 50 mesh size. Heat the end of a 7 inch long glass tube (5 mm outside diameter) until the opening is approximately 2 to 3 mm wide. Close the constricted end with a small wad of glass wool, pour in a 5 inch column of the treated silica gel, then push another small wad of glass wool down on top of the column. Store the tubes in a brown glass bottle. To determine the phosphine content of air, draw a known volume of the air through one of the tubes; measure the length of the black color formed in the tube and compare with a calibration curve obtained with known mixtures. The method is sensitive to parts per billion of phosphine (with a reproducibility of ± 5%). Arsine, stibine, and hydrogen sulfide interfere. Add. Ref.: CA **52**, 4397 (1958); AA **5**, 1380 (1959); Anal. Chem. Anal. Reviews **32**, 54R-63R (1960).

13—THE DETERMINATION OF PHOSPHINE IN AIR

Borrowdale, J. and C. E. A. Shanahan. Ann. Occup. Hyg. **4**, 36-48 (1961).

The authors, using lead acetate, silver nitrate, mercuric chloride, and ammonium cuprous chloride test papers, on acetylene cylinder gas, hydrogen sulfide from a Kipp's generator, and an unknown air in the vicinity of a lathe, proved that the malodorous reducing gas evolved in the machining of graphite iron is phosphine, and not hydrogen sulfide. They present a method for the determination of small amounts of phosphine in air.

14—THE ESTIMATION OF PHOSPHINE IN AIR

Hughes, J. G. and A. T. Jones. Am. Ind. Hyg. Assoc. J. **24**, 164-167 (1963).

Detect as little as 0.05 ppm of phosphine in air visually with silver nitrate impregnated papers, prepared by passing 2″ wide strips of thick chromatographic paper through 0.1 N silver nitrate solution, and hanging to dry in the dark. Cut the dried strips into 3″ lengths and store in an amber bottle covered with black photographic paper. The papers last 2 to 3 weeks before darkening too much to detect low concentrations of phosphine. Make a set of permanent standards by reproducing with water color paints or water based inks the stains made on the impregnated papers with known amounts of phosphine. Add. Ref.: A.P.C.A. Abstr. **9**, No. 2, 5310 (July, 1963).

See Section One
For references 3, 72, 92, 120.

Phosphoric Acid Ester

1—DETERMINATION OF DIETHYL THIONOPHOSPHOR-IC ACID ESTER OF 2-HYDROXYETHYLTHIOETHYL ETHER

Draegerwerk, Heinrich und Bernhard Draeger. Ger. (Pat. No.) 1,006,629, April 18, 1957 (Cl. 42 **1**); CA **54**, 176 (1960).

The samples are treated with a solvent, which is then passed over silica gel impregnated with a chloride of a noble metal, mercury, or copper. The addition of a chromatographic developer such as p-aminobenzoic acid is required to make the reaction products visible.

Phosphorus

1—QUALITATIVE ANALYSES OF ORGANIC PHOSPHORUS COLOR REACTIONS AND SIMPLE DETECTION

Sera, Kansuke, Akira Matsunaga, Akira Murakami, Isao Sato, Kaoru Yamashita, and Haruo Yoshimori.

Kumamoto Med. J. **12**, 193-213 (1959) (in English); CA **54**, 11813 (1960).

The authors investigated 13 colorimetric reactions for the detection of 18 organic phosphorus compounds. The results are tabulated; ethylparathion (EP) could not be distinguished from EPN nor could PM (mixture of parathion and malathion). These tests were also applied to 41 other chemicals which should be distinguished from organic phosphorus compounds in toxicology. Of the 13 tests, 5 were suitable for the simple detection of organic phosphorus compounds: ammonium molybdate for phosphorus; dibromo-N-chloroquinone imine for phosphorus: sulfur; sodium hydroxide and hydrogen peroxide for p-nitrophenol; hydroxylamine for esters; silver nitrate for chlorides.

See Section One
For reference 6.

Phthalocyanines

1—PHTHALOCYANINES IN INORGANIC SPOT TESTS

Ackerman, G., Mikrochim. Ichnoanal. ACTA 1964 (2-4) 222-7 CA **61** 3662 (1964).

A method is presented utilizing phthalocyanine as a reagent for the spot testing analysis of copper, cobalt, nickel, zinc, and cadmium in neutral or slightly alkaline solutions. In the presence of these ions strongly colored phthalocyanines are produced. Limits of sensitivity are: Cadmium 0.007 μg, nickel, copper, and zinc 0.02 μg and cobalt 0.35 μg.

Picric Acid

1—ANALYTICAL CHEMISTRY OF INDUSTRIAL POISONS, HAZARDS AND SOLVENTS

Jacobs, Morris B. Interscience Publishers, Inc., New York (1941) p. 571.

An aqueous solution of picric acid *(sample taken by impingement)* is colored an intense red by potassium cyanide or by ammonium sulfide solution, but the color must be developed by allowing the mixture to stand or by heating. These reactions also are given by trinitrocresol but much more readily. *Aromatic nitro compounds may be detected by various methods, with the reactions carried out in impingers containing a reagent in solution. Example: the alkaline reactions of palladium chloride with aromatic nitro compounds. See "Nitro compounds, Aromatic," p. 214.*

Propane

1—DETERMINATION OF SOLVENT VAPORS IN AIR. V. PROPANE

Kobayashi, Yoshitaka. J. Soc. Org. Synthet. Chem., Japan **12**, 360-363 (1954); CA **51**, 952 (1957).

Silica gel impregnated with a mixture of sulfuric acid and chromic acid was used for the determination of solvent vapors. The effective range is 0.1 to 10.0 per cent.

Propyl Alcohol

1—METHODS FOR THE ANALYSIS OF TECHNICAL SOLVENTS. III. COLOR TESTS FOR PROPYL, BUTYL, ISOBUTYL AND ISOAMYL ALCOHOLS

Weber, Hans H. and Werner Koch. Chem.-Ztg. **57**, 73-74 (1933); CA **27**, 1296 (1933).

The alcohol sample is heated with a solution of Beckmann's chromic acid mixture thereby producing the aldehyde corresponding to the alcohol in question. The sample is centrifuged and upon treatment with sodium hydroxide and o-nitrobenzaldehyde a series of colors is observed. The colors produced are utilized for the identification of the alcohol of interest.

Pyridine

1—DETECTION AND DETERMINATION OF SMALL QUANTITIES OF PYRIDINE

Kulikov, I. V. and T. N. Krestovosdvigenskaya. Z. anal. Chem. **79**, 452-460 (1930); CA **24**, 2083 (1930).

This analytical method is based on the fact that cyanogen bromide combines readily with pyridine and the resulting compound reacts in the cold with aromatic amines to produce intensively colored dyes of a yellow to violet tint, which will serve for the detection and colorimetric determination of small quantities of pyridine. Directions are given for conducting the analysis with aniline as the aromatic amine.

2—ESTIMATION OF PYRIDINE IN AIR

Karlson, L. E. Zhur. Prikladnoi Khimii **4**, 124-136 (1931); CA **25**, 5877 (1931).

Various proposed methods are considered.

3—ACTION OF ULTRA-VIOLET RAYS UPON PYRIDINE. I. A NEW TEST FOR SEVERAL PRIMARY AROMATIC AMINES AND PYRIDINE

Freytag, Hans and Walter Neudert. J. prakt. Chem. **135**, 15-35 (1932); CA **27**, 724 (1933).

Filter paper containing pyridine exhibits a yellow color when exposed to ultra violet light. These papers also exhibit various colors with aromatic amine salts. With this method pyridine can be detected in a dilution of 1:26,840.

4—TOXICOLOGY OF PYRIDINE. I. DETERMINATION IN THE ATMOSPHERE AND IN BIOLOGICAL MEDIA

Fabre, R., R. Truhaut, and M. Herbert. Ann. pharm. franc. **8**, 773-788 (1950); CA **45**, 6969 (1951).

Cyanogen bromide converts pyridine into a pyridium compound which yields colored compounds with aromatic amines. The reagent is prepared in the following manner: Mix a 1 ml solution containing pyridine with 10 ml of 10% sodium acetate buffer solution, add 2 ml cyanogen bromide reagent (dissolve 4 g potassium cyanide in 40 ml water and 5 ml acetic acid; mix with a solution of 3 g potassium bromate and 4 g potassium bromide in 40 ml water, add while cooling 4 ml sulfuric acid dropwise and water to make 100 ml), 5 ml acetone and mix; add 2 ml of a solution containing 0.05 g benzidine in 100 ml ethyl alcohol and 2 ml acetic acid. The red color that develops reaches its maximum after 6 minutes and is stable for 5 minutes. To determine pyridine in air draw a volume of air through 4.4% acetic acid solution which on subsequent neutralization yields approximately 10 g sodium acetate trihydrate.

5—ESTIMATION OF TOXIC GASES IN AIR

Fukuyama, Tomitaro, Tokuro Sato, Aiko Watanabe, and Mieko Yamada. Bull. Int. Pub. (Tokyo) **3**, No. 1, 9 (1953) (English summary) CA **49**, 14236 (1955).

A review of useful and practical methods for the detection and determination of some toxic gases and vapors; pyridine is included.

Radiation Chemical Detectors

1—DETECTION OR DETERMINATION OF RADIOACTIVE GASES IN THE AIR

Auergesellschaft Akt.-Ges. (by Hermann Heidrich).

Ger. (Pat. No.) 1,037,030, Aug. 21, 1958 (Cl. 21. **g**); C. Z. **1959**, 9696; CA **54**, 16215 (1960).

The reagent consists of a phosphor, which is sensitive to alpha rays, mixed with silica gel. The phosphor can be zinc sulfide or zinc-cadmium sulfide.

2—PAINT THAT DETECTS RADIATION

Anon. New Scientist (London) **16**, No. 314, 441 (1962).

A yellow paint, sensitive to radiation, turns red if exposed to gamma rays or high energy electrons. The essential ingredient, a yellow azo dye sensitive to acid, is mixed with a plastic substance such as polyvinylchloride. Radiation releases hydrochloric acid from the plastic and the acid turns the paint red. For practical use the paint is covered with a thin film of lacquer to absorb ultraviolet rays, and to protect the paint from acids in the air and from prolonged exposure to temperatures up to 80° C. The paint is suitable for radiation doses of 100,000 rads up to 10 million rads. Incorporating acid absorbers can change the sensitivity of the paint for detection of very high radiation doses. Add. Ref.: Tech. Survey **19**, No. 1, 13 (1963).

REDUCING SUBSTANCES

1—DETECTING ABSORBABLE OXIDIZING GASES OR VAPORS IN AIR OR OTHER NEUTRAL GASES

Bangert, Friedrich K. G. (to Otto H. Draeger). U. S. (Pat. No.) 2,103,136, Dec. 21, 1938; CA **32**, 1214 (1938).

Absorb the gas on prepared silica gel, and note the color change when the silica gel is treated with an oxidizing agent, such as potassium permanganate.

2—FORMAZAN TEST FOR REDUCING COMPOUNDS

Weiner, S. Chemist-Analyst **37**, 56-59 (1948); CA **43**, 59 (1949).

When 2,3,5-triphenyl tetrazolium chloride is reduced, triphenylformazan is formed. This compound is insoluble in water, dilute acid, and dilute base but is soluble in ethyl alcohol. One ml of water (or isopropyl alcohol if the compound is insoluble in water) $+$ 4 drops of N NaOH and 4 drops of a 0.1% solution of the sodium salt of triphenyl tetrazolium chloride are added to a few drops of the sample. Shake, allow to stand for several minutes, and look for a reddish precipitate or solution if alcohol is present. *This procedure might be applied to a field detector.*

3—REAGENT-PAPER FOR INDICATING REDUCING SUBSTANCES

Eisenbrand, Josef and Franz Wegel (to I. G. Far-

benind. A.-G.) German (Pat. No.) 727,183, Sept. 24 1942 (Cl. 55f. 16); CA **37**, 6214 (1943).

The detection of ascorbic acid involves saturating a filter paper with a solution of phosphotungstic acid adjusted to a pH of 5 to 7. The paper is then rapidly dried. The method might be modified for use as a field detection method.

4—DETECTION OF REDUCING SUBSTANCES

Feigl, Fritz and Giscalo F. Dacorso. Ministerio agr., Dept. nacl. producao mineral., Lab. producao mineral. (Brazil), Bol. No. 5, 89-98 (1942); CA **38**, 2581 (1944).

Spot tests, depending on the formation of molybdenum blue, can serve to distinguish hydrazine from hydroxylamine, to detect zinc in zinc oxide, and to detect solid sulfides. Usually 12 μg or less of reducing agent can be detected.

Selenium

1—APPLICATION OF SPOT REACTIONS. IV. DETECTION OF ELEMENTARY SULFUR AND SELENIUM

Feigl, Fritz and Nicolau Braile. Chemist-Analyst **33**, 28-31 (1944); CA **38**, 3568 (1944).

Soak filter paper in 0.5% thallium carbonate or thallium acetate solution, drain and dry in warm air. Just before using, hold the paper over a warm solution of ammonium sulfide until the paper is covered with a black precipitate of thallium sulfide. Treat the test sample with pyridine to dissolve any free sulfur, then place a drop of the sample solution on the filter paper. Swish the paper in dilute nitric acid to dissolve the black thallium sulfide. If sulfur is present in the pyridine solution, a brownish red spot will remain. Selenium behaves similarly but the final spot is dark brown or black. The tests are very sensitive.

2—SIMPLE AND RAPID DETERMINATION OF DUST AND VAPORS OF SELENIUM AND SELENIUM DIOXIDE IN AIR

Berton, A. Chim. anal. **35**, 91 (1953); CA **47**, 5842 (1953).

A known volume of air is passed through a filter paper previously wetted with a strong cyanide solution. This procedure will dissolve selenium and selenium dioxide. The selenium is reduced with sulfur dioxide and the concentration is estimated by comparing the red stain of the selenium sample with stains produced by known quantities of selenium. The sensitivity is 5 to 500 μg with a reproducibility of $\pm$ 25%. Add. Ref.: IHD **18**, 324 (1954).

Smoke

1—ATMOSPHERIC POLLUTION IN DUBLIN DURING THE YEAR 1938

Leonard, A. G. G. and Bridget P. McVerry. Sci. Proc. Roy. Dublin Soc. **22,** 83-93 (1939); CA **34,** 5581 (1940).

Air was drawn through a rotating filter paper and the dark spot deposited was compared with a set of standard shades. *A grey scale was used.*

2—MEASURING SMOKES AND RATING EFFICIENCIES OF INDUSTRIAL AIR FILTERS

Robertson, A. C., J. G. Mulder, and F. G. Van Suan. Ind. Eng. Chem., Anal. Ed. **13,** 331-334 (1941).

The authors describe a portable impinging device which uses filter paper as the sampling medium and which quantitates the darkened area by a transmitting densitometer.

3—A METHOD FOR THE MEASUREMENT OF SMOKE CONCENTRATION IN THE ATMOSPHERE

Zancani, Cinzio. Termotecnica **8,** 30-37 (1954); CA **49,** 1249 (1955).

The air is filtered through a paper, Schleicher and Schuell (S.S. 589-1 black stripe), and the sediment is determined by the amount of light impinging on a photoelectric cell.

4—CRITICAL EVALUATION OF A FILTER-STRIP SMOKE SAMPLER USED IN DOMESTIC PREMISES

Shephard, Roy J., Geoffrey C. R. Carey, and John J. Phair. A.M.A. Arch. Ind. Health **17,** 236-252 (1958).

The efficiency of the A. I. S. I. smoke sampler, when used with Whatman No. 4 filter paper, is 80% to 90%. The efficiency is not affected by changes of median particle size (0.2 μ to 0.5μ), but does vary with changes in the thickness and texture of the filter paper. This effect is reduced by concomitant variations in sampling efficiency, but there is a residual error of at least $\pm$ 2.5%. Optical tests suggest that the density of smoke deposits is attributable to absorption rather than to scattering of light, and is greatly influenced by the color of the deposit. Add. Ref.: CA **52,** 9496 (1958).

Stibine

1—SENSITIVE TEST FOR THE HYDRIDES OF ARSENIC, ANTIMONY AND PHOSPHORUS BY MEANS OF GOLD CHLORIDE

Zimmermann, W. Apoth. Ztg. **36,** 26 (1921); J. Chem. Soc. **120,** II, 276 (1921); CA **15,** 2691 (1921).

Filter paper containing 1 drop of sodium chloroaurate takes on a violet coloration in the presence of small quantities of the hydrides of arsenic, antimony, or phosphorus. Organic matter must be destroyed prior to analysis and hydrogen sulfide interferes by producing a brown stain.

2—THE USE OF INDICATORS FOR THE DETECTION OF POISONOUS GASES AND VAPORS

Heering, D. Gasmaske **8,** 88-89 (1936).

Paper impregnated with silver nitrate turns dark brownish red to black around the edges in the presence of stibine. Stibine also turns mercuric bromide-impregnated paper yellow. Add. Ref.: CA **30,** 7059 (1936).

3—COLORIMETRIC DETERMINATION OF ARSENIC

Vasak, Vladimir and Vaclav Sedivec. Chem. Listy **46,** 341-344 (1952).

Arsine develops a red-violet color, suitable for colorimetric estimation, with a pyridine solution of silver diethyldithiocarbamate. Stibine produces a different color; phosphine does not interfere. Hydrogen sulfide must be removed first with lead acetate paper. The author suggests the reagent for air analysis. Add. Ref.: CA **47,** 67 (1953). The reagent *is difficult to prepare in extremely pure form and is unstable.*

4—SAMPLING AND ANALYZING AIR FOR CONTAMINANTS IN WORK PLACES

Silverman, Lesie. Encyclopedia of Instrumentation for Industrial Hygiene, edited by Yaffe, Charles D., Dohrman H. Byers, and Andrew D. Hosey. (Univ. of Michigan, Inst. of Industrial Health, Ann Arbor, Mich., 1956) pp. 7-25.

Whatman No. 1 filter paper impregnated with 1% silver nitrate solution turns from brown to black with 1 to 100 ppm of stibine. Arsine and phosphine interfere.

See Section One
For references 76, 119, 125.

Styrene

1—COLORIMETRIC DETERMINATION OF SMALL AMOUNTS OF STYRENE IN AIR

Poletaev, M. I. Gigiena i Sanit. **1952**, No. 3, 46-47; CA **46**, 7000 (1952).

The nitration method is unsatisfactory unless the following procedure is used. The air sample is passed into a nitration mixture consisting of 10 g ammonium nitrate in 100 ml sulfuric acid. The sample is collected in small 1 to 2 ml absorbers and complete retention is obtained even at one liter per minute. In order to stabilize the yellow color, the solution is diluted with 3 ml water and made alkaline with concentrated ammonium hydroxide. The sample color is compared with a standard empirical scale made from styrene in carbon tetrachloride. Ethylbenzene does not interfere, neither does diphenyl and diphenyl oxide.

Sulfate

1—MODIFICATION OF A SPOT TEST FOR SULFATE ION

Fukutomi, Takeo and Michiko Nakahara. Anal. Chem. **31**, 1118 (1959); CA **53**, 15869 (1959).

When thymolphthalein is used instead of phenolphthalein in the spot test for sulfate, the limit of identification is 4 μg of sodium sulfate, and the dilution limit is 1: 10,000. The pink color produced by the indicator suggests that this modification might be applied to a field detector.

Sulfur

1—INVESTIGATION OF ATMOSPHERIC POLLUTION. REPORT ON OBSERVATIONS IN THE YEAR ENDED MARCH 31, 1932.

Simpson, G. C. et al. Dept. Sci. Ind. Research, (London, England) 18th Rept. Investigation Atmospheric Pollution, 102 pp. (1933); CA **27**, 3274 (1933).

Cotton impregnated with lead peroxide was used to detect sulfur compounds in air.

2—A TEST FOR FREE SULFUR

van Itallie, L. Pharm. Weekblad. **75**, 278-280 (1938); CA **32**, 4904 (1938).

The addition of a trace of sulfur and a small quantity of pyridine to a 4N solution of sodium hydroxide produces a blue color which changes through green to brown in the presence of larger quantities of sulfur. *This reaction might be applied to the field detection of sulfur.*

3—COLOR REACTION OF SULFUR

van Itallie, L. Pharm. Weekblad **75**, 1445-1448 (1938); CA **33**, 3529 (1939).

The limit of sensitivity for the analysis of sulfur by the method described above is 0.005 mg.

4—APPLICATION OF SPOT REACTIONS. IV. DETECTION OF ELEMENTARY SULFUR AND SELENIUM

Feibl, Fritz and Nicolau Braile. Chemist-Analyst **33**, 28-31 (1944); CA **38**, 3568 (1944).

Soak filter paper in 0.5% thallium carbonate or thallium acetate solution, drain, and dry in warm air. Just before using, hold the paper over a warm solution of ammonium sulfide until the paper is covered with a black precipitate of thallium sulfide. Treat the test sample with pyridine to dissolve any free sulfur, then place a drop of the sample solution on the filter paper. Swish the paper in dilute nitric acid to dissolve the black thallium sulfide. If sulfur is present in the pyridine solution, a brownish red spot will remain. The test is very sensitive.

5—DETECTION OF ELEMENTARY SULFUR

Pettinger, A. H. Nature **163**, 537 (1949).

Sulfur vapor stains brown a freshly moistened lead acetate paper. Add. Ref.: CA **44**, 2889 (1950).

6—DETERMINATION OF FREE SULFUR IN THE ATMOSPHERE

Magill, Paul L., Myra V. Rolston, and Raymond W. Bremner. Anal. Chem. **21**, 1411-1412 (1949).

Soak Chemical Warfare Service Type 6 untreated filter material, or Whatman No. 1 filter paper, 7 cm diameter, in 0.5% aqueous thallous sulfate solution, then thoroughly dry in an electric oven at 80° to 105° C. Stored in covered glass containers the papers remain stable, with slowly decreasing sensitivity, for at least several weeks. Clamp the treated paper in the holder of the sampling device, and draw through the paper a measured volume of the test gas, then spray the test portion with pyridine from an atomizer. Spot a similarly prepared thallous paper with drops of various strength of standard solution, then allow both standard and test papers to dry thoroughly. Next, suspend the papers from glass rods and again spray with pyridine from the atomizer until the papers are slightly and uniformly damp. When almost dry, place the papers in a jar of hydrogen sulfide for about 30 seconds, then remove and allow the remaining pyridine to evaporate. Wash in 0.5 N nitric acid (to remove the thallous sulfide), then in water (to remove the acid), and compare the intensity of the test spot with those of the standards to determine the quantity of sulfur in the sample. The method can determine as little as 0.05 ppm sulfur in 1 cubic foot of air with 90% accuracy. Selenium interferes, and dust should be prefiltered out with untreated paper. Add. Ref.: CA **44**, 2889 (1950).

Sulfur Dioxide

1—SIMPLE METHODS FOR THE DETERMINATION OF GASEOUS IMPURITIES IN THE AIR OF FACTORIES

Hahn, Martin. Gesundh. Ing. **31**, 693-697 (1910); CA **4**, 1074 (1910).

Colorimetric methods for the determination of sulfur dioxide are described. The sulfur dioxide is determined by noting the amount of air required to discharge the color of a 0.25000 N solution of iodine colored with starch.

2—CHEMICAL DETECTION OF RESPIRATORY POISONS

Smolczyk, E. and H. Cobler. Gasmaske **2**, 27-33 (1930); Wasser u. Abwasser **28**, 95 (1930); CA **26**, 1214 (1932).

The authors describe an apparatus which indicates the composition and concentration of a gas. Sensitized paper strips are used and their reaction and sensitivity to sulfur dioxide are given. Blue litmus paper turns red, at once with 0.04 mg per liter, after 5 seconds with 0.004 mg per liter.

3—ANALYSIS OF ETHYLENE FOR ANESTHETIC USE

Busi, M. and C. Collina. Atti. soc. ital. progresso sci. **19**, 195-199 (1931); CA **26**, 1707 (1932).

The authors describe methods of detection of sulfur dioxide in ethylene.

4—THE MICRO-DETECTION OF GASES AND VAPORS

Blank, Eugene W. J. Chem. Education **11**, 523-525 (1934).

Sulfur dioxide turns a mixture of iodic acid and starch violet to blue. Zinc nitroprusside, exposed to ammonia vapors, then to sulfur dioxide, turns rose-red. Add. Ref.: CA **28**, 6392 (1934).

5—THE DETECTION OF TOXIC GASES AND VAPORS

Leroux, Lucien. Rev. hyg. et med. prevent. **57**, 81-112 (1935).

At a concentration of 41. mg per liter of sulfur dioxide, congo red paper turns blue immediately; after 2 seconds with 1/10 this amount; after 10 seconds with 1/100 as much; and after 1 minute with 1/1000 the concentration (at 20° C). Add. Ref.: CA **29**, 3627 (1935).

6—SIMPLE METHODS FOR THE DETECTION AND DETERMINATION OF POISONOUS GASES, V A P O R S, SMOKES, AND DUSTS IN FACTORY AIR

Weber, Hans H. Zentr. Gewerbehyg. Unfallverhuet. **23**, 177-180 (1936).

Blue litmus paper turns red immediately with 0.04 mg sulfur dioxide per liter, and in 5 seconds with 0.004 mg per liter.

7—THE USE OF INDICATORS FOR THE DETECTION OF POISONOUS GASES AND VAPORS

Heering, D. Gasmaske **8**, 88-89 (1936).

Sulfur dioxide in a concentration of 0.05 mg per liter turns blue litmus paper red immediately; 0.004 mg per liter requires 5 seconds. Congo red paper turns blue in 10 seconds with 0.4 per liter; 0.04 mg requires 25 seconds. Add. Ref.: CA **30**, 7059 (1936).

8—A SIMPLIFIED COLORIMETRIC DETERMINATION OF SULFUR DIOXIDE IN THE AIR

Chumanov, S. M. and M. B. Aksel'rod. J. Applied Chem. (U.S.S.R.) **11**, 720 (1938); CA **32**, 6974 (1938).

A preliminary report describing a colorimetric method for the determination of sulfur dioxide is presented. A small quantity of dilute potassium ferricyanide combined with a solution of ferric ions can be used as an indicator for sulfur dioxide in the absence of other reducing agents. The blue coloration is intensive enough to detect 0.02 mg of sulfur dioxide in a liter of air.

9—METHODS FOR THE DETECTION OF TOXIC GASES IN INDUSTRY. SULFUR DIOXIDE

Anon. Dept. of Scientific and Industrial Research, London, England. Leaflet No. 3 (1939) 7 pp.

A bright blue stain of Prussian blue on potassium ferricyanide-ferric chloride test paper is a sensitive test for sulfur dioxide, but the papers readily become colored during preparation and storage. A more stable test paper is impregnated with a starch-potassium iodate-potassium iodide-glycerol reagent. To prepare the reagent, add 12 ml of approximately N/10 barium hydroxide to 60 ml of distilled water. Make a thin paste with 1 g of soluble starch and approximately 10 ml of the treated water. Boil the remainder of the water, and to the boiling liquid add 1 g of potassium iodate and 2 g of potassium iodide; when these are completely dissolved, add the starch paste and continue boiling for a few minutes. Cool the solution, add 30 ml of pure glycerol, shake the mixture well, and dilute to 100 ml with distilled water. Immerse 2" wide strips of extra thick filter paper in the reagent for 30 seconds, drain, press 2 or 3 times between sheets of dry filter paper, then suspend the strips for 10 minutes at 50°C in a well ventilated oven free from acid fumes. Remove the strips from the oven and cut off and discard 1" from the top and bottom of each white and slightly moist strip, then cut into 3" lengths for use. Store in a well stoppered bottle in the dark if not used immediately. The papers are usable up to 2 days later if not discolored; the reagent keeps for about 7 days. Draw air samples through the papers with a hand pump; compare any stains obtained with standard color stains. The test can detect 1 part sulfur dioxide in 100,000 (approximately 0.03 mg per liter). Other oxidizing gases interfere, and should be removed by entrapment ahead of the test paper. Starch iodate paper without potassium iodide is specific for sulfur dioxide and can identify the contaminant definitely if other iodide-affecting gases are present also.

10—COLOR REACTION OF SULFUROUS ANHYDRIDE

Pagano, Marcelo. Rev. asoc. bioquim. arg. **4**, No. 12, 17-20 (1939); CA **35**, 408 (1941).

Sulfur dioxide can be determined on filter paper moistened with a 0.5 to 1% solution of p-phenylenediamine dihydrochloride and a few drops of a 40% formaldehyde solution. These papers have an adequate shelf life but should be freshly moistened with formalin before using. When placed in air containing sulfur dioxide they turn blue.

11—THE DETECTION OF TOXIC GASES AND VAPORS IN INDUSTRY

Vallender, R. B. Chem. and Ind. (London) **58**, 330-333 (1939).

To detect sulfur dioxide, impregnate paper with potassium iodate, potassium iodide, glycerin, and starch. With 10 strokes on the British hand pump, concentrations as low as 1 part in 250,000 can be determined. Add. Ref.: CA **33**, 4907 (1939).

12—WAR GASES AND THEIR IDENTIFICATION

Twiss, D. F. and A. E. T. Neale. Chem. and Ind. (London) **18**, 13-14 (1940).

The authors describe a method for the identification of war gases. An ethyl alcohol lamp is described for the detection of (a) halogen in war gases by the Beilstein method, and (b) sulfur by the presence of sulfur dioxide in the combustion products; this facilitates recognition of these two characteristics of mustard gas. Add. Ref.: CA **34**, 4828 (1940).

13—WAR GASES AND THEIR IDENTIFICATION. MODIFICATION OF THE TWISS-NEALE LAMP TEST FOR MUSTARD GAS

Edwards, G. H. Chem. and Ind. (London) **18**, 239-240 (1940).

The author describes his modification of the Twiss-Neale lamp technique (see above)) for identifying mustard gas. He burns sulfur-containing organic materials to sulfur dioxide, then identifies the gas on a test filter paper impregnated with phosphotungstate-phosphomolybdate solution and moistened with aqueous ammonia. The author details the preparation of the reagent and the test paper, mentions that the paper is light-sensitive, and claims that if this paper is used instead of starch-iodate paper to detect sulfur dioxide, interference by iodine from ethyl iodoacetate ("K.S.K.") is eliminated. Add. Ref.: CA **34**, 7475 (1940).

14—SODIUM NITROPRUSSIDE TEST PAPERS FOR THE DETECTION OF SULFUR DIOXIDE AND HYDROGEN SULFIDE

Sciacca, N. and E. Solarino. Ann. chim. applicata **30**, 246-247 (1940); CA **35**, 1353 (1941).

Sulfur dioxide concentrations on the order of 1:1,000,000 can be detected on filter papers washed in a solution of 4% sodium nitroprusside and 2% sodium carbonate.

15—IDENTIFICATION OF WAR GASES

Sharman, C. F. Chem. and Ind. (London) **18**, 741-742 (1940).

An incandescent filament is used to burn organic agents, and specially prepared papers to test or the products of combustion. Sulfur dioxide colors starch iodate paper blue. Add. Ref.: CA **35**, 820 (1941).

16—DETERMINATION OF SULFUR DIOXIDE IN THE AIR BY THE DECOLORIZATION OF FUCHSIN

Kastner, E. P. Zavodskaya Lab **9**, No. 1, 111 (1940); CA **36**, 1265 (1942).

Hydrogen sulfide is first removed by aspirating the sample through 50 ml of 2% acidified copper sulfate solution containing 5 ml of ethyl alcohol. Sulfur dioxide is then determined by aspirating the sample through 2 absorbers, each containing 50 ml of fuchsin solution.

17—ATMOSPHERIC POLLUTION BY HEAVY INDUSTRY

Hewson, E. Wendell. Ind. Eng. Chem. **36**, 195-201 (1944); CA **38**, 1812 (1944).

The author describes the operating principle of Thomas autometer type instruments. In this apparatus air is bubbled through an acidified solution of hydrogen peroxide in water, thus changing any sulfur dioxide into sulfuric acid and increasing the electrical conductivity of the solution. Concentrations as low as 0.01 ppm can be thus detected.

18—DETERMINATION OF SULFUR DIOXIDE IN AIR BY MEANS OF THE MIDGET IMPINGER

Pearce, S. J. and H. H. Schrenk. U. S. Bur. Mines, Rept. Invest. 4282, 6 pp. (1948).

Mix 1 g of soluble starch and 5 g of mercuric iodide into a paste with a little cold distilled water. Stir the paste into 500 ml of boiling distilled water. In a conventional midget impinger place 2.5 ml of 10% potassium iodide solution, 2 ml of the starch mixture, 3.5 ml of distilled water, and 2 ml of 0.0025 N iodine solution. Draw air suspected of containing sulfur dioxide through the reagent at 2.83 liters per minute until the blue color disappears; note the length of time required to decolorize the starch-iodine solution. As little as 2 ppm can be determined by this method; other oxidizing gases interfere. Add. Ref.: CA **42**, 5376 (1948).

19—DETECTION AND DETERMINATION OF SMALL QUANTITIES OF SULFUR DIOXIDE

Gandolfo, Nicolo. Rend. ist. super. sanita (Rome) **11**, 1268-1274 (1948); CA **43**, 8308 (1949).

Sulfur dioxide concentrations on the order of 0.0005 mg can be detected by sweeping gases from acidified sulfite or bisulfite solutions over test papers impregnated with ammoniacal zinc nitroprusside. The reaction produces a brick-red coloration which is due to zinc nitroprusside-ammonium sulfite. The method can be made quantitative as shown by an intensity chart for known amounts of sulfur dioxide from 0.001 to 1.0 mg. The test papers are freshly made by immersing strips of filter paper in an ammonia-cleared solution prepared by mixing 10 cc of zinc sulfate (0.6 g) solution and 10 cc of sodium nitroprusside (1. g) solution.

20—THE USE OF SILVER VANADATES AS ABSORBENTS FOR SULFUR DIOXIDE

Ingram, G. Anal. Chim. Acta **3**, 137-143 (1949) (in English); CA **43**, 8308 (1949).

A new solid absorbent for sulfur dioxide is described. The absorbent is effective at room temperature and does not absorb carbon dioxide. A color change from green to brown indicates that the absorbent is exhausted. While an active product, which will absorb sulfur dioxide when dry, can be prepared by precipitation methods, this investigation confirms the uncertainties involved in this procedure; and it is recommended that the reagent be made by heating molecular quantities of silver oxide and silver vanadate together at 150°. It is shown that under this treatment the 2 silver compounds combine to form a product having the same empirical composition as the ortho-vanadate, but with very different properties from that produced by the usual precipitation method. *This procedure might be applicable to a field detector.*

21—SULFUR DIOXIDE DETECTOR

Kitagawa, Tetsuzo (to Tokyo Industrial Research Institute). Japan (Pat. No.) 178,082, March 7, 1949; CA **45**, 5983 (1951).

Silica gel is impregnated with one or more of the following compounds: aqueous potassium permanganate, chromium trioxide, potassium dichromate, or potassium chromate. The prepared reagent is dried and placed in a glass tube. The color development is not influenced by the presence of oxygen, nitrogen, hydrogen, carbon monoxide, carbon dioxide, or nitrogen oxide.

22—DETERMINATION OF SULFUR DIOXIDE BY COLOR-CHANGING GELS

Patterson, Gordon D., Jr., with M. G. Mellon. Anal. Chem. **24**, 1586-1590 (1952).

In the author's simple, portable apparatus, 150 ml air samples with 10 ppm of sulfur dioxide, are passed through glass tubes containing various granular gels which change color when exposed to low concentrations of sulfur dioxide. The colors which appear on the various gels may be matched with those on standard color cards, or the length of the colored column may be measured, or the sample volume necessary to produce a desired color or length of colored column may be observed. Vanadate-silica gels and gels containing iodates or periodates, erioglaucine, 8-nitroquinoline, rosaniline hydrochloride, or p,p'-tetramethyldiaminodiphenylmethane are among those studied by the authors and found suitable for field detection and determination of sulfur dioxide. Add. Ref.: CA **47**, 71 (1953).

23—A SIMPLE DEVICE FOR AIR ANALYSIS

Gisclard, J. B., J. H. Rook, M. V. Andresen, and W. R. Bradley. Am. Ind. Hyg. Assoc. Quart. **14**, 23-25 (1953).

The authors' device is a 100 ml syringe mounted on a plywood frame. They draw the air sample through 2 side arm test tubes containing an absorbing reagent which, for sulfur dioxide, is 0.0001 N iodine (1 ml = 0.0032 mg sulfur dioxide), with starch as the indicator. The air titration unit is convenient for field use.

24—ANALYSIS OF MEDICALLY IMPORTANT GASES USING SPOT TESTS

Massmann, W. Arch. Gewerbepathol. Gewerbehyg. **13**, 262-275 (1954).

Draw a measured volume of air through filter paper moistened with potassium chromate solution, which turns brown if sulfur dioxide is in the air. Prepare the reagent solution by dissolving 5 g of potassium chromate and 20 g of sodium acetate in water and diluting the mixture to 100 ml. Pull air containing 5 to 50 ppm of sulfur dioxide per liter through filter paper moistened with the reagent, at a rate of 1 liter in 10 minutes. Remove the paper, dry it in a desiccator, and compare with previously prepared standards. None of the following interferes: carbon monoxide at 500 ppm, carbon disulfide at ordinary concentrations, arsine below 2 ppm, oxides of nitrogen below 50 ppm, chlorine below 20 ppm, hydrogen sulfide up to 20 ppm. High concentrations of hydrogen sulfide definitely interfere. Add. Ref.: IHD **19**, 599 (1955).

25—REAGENT FOR SULFUR DIOXIDE

Liddell, H. F. Analyst **80**, 901 (1955).

Dissolve 0.1 g of Astrazone Pink FG (Bayer) in 20 ml of hot water and allow to cool. Dissolve 5 g of sodium bicarbonate in 50 ml of cold water, mix the 2 solutions, add 25 ml of glycerol, and dilute to 100 ml. In the dark the reagent solution is stable for more than 1 week, the dye solution alone for several months. Place 1 drop of the reagent on filter paper and draw air through the wet paper at 250 ml per minute until bleaching occurs. The sensitivity is 1.5 μg of sulfur dioxide in 500 ml of air. Add. Ref.: CA **50**, 4715 (1956); IHD **20**, 935 (1956).

26—LIMITS OF ALLOWABLE CONCENTRATIONS OF ATMOSPHERIC POLLUTANTS. Book 2

Ryazanov, V. A., Editor, translated by B. S. Levine. U. S. Dept. of Commerce, Office of Technical Services, Washington, D. C. (1955).

In a discussion of sulfur dioxide the following reference is cited. Alekseeva, M. V. and R. Ya. S. Samorodina, Gigiena i Sanit. **1953**, No. 10, p. 42, and a non-specific method is described in which sulfur dioxide reacts with fuchsin-formaldehyde to produce a violet color which then may be compared with a standard color scale. The absorbing medium is a 0.01 N sodium hydroxide solution made 5% with glycerin. Two ml of this solution, after treatment with the fuchsin-formaldehyde reagent, is compared with synthetic standards. The sensitivity of the method is 0.00002 mg sulfur dioxide per liter when a 7.5 liter air sample is drawn through 3 ml of the absorbing solution. The range of the fuchsin-methyl violet synthetic standard curve is from 0.0 to 0.010 mg of sulfur dioxide.

27—DETERMINATION OF TOXIC GAS COMPONENTS IN AIR BY THE REICH STOP-METHOD

Kraus, E. Chem. Tech. (Berlin) **7**, 552-555 (1955); AA **3**, 1893 (1956); CA **50**, 12750 (1956).

A method for the determination of traces of sulfur dioxide is "based on the Reich method for the estimation of sulfur dioxide in roast gases." The gaseous mixture is drawn from a measuring cylinder through a known concentration of starch-iodide solution in an absorption flask until the starch solution is decolorized. The sulfur dioxide concentration then is calculated from the remaining volume of gas.

28—DETERMINATION OF SULFUR DIOXIDE IN AIR

Ishizaka, Otoharu, Hideo Nagano, and Yoshiki Hamada. Bull. Nagoya City Univ. Pharm. School **2**, 31-32 (1954); CA **50**, 12749 (1956).

The sample is aspirated through 0.03 cc of 0.01 N potassium permanganate solution at a constant rate of approximately 100 cc per 50 seconds. If the volume of air needed for the decolorizing of potassium permanganate solution is **V**, the per cent sulfur dioxide in the air is given as (0.25/V). The measurable sulfur dioxide concentration range is 5 to 50 ppm; the error, less than 5%.

29—AIR SANITATION. VII. ASSAY OF SULFUR DIOXIDE IN AIR BY THE DROP SURFACE REACTION

Ishizaka, Otoharu, Hideo Nagano, Tae Nishizaki, and Miyo Okabe. Bull. Nagoya City Univ. Pharm. School **4**, 18-22 (1956); CA **51**, 6747 (1957).

Identical with the article above.

30—SAMPLING AND ANALYZING AIR FOR CONTAMINANTS IN WORK PLACES

Silverman, Leslie. Encyclopedia of Instrumentation for Industrial Hygiene, edited by Yaffe, Charles D., Dohrman H. Byers, and Andrew D. Hosey. (Univ. of Michigan, Inst. of Industrial Health, Ann Arbor, Mich., 1956) pp. 7-25.

A column of inert granules impregnated with ammonium vanadate turns from blue to yellow with from 0 to 50 ppm of sulfur dioxide, the length of the stain being proportional to the amount of the gas present. Four to 200 ppm turn S and S No. 598 filter paper impregnated with starch-potassium-iodide iodate-glycerine from light brown to black. Other oxidizing gases which reduce iodides interfere. Reagent solution containing 0.0025 N iodine and 10% potassium iodide with starch indicator in a midget impinger turns from blue to colorless with less than 1 ppm of sulfur dioxide. Hydrogen sulfide, nitrogen dioxide, and other oxidizing gases interfere.

31—FIXATION OF SULFUR DIOXIDE AS DISULFITO-MERCURATE AND SUBSEQUENT COLORIMETRIC ESTIMATION

West, Philip W. and G. C. Gaeke. Anal. Chem. **28**, 1816-1819 (1956).

Sulfur dioxide in the atmosphere was collected into 0.1 M sodium tetrachloromercurate reagent, prepared by dissolving 27.2 g of reagent grade mercuric chloride and 11.7 g of reagent grade sodium chloride in water and diluting to 1 liter. Addition of p-rosaniline hydrochloride-hydrochloric acid mixture (0.04% dye-6% concentrated acid, prepared by mixing 4 ml of a 1% aqueous solution of p-rosaniline hydrochloride and 6 ml of concentrated hydrochloric acid, then diluting to 100 ml) and 0.2% formaldehyde (5 ml of 40% formaldehyde diluted to 1000 ml with distilled water) produced a red-violet color with sulfur dioxide. This method was adapted to field use with migdet impingers by Welch and Terry in 1960 (see below). Add. Refs.: CA **51**, 11930 (1957); IHD **21**, 121 (1957).

32—DETECTION OF SULFUR DIOXIDE

McConnaughey, Paul W. (to Mine Safety Appliances Co.). U. S. (Pat. No.) 2,736,638, Feb. 28, 1956; CA **50**, 8402 (1956).

Nitric acid washed silica gel, impregnated with an iodine solution which has been mixed with tetramethyldiaminodiphenylmethane until the blue color appears, is a useful reagent for the detection of sulfur dioxide in air. In the presence of sulfur dioxide the blue color changes to white. This method is also applicable to a determination of sulfur dioxide when a measured volume of gas is passed through the tube. The length of the bleached column is a direct measurement of the sulfur dioxide. It is possible to detect 0.1 ppm by volume of sulfur dioxide in air. The reagent is prepared by impregnating 100 g silica gel, washed and purified with nitric acid, with 30 cc of iodine solution; then 0.2 g of TDD is added and agitated until the blue color appears. Add. Ref. AA **4**, 3145 (1957).

33—INFORMATION ON THE DRAEGER GAS DETECTOR

Draegerwerk Heinr. und Bernhard Draeger, Luebeck, Germany (distributed by N. J. Safety Equipment Co., 299 Park Ave., East Orange, N. J.). SULFUR DIOXIDE DETECTOR TUBE 0.01 - Information Sheet No. 8 (Sept. (1957).

The 0.01 Sulfur Dioxide Detector Tube, for use with the Draeger Multi-Gas Detector, is sensitive to 0.01 mg sulfur dioxide per liter of air, or approximately 3.5 ppm, in the range from 0.01 to 0.4 mg per liter (approximately 3.5 to 150. ppm), and the measured result is independent of the ambient temperature. The tube may be stored for 2 years provided the temperature is under 40° C.

34—AIR SANITATION. VIII. ASSAY OF SULFUR DIOXIDE AND HYDROGEN SULFIDE IN AIR BY THE SPOT REACTION

Ishizaka, Otoharu, Hideo Nagano, Kazuko Okamura, Masami Saburi, Saeko Koide, and Michiko Goto. Nagoya Shiritsu Daigaku Yakugakubu Kiyo **5**, 14-20 (1957); CA **52**, 4076 (1958).

Cf. CA **51**, 6747 (1957) (above). The coloration of potassium iodate-starch paper by sulfur dioxide or hydrogen sulfide gas is applied on a spot of the filter paper, and a measuring formula is introduced. Error is less than ± 5% for 5 to 50 ppm of sulfur dioxide or hydrogen sulfide under the condition of 0 to 40° and 40 to 80% humidity.

35—QUANTITATIVE DETERMINATION OF SULFUR DIOXIDE IN AIR

Auergesellschaft Akt.-Ges. (by Andreas A. Hauch and Hermann Heidrich). Ger. (Pat. No.) 1,021,186, Dec. 19, 1957 (Cl. 42.**1**); CA **54**, 24135 (1960).

A test tube for the quantitative determination of sulfur dioxide contains silica gel impregnated with a potassium iodide-starch solution and a small quantity of nitric acid. The reagent is introduced into the tube while still wet, and the tube is sealed. Preferably, the reagent is exposed to ultra-violet light to develop the blue color in the gel more rapidly and completely.

36—COLORIMETRIC DETERMINATION OF SULFUR DIOXIDE

Patterson, G. D., Jr. and M. G. Mellon. U. S. (Pat. No.) 2,785,959, Mar. 19, 1957; AA **5**, 1828 (1958).
Sulfur dioxide can be determined with silica gel mixed with 10 times its volume of saturated aqueous ammonium vanadate. The gel is then dried at 60°. A measured volume of air, drawn through a tube containing the gel, forms 5 bands of color. The concentration of sulfur dioxide is determined by color comparison with a standard set of colors

or by a photocell. Tetraethoxysilane or sodium vanadate can be used instead of ammonium vanadate.

37—INSTRUMENTS FOR MEASURING SMALL QUANTITIES OF SULFUR DIOXIDE IN THE ATMOSPHERE

Cummings, W. G. and M. W. Redfearn. J. Inst. Fuel **30**, 628-635 (1957); AA **5**, 3225 (1958).

The authors describe a portable sulfur dioxide analyzer. The sulfur dioxide in the air reacts with a starch-iodine reagent in a countercurrent absorption column, and the amounts of light absorbed by the unchanged and the partially decolorized reagent are determined by photoelectric cells connected to a galvanometer. The instrument is sensitive to 1 part of sulfur dioxide in 100 million parts of air over the range 0 to 0.5 ppm.

38—DETECTION OF SULFUR DIOXIDE

McConnaughey, Paul W. (to Mine Safety Appliances Co.). Brit. (Pat. No.) 793,727, Apr. 23, 1958; CA **52**, 19726 (1958).

Sulfur dioxide can be determined qualitatively and quantitatively by means of a glass detector tube containing an inert granular solid impregnated with iodine and tetramethyldiaminodiphenylmethane.

39—PHOTOELECTRIC ABSORPTIOMETER FOR DETERMINATION OF SMALL AMOUNTS OF GASES IN AIR

Barley, Thomas, Joseph H. Elliott, and Richard P. Kinsey. U. S. (Pat. No.) 2,829,032, Apr. 1, 1958; CA **52**, 11490 (1958).

The authors describe an apparatus which is capable of determining the concentration of one gas in another with an accuracy of 0.5 ppm. It records continuously the color changes in a specific solution.

40—SULFUR DIOXIDE GAS DETECTOR

Mine Safety Appliances Co., 201 N. Braddock Ave., Pittsburgh 8, Penna. Bull 0811-2 (1959).

Three squeezes of the rubber aspirator bulb draw in an adequate air sample through a glass detector tube containing a sensitive chemical. Any sulfur dioxide present causes the blue reagent granules in the detector tube to turn white. Mounted on the tube holder with the aspirator bulb is a graduated sliding scale against which the bleached portion of the detector tube is measured to give the concentration of sulfur dioxide in parts per million. The range of sensitivity is from 0 to 50 ppm, and all items in the detector kit fit into a convenient carrying case. The chemicals have infinite shelf life before mixing; the mixed chemicals can be stored for 3 days at 90° F and for 2 weeks at 40° F without loss of sensitivity. Add. Ref.: M.S.A. Catalog 8B3621, Sect. 3, p. 17 (1961).

41—AIR POLLUTION SAMPLING AND ANALYSIS WITH SPECIAL REFERENCE TO SULFATE PULPING OPERATIONS

Hendrickson, E. R. Tappi **42**, No. 5, 173A-176A (1959); CA **53**, 17392 (1959).

The West and Gaeke method (see above) is used to determine sulfur dioxide. The sulfur dioxide is absorbed in 0.1 M sodium tetrachloromercurate solution and the red-violet color is developed by the addition of acid bleached p-rosaniline hydrochloride and formaldehyde. The resulting color is compared to color standards. A paste of lead peroxide which will react with sulfur dioxide to form lead sulfate is also described.

42—DEVELOPMENTS IN THE MEASUREMENT OF ATMOSPHERIC SULFUR DIOXIDE

Welch, Allan F. and James P. Terry. Am. Ind. Hyg. Assoc. J. **21**, 316-321 (1960).

The authors describe field experiences with several techniques for the determination of sulfur dioxide. The sodium tetrachloromercurate method of West and Gaeke (see above), for collection and analysis of low concentrations of sulfur dioxide, was accurate, sensitive, flexible, practical, and adaptable to rapid midget bubbler handling methods. Add. Ref.: Anal. Chem., Anal. Reviews **33**, No. 5, 3R-13R (1961).

43—A FIELD METHOD FOR THE DETERMINATION OF SULFUR DIOXIDE IN AIR

Hands, G. C. and A. F. F. Bartlett. Analyst **85**, 147-148 (1960).

Impregnate 1" wide strips of extra-thick filter paper with a solution of ammoniacal zinc nitroprusside, dry at not over 40°C in a fume-free atmosphere, and store in a stoppered container in the dark. To use, spray the dried paper with water from an insufflator, fix in a previously described holder (Analyst **83**, 199 (1958)) and draw 360 ml of air through the paper. Compare the brick-red stain produced by the sulfur dioxide with a standard stain chart or with a disc of standard tints. With a 360 ml sample 1 to 20 ppm can be determined with ±20% accuracy. Add. Refs.: AA **7**, 4509 (1960); IHD **25**, 182 (1961); Anal. Chem., Anal. Reviews **33**, No. 5, 3R-13R (1961); CA **54**, 18840 (1960).

44—SELF-RECORDING AIR ANALYZER WITH A CHEMICAL ABSORBENT FOR SULFUR DIOXIDE

Lyubimov, N. A. Gigiena Truda i Prof. Zabolevaniya **5**, No. 12, 49-51 (1961); CA **56**, 13979 (1962).

An automatic air analyzer for the determination of sulfur dioxide is described. The absorbent contains 1 part of 0.1 N hydrochloric acid, 1 part of hydrogen peroxide, and 9 parts of starch paste. The minimum time required for an accurate determination was inversely proportional to the rate of aspiration, and the latter could be increased to 2 liters per minute.

45—SIMPLE AND RAPID METHOD FOR DETERMINING SULFUR DIOXIDE IN THE ATMOSPHERE OF INDUSTRIAL PLANTS

Ioanid, N., G. Bors, I. Popa, L. Armasescu, T. Stan, and N. Popovici. Farmacia (Bucharest) **9**, 223-224 (1961); CA **56**, 5076 (1962).

The sample to be analyzed is aspirated through a dilute solution of acid potassium dichromate containing a small quantity of potassium iodate and starch as indicator. When the entire quantity of bichromate as well as that of liberated iodine is consumed, the blue coloration disappears indicating the end of the reaction.

46—THE DETERMINATION OF SULFUR DIOXIDE IN THE ATMOSPHERE BY FUCHSIN FORMALIN METHOD

Arai, Kuichiro and Koichiro Shinra. Sci. Rept. (Osaka Univ.) **9**, 47-58 (1960); CA **56**, 1722 (1962).

The authors describe a slightly modified fuchsin-formaldehyde method for the determination of sulfur dioxide. An aqueous solution containing 0.1 M mercuric chloride, 0.2 M sodium chloride, and 5% glycerol was used to avoid the oxidation of sulfur dioxide. The glycerol prevents the solution from splashing. The most sensitive color reagent is an aqueous solution containing 0.02% basic fuchsin, 0.36 N hydrochloric acid, and 0.05% formaldehyde.

47—IMPINGER TECHNIQUES FOR GAS AND PARTICLE SAMPLING

Robrecht, Charles. Dust Topics (published by Gelman Instrument Co., Ann Arbor, Mich.) Vol. **3**, No. 2, (1966).

Describes impinger sampling techniques for particles and gases. Tells how to prepare reagents for sampling SO_2 and how to prepare a calibration curve.

See Section One

For references 6, 15, 69, 81, 90, 106, 109, 129.

Sulfuric Acid

1—DETERMINATION OF SMALL AMOUNTS OF SULFURIC ACID IN THE ATMOSPHERE

Mader, Paul P., Walter J. Hamming, and Anthony Bellin. Anal. Chem. **22**, 1181-1183 (1950).

The authors present a method for determining small concentrations of sulfuric acid mist in the atmosphere. They trap air samples on 2 specially prepared Whatman No. 4 filter papers in a glass filter paper holder, at a rate of 50 to 60 cubic feet per hour. They then macerate the filters in 20 ml of distilled water, measure the pH of the solution, and titrate the acid with 0.002 N sodium hydroxide. The efficiency of the filter papers for trapping the acid is

91 to 97% under the authors' conditions. *This abstract is included here because of these reported efficiency factors.* Add. Ref.: CA **45**, 4174 (1951).

2—ESTIMATION OF THE CONCENTRATION OF SLIGHTLY DISSOCIABLE GASES

Nogami, Kinzo. Japan (Pat. No.) 6345, Dec. 9, 1953; CA **48**, 12618 (1954).

The authors describe a series of indicators for determination of sulfuric acid concentrations. Concentration differences are indicated by changes in pH.

Sulfuric acid is determined conveniently by a number of reactions and in various types of equipment. Most common is absorption of the acid mist in an aqueous solution containing an indicator, followed by an air titration. A similar procedure uses a filter paper treated with an alkali and an indicator for the air titration. Color intensity reactions for sulfuric acid have not been developed.

3—A QUICK SEMIQUANTITATIVE METHOD OF DETERMINATION OF SULFURIC ACID IN THE AIR

Gernet, E. V. and A. A. Russkikh. Trudy po Khim. i Khim. Tekhnol. **3**, No. 1, 64-66 (1960); CA **55**, 25112 (1961).

Filter paper treated with a suspension of barium rhodizonate in a 20% glycerol solution is utilized for the determination of sulfuric acid. Barium rhodizonate is prepared reacting barium chloride with sodium rhodizonate. To determine the sulfuric acid content of air, 25 to 500 ml is drawn through a filter containing barium rhodizonate in the presence of the acid. The barium rhodizonate is discolored. A standard scale is prepared with air containing various amounts of the acid. Results obtained by the method are shown in a table. The lower limit of sensitivity is 0.001 mg per liter. Vapors of hydrogen chloride, sulfur gas, and hydrogen sulfide do not interfere, whereas nitric acid vapors and oxides of nitrogen interfere, if the sample contains 0.2 mg or more.

Sulfur Trioxide

See Section One
For references 8, 90.

Tetryl
(2,4,6-Trinitrophenylmethylnitramine)

1—THE ANALYSIS OF ATMOSPHERIC SAMPLES OF EXPLOSIVE CHEMICALS

Goldman, Frederick H. J. Ind. Hyg. Toxicol. **24**, 121-122 (1942).

The author reports a preliminary investigation of some color reactions of alkylaminoethanols with explosives. Diethylaminoethanol, the preferred reagent, turns deep red with tetryl and deep violet with trinitrotoluene. The reagent gives no color with dinitrotoluene until treated with alkali, when a deep blue-green appears. The concentrations of the explosives may be determined directly in the field with diethylaminoethanol as the sampling medium. Add. Ref.: CA **36**, 5349 (1942).

2—THE ESTIMATION OF MINUTE AMOUNTS OF TETRYL IN THE ATMOSPHERE

Goldman, F. H. and D. E. Rushing. J. Ind. Hyg. Toxicol. **25**, 195-196 (1943).

Diethylaminoethanol is the collecting medium for the direct determination of tetryl in air. Trinitrotoluene interferes. Add. Ref.: CA **37**, 5927 (1943).

3—DETERMINATION OF AIR-BORNE TRINITROTOLUENE, TETRYL AND DINITROTOLUENE

Cumming, W. M. and W. G. D. Wright. Brit. J. Ind. Med. **2**, 83-85 (1945).

Airborne tetryl is estimated colorimetrically *in situ* by absorption into a 1:1 mixture of methyl ethyl ketone and cyclohexanone to which potassium hydroxide solution is added (0.5 ml of 12% aqueous potassium hydroxide to 10 ml of solvent mixture). The red color is assessed in a Lovibond comparator (Tintometer) against a standard disc. Add. Ref.: CA **39**, 5209 (1945).

4—A METHOD FOR THE DETERMINATION OF TRINITROTOLUENE IN AIR

Mackay, J., K. W. Holmes, and R. E. Wilson. Brit. J. Ind. Med. **15**, 126-129 (1958).

Air to be analyzed is sampled automatically with a glass aspirator, to obviate the risk of explosion. Tetryl can be determined in the apparatus by using a suitable solvent. Add. Ref.: CA **52**, 21108 (1958).

Tin

1—DETECTION OF TIN AND MERCURY BY MEANS OF SPOT TESTS

Tananaev, N. A. Z. anorg. allgem. Chem. **133**, 372-374 (1924); CA **18**, 1628 (1924).

Moisten a strip of filter paper with mercuric chloride solution, add a drop of the solution to be tested for tin, and dry; then add a drop of aniline. A dark stain indicates the presence of tin.

2—NEW REAGENT PAPERS FOR POROSITY TESTING AND FOR THE DETERMINATION OF METALS

Kutzelnigg, Arthur. Metalloberflaeche **5**, B 113-115 (1951); CA **46**, 56 (1952).

Methylene blue, absorbed on filter paper, is useful for the determination of tin. The paper should be moistened with dilute hydrochloric acid.

3—SPECIFIC REAGENT FOR THE MICRODETECTION OF STANNOUS IONS

Ruzicka, Eduard. Chem. Listy **47**, 1014-1016 (1953); CA **48**, 3849 (1954).

The author describes a reagent which is specific for stannous ions. Oxidation products of o-aminophenol in an acidic medium form a suitable reagent for the detection of stannous ions. The brown-red reagent is prepared by boiling 0.5 g of o-aminophenol in 100 ml of water for 1 hour and then adding to the hot solution 50 ml of dilute hydrochloric acid containing 15 ml of concentrated hydrochloric acid. The addition of stannous ion to a solution of 0.2 ml of o-aminophenol in 1 ml of water develops a brown-green to emerald-green coloration which is extractable into ether or ethyl acetate. *This might be applied to a field detector.*

4—A NEW REAGENT FOR STANNOUS TIN

Anderson, J. R. A. and J. L. Garnett. Anal. Chim. Acta **8**, 393-396 (1953).

As little as 1 μg of tin can be detected in a spot test which uses the ammonium salt of 6-nitro-2-naphthylamine-8-sulfonic acid as reagent. Tin causes an intense blue fluorescence with the reagent under ultraviolet light; 46 other metallic ions do not fluoresce under the conditions of the test. Add. Ref.: CA **47**, 12102 (1953).

5—A NEW SPOT-PLATE TEST FOR TIN WITH MORIN

Feigl, F. and V. Gentil. Mikrochim. Acta **1954**, 90-92 (in German); CA **48**, 4362 (1954).

The spot test for tin depends on the fact that tin hydroxides form blue-green fluorescent compounds with morin which resist the action of acetic acid. Trivalent aluminum ions, trivalent antimony ions, and divalent zirconium oxide interfere. A drop of the acid solution to be tested is placed on filter paper, the spot is evaporated over ammonium hydroxide, and then the paper moistened with a solution of morin in acetone. The paper is placed in dilute acetic acid, and examined under ultraviolet light.

See Section One

For reference 98.

Toluene Diisocyanate

1—RAPID COLORIMETRIC DETERMINATION OF DESMODUR T

Bank, H. Kunststoffe **37**, 102 (1947); Chimie et industrie **59**, 168 (1948); CA **42**, 7663 (1948).

The determination depends on the fact that Desmodur T (1,6-hexamethylenediisocyanate) produces a color reaction with nitrite ion in alcoholic solution in the presence of acetone. A standard curve must be plotted. The maximum amount of Desmodur T that can be determined is 25 mg.

2—CONTROLLING TDI HAZARDS

Anon. Chem. and Eng. News **34**, 4826 (1956).

Kalman Marcali and other DuPont researchers have developed a chemical monitoring method which quickly evaluates TDI level in air. The technique depends on rapid hydrolysis of the diisocyanate to the corresponding diamine derivative, diazotization of the diamine in the presence of nitrous acid, destruction of the excess nitrous acid with sulfamic acid, and finally coupling of the stable diazo compound at room temperature with N 1-naphthylethylene diamine to produce a reddish-blue color measurable spectrophotometrically at 550 mu. This diazometric method is incorporated into a portable analytical kit that allows the entire analysis, from air sampling and color formation through color comparison with stable plastic standards.

3—TDI DETECTOR KIT

Mine Safety Appliances Co., 201 N. Braddock Ave., Pittsburgh 8, Pa. Bull. No. 0811-4 (1956).

A small, compact field kit rapidly determines low concentrations of vapors of toluene diisocyanate and toluene diisocyanate urea. The kit consists of a hand cranked, 4 cylinder pump with regulator for drawing atmospheric samples at the rate of 1 liter per minute, a 3-minute timer for controlling the sampling period for each test, 6 all glass impinger tubes for absorbing TDI in dilute aqueous acid solution, replaceable reagent package containing all necessary solutions in polyethylene bottles, and transparent color standards laminated between plastic and representing concentrations of 0.05, 0.10, and 0.20 ppm. Operating the pump for 3 minutes draws a 3 liter air sample through the 15 ml of acid solution in the impinger flask. Absorbed in the solution, the TDI or TDI-urea hydrolyzes to an amine. Adding 15 drops of sodium nitrite-sodium bromide solution in the impinger and mixing for 1½ minutes, followed by 15 drops of sulfamic acid and mixing for another 1½ minutes, forms a diazo-amine compound. Upon adding 15 drops of the final test reagent (N-1-naphthylethylene diamine dihydrochloride) a rose pink color develops immediately, and is compared on a white background with the color standards. Add. Ref.: M. S. A. Catalog 8B3621, Sect. 3, p. 26 (1961).

4—MICRODETERMINATION OF TOLUENEDIISOCYANATES IN ATMOSPHERE

Marcali, Kalman. Anal. Chem. **29**, 552-558 (1957).
A rapid, sensitive, colorimetric method for determining toluene diisocyanates in air depends on hydrolysis of the toluene diisocyanate to the corresponding diamine, diazotization, coupling to N-1-naphthylethylenediamine, and final color measurement at 550 mμ. The method can detect 0.01 ppm of toluene-2,4-diisocyanate. With a portable field analytical kit a complete analysis takes 15 minutes, with a sensitivity of 0.02 ppm of toluene-2,4-diisocyanate. As little as 0.03 ppm of 3,3'-diisocyanato-4,4'-dimethylcarbanilide may be determined in the presence of toluene-diisocyanate. The method depends on measurement at 450 mμ of the yellow color formed when the dimethylcarbanilide is absorbed in an aqueous solution of ethyl Cellosolve containing sodium nitrite and boric acid. The author details his apparatus, procedures, and preparation of reagents and color standards. Add. Refs.: IHD **21**, 670 (1957); Health Hazards of Spraying Polyurethan Foam Out-of-Doors. Peterson, J. E., R. A. Copeland, and H. R. Hoyle. Am. Ind. Hyg. Assoc. J. **23**, 345-352 (1962).

5—HAZARDS OF ISOCYANATES IN POLYURETHANE FOAM PLASTIC PRODUCTION

Zapp, John A., Jr. A.M.A. Arch. Ind. Health **15**, 324-330 (1957).
In the analytical method developed by K. E. Ranta of the Haskell Laboratory, air passes through a glass bubbler into 15 ml of a reagent solution consisting of 200 ml of 1% aqueous sodium nitrite and 800 ml of ethylene glycol monoethyl ether (Cellosolve). TDI produces a yellow-orange color which develops on standing at room temperature, reaches maximum at 1 hour, then is read at 420 mμ and compared against standards containing known amounts of TDI. *Other authors have used this procedure as a field test, comparing the color with fixed standards.*

6—TOLUENE DIISOCYANATE DETECTOR KIT

U. S. Industrial Chemicals Co., Division of National Distillers and Chemical Corp. 99 Park Avenue, New York 16, New York.
A small, compact, practical detector kit rapidly determines low concentrations of vapors of toluene diisocyanate and toluene diisocyanate urea.

7—UNICO TDI REAGENT KIT

Union Industrial Equipment Corp., Port Chester, N. Y.
The TDI Reagent Kit, used with the Unico TDI detector, consists of 2 bottles of acid absorber solution, and 1 bottle each of nitrite-bromide (Solution No. 1), sulfamic acid (Solution No. 2), and amine (Solution No. 3), together with a set of permanent TDI color standards, representing 0.01, 0.02, 0.04, and 0.08 ppm, for visual comparison of the blue-red color produced in the reaction.

8—AUTOMATIC UNI-JET TDI ANALYZER

Union Industrial Equipment Corp., Port Chester, N. Y. Brochure (1962).
The lightweight, portable, explosion proof instrument samples automatically with a Freon 12 powered aspirator. The TDI reagents, based on Marcali's method (see above), determine colorimetrically atmospheric concentrations of toluene diisocyanate from 0.01 to 0.08 ppm in less than 20 minutes. The TDI, removed from the air sample by passage through a dilute acid reagent, is hydrolyzed to toluene diamine. The unit diazotizes this through addition of sodium nitrite and couples it to produce a blue-red azo dye. The color density is translated to a reading of ppm concentration of TDI by comparison with hermetically sealed, nonfading color standards.

9—ATMOSPHERIC DETERMINATION OF TOLYLENE DIISOCYANATES

Robinson, Donald B. Am. Ind. Hyg. Assoc. J. **23**, 228-230 (1962).
In a midget impinger tube containing 15 ml of 0.6 ml of 0.6 N acetic acid (34 ml of glacial acetic acid, C. P., diluted to 1 liter with distilled water) collect an air sample of at least 10 liters at approximately 1 liter per minute. Transfer the solution to a colorimeter tube and dilute to 20 ml with 0.6 N acetic acid. Mix well and add 1 ml of 1% dimethylaminobenzaldehyde reagent (0.5 of dimethyl-aminobenzaldehyde dissolved in 25 ml of glacial acetic acid, diluted with 25 ml of water, stored in a brown bottle in a refrigerator and prepared fresh daily). Mix again and let stand for 1 hour, then read the transmission at 425 mμ. Compare with a calibration curve in the range from 0 to 50 μg of TDI per 20 ml of 0.6 N acetic acid. Calculate results to ppm. This procedure appears more suited for sampling for TDI vapors at elevated temperatures than the kit method because of fewer interferences. Add. Ref.: IHD **26**, 883 (1962).

10—A FIELD AND LABORATORY EVALUATION OF THE RANTA AND MARCALI METHODS FOR TDI

Skonieczny, R. F. Am. Ind. Hyg. Assoc. J. **24**, 17-22 (1963).
The author investigates 2 methods for the determination of TDI. In the Ranta method, the air sample is bubbled through 15 ml of a reagent, consisting of 200 ml of 1% aqueous sodium nitrite and 800 ml ethylene glycol monoethyl ether (cellosolve), at a rate of 1 liter per minute for 10 to 30 minutes. The collecting reagent develops a yellow-orange color in the presence of TDI and the color intensity is spectrophotometrically determined at 440 mμ against a reagent blank. The Marcali method utilizes the hydrolysis of TDI to an amine by bubbling the air sample

at 0.1 cubic foot per minute for 10 to 15 minutes through a hydrochloric acid absorbing solution, a subsequent diazotization of the amine, and a final coupling with N-1-naphthylethylenediamine. The concentration is determined by measuring the final reddish-blue color spectrophotometrically at 550 mμ.

Toluidine

1—DETERMINATION OF VAPORS OF p-TOLUIDINE IN THE AIR OF INDUSTRIAL ESTABLISHMENTS

Vinogradova, V. A. Gigiena i Sanit. **1954**, No. 11, 48; CA **49**, 3736 (1955).

p-toluidine can be determined in 0.1 N hydrochloric acid by mixing the sample with varying amounts of 20% ferric chloride, which yields a brown to red color depending on concentration, which is readily compared with a standard scale. The reaction of p-nitrophenyldiazonium chloride yields a red-yellow coupling product, but the reaction is not specific and its sensitivity is not better than that with ferric chloride (0.001 mg per 5 ml). Add. Ref.: IHD **19**, 606 (1955).

Trichloroacetaldoxime

See Section One
For reference 37.

Trinitrotoluene

1—THE DETECTION AND ESTIMATION OF SMALL AMOUNTS OF CERTAIN ORGANIC NITRO COMPOUNDS WITH SPECIAL REFERENCE TO THE EXAMINATION OF THE URINE OF TNT WORKERS

Elvove, Elias. J. Ind. Eng. Chem. **11**, 860-864 (1919); CA **13**, 2654 (1919).

A modification of the Griess nitrite test is described for the determination of certain organic nitro compounds.

2—DETERMINATION OF TNT (2,4,6-TRINITROTOLUENE) IN AIR

Kay, Kingsley. Can. J. Research **19**, B, 86-89 (1941); CA **35**, 3562 (1941).

A red color appears when 2,4,6-trinitrotoluene in acetone is treated with aqueous sodium hydroxide.

3—THE ANALYSIS OF ATMOSPHERIC SAMPLES OF EXPLOSIVE CHEMICALS

Goldman, Frederick H. J. Ind. Hyg. Toxicol. **24**, 121-122 (1942).

The author reports a preliminary investigation of some color reactions of alkylaminoethanols with explosives. Diethylaminoethanol, the preferred reagent, turns deep red with tetryl and deep violet with trinitrotoluene. The reagent gives no color with dinitrotoluene until treated with alkali, when a deep blue-green appears. The concentrations of the explosives may be determined directly in the field with diethylaminoethanol as the sampling medium. Add. Ref.: CA **36**, 5349 (1942). *The deep violet reaction with TNT may be used directly in the field as indicated, but the airborne concentration must be relatively high. The reaction is better under the conditions reported by the author in 1943 (see below).*

4—DETERMINATION OF TRINITROTOLUENE IN AIR

Cone, Thomas E., Jr. U. S. Naval Bull. **41**, 219-220 (1943); CA **38**, 529 (1944).

A modification o the Kay method is described for the determination of TNT. Two liter air samples are used and semipermanent standard tubes were prepared. The standard preparation consisted of various dilutions of TNT in butanone made alkaline with 0.1 cc of 0.1 N potassium hydroxide per 10 cc.

5—DIETHYLAMINOETHANOL AS A REAGENT FOR THE DETECTION AND COLORIMETRIC DETERMINATION OF SMALL AMOUNTS OF TRINITROTOLUENE IN AIR

Goldman, F. H. and D. E. Rushing. J. Ind. Hyg. Toxicol. **25**, 164-171 (1943).

Determine trinitrotoluene in air by bubbling air directly through diethylaminoethanol. The red violet color formed fades to a stable yellow brown in 48 hours. The reaction is relatively specific and is sensitive to 1 μg of TNT per 10 ml of sample. A modification of this procedure is outlined in "Analytical Procedures of the Industrial Hygiene Group," Los Alamos Scientific Laboratory LA-1858 (2nd Ed.) (1958). Add. Ref.: CA **37**, 5927 (1943).

6—DETERMINATION OF AIR-BORNE TRINITROTOLUENE TETRYL AND DINITROTOLUENE

Cumming, W. M. and W. G. D. Wright. Brit. J. Ind. Med. **2**, 83-85 (1945).

Airborne trinitrotoluene is estimated colorimetrically *in situ* by absorption into a 1:1 mixture of methyl ethyl ketone and cyclohexanone to which potassium hydroxide solution is added, 0.5 ml of 12% aqueous potassium hydroxide to 10 ml of solvent mixture. The red color is assessed in a Lovibond comparator (Tintometer) against a standard disc.

Airborne dinitrotoluene is absorbed in a naphthalene filter which then is dissolved in acetone and cyclohexanone containing potassium hydroxide. The violet color produced is matched against aqueous standards containing gentian violet. Add. Ref.: CA **39**, 5209 (1945).

7—A METHOD FOR THE DETERMINATION OF TRINITROTOLUENE IN AIR

Mackay, J., K. W. Holmes, and R. E. Wilson. Brit. J. Ind. Med. **15**, 126-129 (1958).

Air to be analyzed for trinitrotoluene is sampled automatically with a glass aspirator, without using an electric motor or vacuum pump, to obviate the risk of explosion. Peroxide-free ethylene glycol monoethyl ether (Cellosolve) is the solvent, in which trinitrotoluene gives a violet color with postassium hydroxide solution (0.1 ml of 25% potassium hydroxide per 10. ml of solvent). The color is measured in a Hilger photoelectric absorptiometer and the concentration of trinitrotoluene determined from a graph prepared from a series of standard solutions. The depth of color is proportional to the concentration of the trinitrotoluene up to 16 μg per ml of solvent. With suitable solvents, the same apparatus can be used for determining other airborne contaminants, e. g., tetryl. Add. Ref.: CA **52**, 21108 (1958).

with various concentrations of turpentine under different conditions is given in a 2-page table.

3—COLOR REACTION OF ROTENONE FOR THE DETERMINATION OF DERRIS ROOTS AND DERRIS-ROOT EXTRACTS

Haeusler, E. P. Mitt. Gebiete Lebensm. Hyg. **38**, 301-303 (1947); CA **42**, 3287 (1948).

Turpentine, some ethereal oils, menthol, and cineole give a blue color reaction with vanillin and sulfuric acid. A method for distinguishing the ethereal oils from the hydro-aromatic compounds is described.

4—SEPARATE DETERMINATION OF TURPENTINE, GASOLINE, AND ROSIN IN AIR

Lipina, T. G. and A. A. Belyakov. Gigiena i Sanit. **1953**, No. 4, 47; CA **47**, 11081 (1953).

Draw the air specimen through a cotton plug, then through 2 bulbs containing concentrated sulfuric acid, and finally through 4 bulbs with 1% potassium dichromate in sulfuric acid. The cotton filter retains the rosin dust and about 2% of the turpentine but no gasoline. The chromic acid bulb retains the gasoline, while the sulfuric acid bulbs absorb most of the turpentine. Determine the concentration of the turpentine by comparing the colors formed in the sulfuric acid bulbs with those of known specimens. *The sensitivity may be improved, and the color intensified by adding a trace of nitric acid to the commercially available Analytical Reagent grade of sulfuric acid.*

Turpentine

1—COLORIMETRIC DETERMINATION OF TURPENTINE IN AIR I. II.

Andreev, P. and A. Gavrilov. Chem.-Ztg. **53**, 870-871, 889-891 (1929); CA **24**, 564 (1930).

A color is formed when turpentine is absorbed by concentrated sulfuric acid. Enough air to contain 0.02 mg of turpentine should be absorbed in 20 cc of concentrated sulfuric acid, and the color compared either with freshly-prepared liquid standards or with more permanent synthetic standards.

2—COLORIMETRIC METHOD FOR DETERMINING TURPENTINE OIL IN THE ATMOSPHERE

Korenman, I. M. Z. anal. Chem. **82**, 429-438 (1930); CA **25**, 897 (1931).

The article describes an investigation of a colorimetric method for the determination of turpentine. The colorimetric determination of turpentine-oil vapors in air by absorbing in ethyl alcohol and further treatment with vanillin-hydrochloric acid is shown to be inaccurate. Attempts to improve the accuracy did not prove successful. Considerable information concerning the colors obtained

Unsymmetrical Dimethylhdrazine

1—UNSYMMETRICAL-DIMETHYLHYDRAZINE DETECTOR

Mine Safety Appliances Co., 201 N. Braddock Ave., Pittsburgh 8, Pa. Bull. 0811-9 (1959); M.S.A. Catalog 8 B 3621, Sect. 3, p. 20 (1961).

The Unsymmetrical-Dimethyl Hydrazine (UDMH) Detector consists of a rubber bulb aspirator, filter head and covers, filters, reagents, and 2 standard stains (1 and 4 ppm) for visual comparison of colors. The sensitivity is 0.5 ppm with 10 aspirations and 10 ppm with 1 aspiration. The concentration of UDMH in the range of 0.5 to 10 ppm is determined by comparing the number of squeezes of the aspirator bulb with the values on the calibration chart for the color standard matched. The reagents do not react with hydrazine.

2—A COLORIMETRIC DETERMINATION FOR 1,1-DIMETHYLHYDRAZINE (UDMH) IN AIR, BLOOD AND WATER

Pinkerton, Mildred K., Jay M. Lauer, Philip Diamond,

and Anton A. Tamas. Am. Ind. Hyg. Assoc. J. **24,** 239-244 (1963).

The authors describe a specific, sensitive, simple, and relatively rapid procedure for determining the presence of UDMH in air in the 2.5 to 50 ppm range, using trisodium pentacyanoamino ferroate (TPF). The TPF (0.1% solution in distilled water) is unstable and should be prepared fresh daily. Prepare pH 5.4 buffer solution by dissolving 1.92 g citric acid crystals and 5.65 g disodium acid phosphate septahydrate in water and diluting to 2 liters. Scrub 2 liters of air sample, at 1 liter per minute, in a polyethylene bubbler containing 20 ml of the buffer solution. Treat a 10 ml aliquot of the sample, and 10 ml of a buffer solution blank, each with 1 ml of the TPF color reagent. Let stand at room temperature for 1 hour, agitating occasionally. Read against a similarly prepared standard curve at 500 mμ. *The reaction might be applied to a field detector.*

Water

1—CHEMICAL MOISTURE DETERMINATION

Societe anon. des manufactures des glaces et produits chimiques de Saint-Gobain, Chauny et Cirey. Fr. (Pat. No.) 1,005,351, Apr. 9, 1952; CA **51,** 7246 (1957).

Silica gel impregnated with an aqueous solution of vanadium salts e.g., alkali metavanadates or vanadium tetroxide compounds, can be used for the determination of water. The impregnated gel is dried at 80 to 90° and calcined at 450°.

2—DETERMINATION OF MOISTURE IN GASES

Roman, W. and C. Akehurst. Rev. fac. cienc., Univ. Lisboa, Ser. 2B, **3,** 5-22 (1954) (in English); CA **50,** 3157 (1956).

A review with 49 references is provided.

3—DETERMINATION OF THE MOISTURE IN THE AIR BY MEANS OF AN INDICATOR TUBE

Demidov, A. V. and L. A. Mokhov. Gigiena i Sanit. **22,** No. 2, 64-66 (1957); CA **51,** 12737 (1957).

One g silica gel is mixed with 2 ml of a 5 percent zinc chloride solution, 4 ml 1 per cent manganous sulfate, and 2.5 ml 0.005 per cent malachite green solution. The mixture is dried until it is orange and placed in a tube. Air is drawn through the tube yields a green coloration. The color is matched with a standard. The amount of air drawn through is an inverse measure of humidity. The tube is reusable.

4—A SIMPLE MOISTURE-INDICATING DEVICE FOR REFRIGERATING SYSTEMS

Krause, Walter O. and Arthur B. Guise. Refrig. Eng. **65,** 39-44 (1957); CA **52,** 18960 (1958).

Cobalt bromide was found best for detecting moisture in refrigeration systems.

See Section One
For reference 6.

Welding Fumes

1—SHIPYARD HEALTH PROBLEMS

Drinker, Philip. J. Ind. Hyg. Toxicol. **26,** 86-89 (1944).

When iron is boiled in the electric arc, its vapor is burned to form ferric oxide, which has a distinctive rouge coloration. A small hand pump serves to draw a known volume of air through a white filter paper disc about 1″ in diameter. The resulting discoloration is then matched against standards. Results accurate to within 15% are obtained.

2—A WELDING FUME SAMPLER

Silverman, Leslie and John F. Ege, Jr. J. Ind. Hyg. Toxicol. **26,** 316-318 (1944).

The sampler consists of a foot-operated tire pump and a sampling head or holder for 37 mm diameter filter papers. The color of a sample after 1 to 5 pump strokes is compared with the reddish brown colors of a standard set of iron stains, from 30 to 150 mg per cubic meter or 1 to 5 strokes at 30 mg per cubic meter. A faint stain after 1 pump stroke indicates an air fume concentration of approximately 30 mg or less. The authors' standards, cemented between 2 sheets of Lucite, were stable for more than 2 years. Add. Ref.: IHD **9,** 938 (1945).

Xylyl Bromide
Xylylene Bromide

See Section One
For references 33, 37.

Zinc
Zinc Oxide

1—DETERMINATION OF ZINC OXIDE FUMES IN AIR
Silverman, Leslie. Harvard School of Public Health,

unpublished data (1947).

Filter paper stained black with nigrosine, or commercial black filter paper, changes from black to gray to white as zinc oxide is captured on the paper, with a sensitivity of 10 to 50 mg per cubic meter. Any dust that alters the density of the color causes error in the interpretation.

2—NEW REAGENT PAPERS FOR POROSITY TESTING AND FOR THE DETERMINATION OF METALS

Kutzelnigg, Arthur. Metalloberflaeche **5**, B 113-115 (1951); CA **46**, 56 (1952).

Dithizone absorbed on filter paper gives a raspberry red color with zinc. The paper should be moistened with an organic solvent.

3—A SPOT TEST ANALYSIS OF THE GROUP III CATIONS

Marion, Stephen P. and Isaac Zlochower. J. Chem. Educ. **36**, 379-380 (1959).

Paper spot test: Soak filter paper in dithizone reagent (10 mg diphenylthiocarbazone in 100 ml carbon tetrachloride) and dry. Mix on a watch glass 1 drop of the test solution and 4 drops of 2 M sodium hydroxide. Press the dithizone paper into the mixture; if zinc is present, a pink stain will appear. Add. Ref.: CA **54**, 2093 (1960).

4—NEW SENSITIVE SPOT REACTION FOR ZINC

Anger, V. Mikrochim. Acta **1959,** 473-475 (in German); CA **56**, 9391 (1962).

Place 1 drop of neutral or acidic test solution on a filter paper. Add 1 drop of reagent solution (20 mg penta-cyanoaminoferroate and 10 ml p-nitrosodimethylaniline in 100 ml of water). Then drop 2 N sulfuric acid on the spot. Zinc forms a blue ring. Mercury, copper, cadmium, cobalt, nickel, iron, and uranium dioxide ions interfere. Detection limits are 0.05 μg zinc at 1:1,000,000.

See Section One

For references 5, 98.

DATE DUE